From Shell Shock to Combat Stress

From Shell Shock
to Combat Stress

A Comparative History of Military Psychiatry

Hans Binneveld
Translated from the Dutch by John O'Kane

AMSTERDAM UNIVERSITY PRESS

This translation was made possible by a generous gift from Vereniging Trustfonds Erasmus Universiteit Rotterdam.

Cover design: NAP Ontwerpers/Sabine Mannel, Amsterdam
Lay-out: Fontline/Marc Regenboog, Nijmegen

ISBN 90 5356 270 2

© Amsterdam University Press, Amsterdam, 1997

FOREWORD

In this study of the history of military psychiatry two separate worlds are brought together which have interested me for quite some time: mental health care and the army.

My interest in mental health care began in the early 1970s. It was at a time when the antipsychiatry movement and the patients' movement were receiving much attention in the Netherlands. Publicly voiced criticism of the existing psychiatric institutions naturally aroused my intellectual curiosity about psychiatry's historical roots. I have given an account, in various books and articles, of the research which sprang from this curiosity.

My interest in the military goes back even further in my personal development. While still in high school I had entertained the idea of pursuing a military career. During my first year at the Koninklijke Militaire Academie, it became clear to me that this ambition was based on a misunderstanding. Nonetheless, the soldier's life has always retained a fascination for me. The path to the study of military history was opened for me by Jan Schulten. Without his stimulating example my fascination would never have been translated into academic study and research.

When at the end of the 1980s I became occupied with the present research topic, some of my colleagues appeared to be less than enthusiastic. After all, was a subject of this kind not simply something of an intellectual hobby? What was the social relevance of research along these lines? Since the Gulf War and the UN interventions in Bosnia, doubts of this type have decreased considerably. What at first sight seemed to be a purely academic subject, has come to occupy a central position in the public's interest.

While writing this book I received help and useful suggestions from a number of people. Due to limits of space I will confine myself to mentioning only a few of them by name. While I was preparing this work, Marja Griffioen and Bert Schonewille provided me with research assistance. Gea Binneveld-de Visser and Peter Verhoef gave me many pointers which were useful in improving the readability of the text. And Anna den Boer worked with incredible dedication to see that the manuscript was ready for publication on time. I hope that all those who have been involved will feel pleased with the book's final form.

Hans Binneveld

PREFACE

Hans Binneveld has written an astonishing book, combining the worlds of war and madness. It gives the facts behind Pat Barker's prize-winning novel *Regeneration* (1995), the military and psychiatric history behind Robert Graves' black comedy of *Goodbye to All That* (1929) and Erich Maria Remarque's *All Quiet on the Western Front* (1928). It contributes to historical revisionism in the history of science, which sees science as human rather than heroic; and it contributes to the new military history, which sees how men fight as part of how they live. Researched from wide sources, *From Shell Shock to Combat Stress* is a tale of success and failure – the 'success' of modern warfare as it industrialized and the failure of psychiatry to cure men driven mad by the 'shrill, demented choirs of wailing shells'.

Battlefields in olden times were terrible enough, as one can read in John Keegan's account of Agincourt in *The Face of Battle*, or for that matter books 11-15 of *The Iliad*. From the middle of the nineteenth century, though, transport improved and weapons increased their range. Bigger armies could be fed longer, and massed ranks could be mown down at greater distances. The battles got longer and the soldiers more thinly deployed. It went on and on, this isolating cacophony of guns, and the madness spread. A British Tommy who had served at Mons, the Marne, the Aisne, first and second Ypres, Hill 60, Neuve Chapelle, Loos, and Armentière went mute. An American marine who had seen the faces of his friends disintegrate in a land mine could not sleep. 'Surely we have perished/ Sleeping', said Wilfred Owen's 'Mental Cases'. 'These are men whose minds the Dead have ravished.'

The rehearsed horror of 'over the top', the assault on an enemy trench or beach, was especially deranging. My uncle Jock had nightmares for years after the island-hopping campaign in the Pacific – and he was only watching, a naval officer directing fire for the marines. He was a 'witness' in Binneveld's triad of witness, victim, and perpetrator. Each had its own cause of madness: frustration, powerlessness, and guilt.

In dealing with madness one must have a theory. I know an elderly man who throughout his wife's declining course of Alzheimer's disease thought she was merely acting badly, and could pull up her socks. The British aristocracy had a similar theory about shell shock: 'Pull yourself together, man', a lack of sympathy for psychiatric casualties evident in the British army as late as the Falklands War.

The professional theorists of madness, the military psychiatrists, had to struggle against the commonsense conviction of officers like General Patton that madmen were shirkers. They struggled without easy cures at hand. That psychiatry does not know what to do in most cases is a sad fact, though merely an instance of the wider failure of Experts in modern times. Psychiatry is of course not unusual in its failures. Physical medicine has seen fads taken as wonders come and go, from bleeding to radical mastectomies. The various solutions to the urban slum, urged in succession since the mid-nineteenth century, failed. The experts, often as not, don't know what they are talking about.

Psychiatrists desperate to please their military superiors resorted to every inexpensive measure they could think of. 'Electrotherapy' has a nice Greek and scientific sound to it; but of course it means plugging the patient into an electric socket and hoping for the best. In the First World War on the German side the Kaufmann Method, Binneveld shows, was designed to reduce the prospect of military pensions. It amounted to torture by electrotherapy, and was quickly imitated, or (to the glory of British medicine) independently discovered, on the Allied side. It and insulin 'therapy' were revived in the Second World War. It was, Binneveld notes, a revival of 'moral' therapy popular in the early nineteenth century, in which the insane are treated as naughty children to be punished.

Is modern war especially damaging to men's minds? The makers of dive-bombers and booby traps hope so. As Binneveld emphasizes, it is a puzzle, since the solution of one problem will highlight another in a merely statistical way. In peace the decline of infectious disease has exposed degenerative diseases such as heart disease and cancer. In war the decline of disease and physical injury as a cause of casualties highlighted the psychological injuries of battle that were always present. Likewise the abolition of the asylum highlighted the problem of psychoses on the street. Better physical medicine on the battlefield exposed the inadequacies of the psychological medicine.

And that on the whole is the sad conclusion of Binneveld's book. Psychiatry is a crude science, too unaware of its own crudeness, and therefore easily corrupted by social pressures, as in the old Soviet Union for politics and everywhere for war. We do not know what drives some men mad and leaves others merely wiser. Binneveld shows that the frustrations of war made psychiatry turn against itself, often in the same terms as the anti-psychiatry movement of the 1960s. Treatment of battle fatigue was to be immediate, short-term, and in proximity to the front – all of which were contrary to the banishment and long-term treatment in civilian psychiatry during the age of the asylum. Unhappily the military psychiatrists did not have the psychotropic drugs that make it possible now to let a psychotic person wander about the community. They did have testing before recruitment, though, and the American military used it with special enthusiasm in the Second World War. Binneveld recounts the psychiatric breakdown, offset by massive doses of Nazi propaganda, of German soldiers on the Eastern front after Stalingrad. Late in the war they could not select their gun fodder well enough to keep the madness out.

Keeping the madness out had never worked very well. In the special madness of modern war it is doubly hard. The wonder is that anyone survives a modern battlefield without Post Traumatic Stress Disorder, as the Americans call it: PTSD, with teams of psychiatrists to 'treat' it. A sad tale, funny in a manic way, sobering about our childish hopes that experts will take care of us always.

Deirdre N. McCloskey
University of Iowa and Erasmus University

Table of Contents

I - INTRODUCTION

Introduction

The soldiers of Dutchbat, having completed their mission in Bosnia, were received with magnificent fanfare. Numerous civilian and military authorities travelled to Zagreb to bid them a warm welcome. In the wake of these official dignitaries, social workers, therapists, psychologists and psychiatrists appeared on the scene. During the Gulf War in 1991 therapists of this sort were present in abundance, in particular among the American forces. On that occasion they were not there to provide follow-up care but to give support during the actual fighting.

One can no longer imagine a battlefield without psychiatrists and psychologists. Their presence is due to the fact that participation in a war, for many of those involved, is an extremely traumatic experience. Not every soldier is capable of dealing with the situation. Those who are unable to do so suffer mental breakdown. Along with the dead and wounded, war – and in particular a modern war – produces soldiers who have been psychologically wounded.

The great philosopher of war, Carl von Clausewitz (1780–1831), was eminently aware of the emotions that battle is capable of arousing in a soldier. In one passage in his standard work *Vom Kriege*, he leads an imaginary recruit by the hand through a typical battlefield:

Let us escort the novice to the battlefield. As we draw closer to the fighting, along with the roar of the artillery which is becoming increasingly louder the whine of the shells is finally heard, which attracts the attention of the inexperienced youth. Directly behind and in front of us shells begin to burst. We quickly make our way to the hill where the commanding general has installed himself with his extensive staff. Here cannon-balls and exploding grenades follow upon one another so closely that concern for his life begins to penetrate the recruit's youthful imagination. Suddenly, an acquaintance is hit and falls to the ground – a grenade lands in the midst of the troops and causes some involuntary commotion – everyone starts to feel he is no longer calm and under control, even the bravest experience a bit of confusion. – Now we take one more step toward the center of the battle which rages before us as if it were a scene in the theater, toward the nearest divisional commander; here one shell follows another, and the noise of our own artillery further intensifies the confusion. Everyone from the divisional commander to the brigadier general – the latter a man of proverbial bravery – has temporarily taken shelter behind a hill, a house or behind some trees; – a clear sign of the growing danger. Case shot rattles on the roof-tops and in the fields, from every direction cannon-balls whizz towards us and past us, and now the whistling of rifle-bullets is starting to be heard more frequently. Still one more step and we reach the troops, the infantry that for hours have been holding fast under fire with indescribable tenacity. Here the air is filled with hissing bullets that betray their close proximity by a brief high-pitched sound as they fly past, one inch from the ear, the head and the soul. On top of it all, our pounding heart is overcome with pity at the sight of the dead and the maimed.[1]

What Clausewitz vividly illustrates in this passage are particular fears that the soldier experiences. The fear of dying or of being maimed. The description given here is of very basic reactions, whereas in reality the range of emotions that accompany direct involvement in combat is much broader.

The Duke of Wellington, in one of his rare candid moments, has given evidence of the emotional effect that years of waging war had on him. One month after the Battle of Waterloo he confided the following in a letter to Lady Shelley:

I hope to God I have fought my last battle. It is a bad thing always to be fighting. While I am in the thick of it I am too much occupied to feel anything; but it is wretched just after. It is quite impossible to think of glory. Both mind and feelings are exhausted. I am wretched even at the moment of victory, and I always say that next to a battle lost, the greatest misery is a battle gained. Not only do you lose those dear friends with whom you have been living, but you are forced to leave the wounded behind you. To be sure one tries to do the best for them, but how little that is! At such moments every feeling in your breast is deadened. I am now just beginning to regain my natural spirits, but I never wish for any more fighting.[2]

Thus the endless fighting was beginning to evoke in Wellington feelings of revulsion and mental exhaustion. It is also clear that he felt a sense of guilt. He did, after all, bear ultimate responsibility for the dead and the wounded whom, as he points out, he was forced to abandon to their fate. But the Duke was a very strong personality who, in contrast to many other commanders, never relinquished the helm under pressure. John Keegan has said of Wellington that he succeeded in banishing from his personality everything that had to do with feelings. Most ordinary mortals, on the other hand, are not capable of effecting such a psychological *tour de force*. One of Wellington's subordinates, general Picton, who was a war-horse of the old school, confessed to his commander-in-chief during the campaign in France that he was no longer competent to face up to his duties. He was what we would nowadays describe as completely burnt out, and he gave advance notice of his resignation. But before his resignation came into effect, Picton met his death at the Battle of Waterloo.[3]

A war inevitably confronts those involved in it with traumatic experiences. In addition, quite often certain physical circumstances play a role. Soldiers who join battle are all too often exhausted from lack of sleep and inadequate nourishment. The armies that fought one another at Waterloo already had many days of marching behind them, and food supplies during the campaigns left much to be desired. During the First World War, the troops who left the trenches to take part in the major offensives were often suffering from a bad cold or the flu. At home, in normal life, they would undoubtedly have reported themselves sick and not gone in to work.

Thus the psychological stress which takes place in war rarely occurs on its own. It takes place at the moment that the soldier is also being driven to the furthest extreme in the physical sense. It is this combination which has proved fatal for many soldiers and which, most notably, has led to the category of the psychologically wounded soldier.

That soldiers can become wounded not only in the physical sense, but mentally as well, has been recognized for centuries.[4] During the Thirty Years War (1618–1648), Spanish military doctors used the expression *estar roto* (to be on the point of breakdown) to characterize the situation of soldiers who could no longer endure combat. Swiss medical practitioners, during the sixteenth and seventeenth centuries, regularly diagnosed *nostalgia*. This disorder was distinguished, among other things, by overtiredness, faulty concentration, and a greatly decreased appetite. Their German colleagues in the same period made use of the term *Heimwee*. Nostalgia is the most widespread concept one meets with throughout the pre-industrial era. This diagnosis was also regularly applied to French soldiers who took part in the Napoleonic wars of conquest, and especially during the retreat from Moscow and the campaign in Egypt.

The American Civil War (1861–1865) was the last conflict in which the appearance of nostalgia on a large-scale was confirmed. Thereafter new terms and new labels came into use but the psychologically wounded soldier remained. During the First World War, soldiers who had been clearly driven round the bend were transported in special sealed ambulances to areas behind the front line. In those areas behind the lines, dazed, completely disoriented soldiers were regularly encountered who could not account for their presence there. The situation remained the same in the Second World War. Then as well thousands of soldiers experienced breakdowns as individuals or in groups. In July 1944, this form of mental collapse among the Allied troops who fought in Normandy actually took on epidemic proportions. The Israeli army went through the same experience during the Yom Kippur War in 1973 when the intensive fighting became too much to bear for countless soldiers.

The phenomenon is therefore age-old. Only the manifestations and the symptoms have changed their character over the centuries. The same can be said of the diagnostic methods and the relevant terms employed in dealing with the problem.

During the Second World War, the expression 'combat exhaustion' or 'battle exhaustion' came into vogue. Since the 1960s it has become established usage to speak of 'combat stress'. But the most famous term, and one that appeals most vividly to the imagination, emerged in the First World War, namely 'shell shock'. This concept was a blanket-term that covered numerous disorders which, as the doctors of the time would have it, could all be associated with the effects of artillery shelling. Although the term was quickly brought into discredit by the experts, the concept proved to be so popular with the wider public that it was impossible to suppress it. When a Dutch UN observer who was serving in the former Yugoslavia in 1992 described the behavior of a highly overwrought colleague, he once again made use of the term shell shock.[5]

In contrast to the centuries-old history of the psychologically wounded soldier, recent developments in the response to this phenomenon on the part of military organization can be reviewed in a brief space. For the generals during the pre-industrial period casualties of this type did not represent a serious problem. These officers had a series of other important problems on their minds. Compared with the notorious epidemics, frequent desertion and faulty logistical organization which constantly threatened the army with starvation, the psychiatric problem was of a subordinate nature. In modern times this situation began to change. The fruits of the industrial revolution made it possible to do something effective against the above-mentioned classic menaces. As a result, more attention could be given to the psychologically wounded soldier. Simultaneously, the same industrial developments led to revolutionary changes in the way of waging war and the production of violence. One of the consequences was the emergence of an enormous psychiatric problem. The numbers of soldiers who experienced breakdowns became so great that the military organization had no choice but to seek a practical solution. The result of their efforts in this direction was the establishment of military psychiatry. This institution consists of a whole complex of specialized knowledge along with a range of more or less related therapies and established services. From the organizational point of view, military psychiatry became a separate branch within the military medical services which had existed from time immemorial.

The history of this medical discipline has been characterized by many vicissitudes. In the American Civil War the Northerners alone were forced to withdraw five to seven thousand of their men from the fighting because the latter were rendered ineffective due to psychological disorders.[6] The Surgeon-General William Hammond took great personal interest in these casualties. But in this respect he stood alone within the army. The military doctors gave no attention whatsoever to this category of wounded. Nor did civilian psychiatrists show any interest in the matter. The few books and articles that were devoted to this subject remained unread both during and after the Civil War. Certainly no system for treatment was organized. Psychologically wounded soldiers were simply escorted to the gate of the barracks or the military encampment and abandoned to their lot. If they were lucky, they were put on a train with their name and place of residence pinned on their jacket. From a scientific point of view, it was especially neurology which was able to profit from the Civil War. This discipline entered upon a flourishing phase in the United States after the signing of peace. For psychiatry the conflict proved to be of no significance. The psychologically wounded soldier passed into oblivion.

The Russo-Japanese War (1904–1905) once more brought to the fore a wide range of psychiatric problems. In this case it was especially Russian doctors who recognized the problem and made a serious attempt to set up a system of treatment.[7] However, the system in question did not prove to be a match for the enormous stream of casualties on hand. Nevertheless, both in clinical and organizational terms the Russians laid the foundation for military psychiatry. But their innovations in this specialized field remained, for the most part, unrecognized because of the low level of performance of the Russian medical services in general. In

1905, Russian military medicine did not represent a model which other countries wished to emulate. Consequently, during the First World War military psychiatry had to be discovered all over again. By the time an armistice was signed in 1918, all the armies involved had provided their medical services with a psychiatric section.

The Present Study: Its Limits and Structure
The origins and subsequent development of military psychiatry are the subject of this book. The chief questions which we will attempt to deal with concern diagnostic methods, as well as curative and preventive procedures. Attention will also be given to what causes soldiers to experience breakdowns and how their breakdowns are related to the particular kind of war being waged.

In order to depict the distinctive countenance of military psychiatry as effectively as possible, comparison of crucial points will be made with the discipline's civilian variant. In so doing, we will consider the mutual influence which both sectors have exerted on one another. In addition, we will attempt to sketch the differences that have appeared between various countries, and where possible give some explanation of the causes of these differences.

The present author is not a psychiatrist or a psychologist but a social historian. This background has led to the choice of a particular line of approach which focuses attention on the organizational and social context within which military psychiatry took shape.

In the presentation of this study a thematic and a chronological approach has been combined. That is to say, in each chapter a particular subject will be analyzed, such as for example the therapeutic instrumentarium. The same subjects will then be treated once again chronologically. Occasionally, this may mean that a certain degree of overlapping will take place.

In writing this work the author has been obliged to adopt certain necessary limits. The first is of a regional nature. In fact, the present study, apart from a few exceptions, deals exclusively with European and American armies. This narrowed focus is not only due to the author's area of competence but results as well from the availability of source materials. Furthermore, attention has been chiefly allotted to developments which took place within the land forces. This does not mean that psychological problems did not arise in the navy and the air force as well. Nor does it mean that the problems encountered in those branches of the armed forces would have been less interesting to investigate. In view of the limited time at his disposal, the author simply found himself obliged to exclude these further areas of study. The same can be said regarding those areas dealt with by military psychiatry which are not more or less directly involved with problems related to violence. An example that immediately comes to mind is the treatment of drug abuse in the armed forces. Problems of this nature will also not be examined in the present study.

The structure of this book is as follows. The whole is divided into two parts. Part One examines the military and the civilian background to the development of psychiatry. To begin with, a brief survey is given of the history of waging war in the pre-industrial and the industrial periods. The overall significance which psychiatric problems, in absolute and relative terms, posed for military organization provides the narrative thread (Chapters II and III). Next, an attempt is made to convey the heterogeneous nature of modern warfare. This is essential because the conflicts fought out in the twentieth century have not been particularly homogeneous but have consisted of a number of widely divergent situations. In order to illustrate this complexity three situations will be sketched in which a soldier can become involved in applying violence (Chapter IV). At the end of Part One the civilian discipline of pyschiatry is treated. Naturally, in this chapter only such matters as are of significance for the development of military psychiatry are examined (Chapter V).

In Part Two military psychiatry forms the central focus of attention. The actual complaints of soldiers and the attempts by psychiatrists to interpret the disorders are taken as the starting point (Chapter VI). Next, the therapies which were applied and the problems which were encountered in their application are considered (Chapter VII). A separate chapter is devoted to what the psychiatrists themselves see as the most crucial aspect of their activity. Here we take a closer look at what have been deemed the fundamental principles of military psychiatry (Chapter VIII). Military psychiatry consists not only of curative procedures but has a preventive component as well. Preventive efforts are examined in Chapter IX. An extremely topical problem concerns the psychological complaints which some soldiers experience after a war. These post-traumatic stress disorders (PTSD) form the subject of Chapter X. Finally, in a section entitled Concluding Observations the chief results of this study will be summarized and a number of conclusions will be drawn.

PART ONE

THE BACKGROUND

II - The Psychologically Wounded Soldier: An Actor without a Speaking Part in the Theater of War

Introduction

Wherever fighting occurs, there are casualties: dead, wounded and the psychologically wounded. In principle every casualty represents a loss to fighting power. It is to be expected that generals will attempt to minimize potential threats to an army's fighting power, certainly where the soldiers concerned have special skills and cannot easily be replaced in the short term.

With military psychiatry the military authorities came to have at their disposal an instrument by means of which they could address a particular form of attrition of the army's strength. But why was it not until the twentieth century that this weapon was brought into operation? Various reasons can be given to explain this late emergence of military psychiatry. In the present chapter we will limit ourselves to considering a number of factors of a military nature. Put in the simplest terms, it comes down to the fact that generals in the pre-industrial age had more pressing matters on their mind. The psychologically wounded soldier was not seen as a crucial problem in comparison with other factors which threatened an army's existence. Far more important in this respect were inadequate logistics, commonly occurring epidemics, and desertion.

In what follows a description will be given of how military organization reacted to these logistical and medical questions and how it dealt with the problem of ensuring loyalty. A brief sketch of the emergence of modern military organization, a process which took place in the years around 1600, will not be amiss by way of introduction.

The Genesis of Military Organization

The sixteenth century, from a military point of view, was one of the most turbulent periods in Western history. Along with the well-known feudal rivalries civil wars occurred. The religious wars, which would last well into the following century, also broke out in all their destructiveness.

In waging war rulers made use of mercenary armies which were recruited for individual campaigns. This was the golden age of the so-called military entrepreneurs. These figures, for a sizeable fee of course, would put together armies for

kings and dukes who had money at their disposal but who lacked the necessary organizational capacities to do this themselves.

Generally speaking, it can be said that, from a military standpoint, these mercenary armies were far from being efficiently functioning enterprises. The weapons
they had were rarely used effectively and their cumbersome, inflexible formations
proved to be increasingly vulnerable to enemy fire. During the military revolution,
which went on between 1580 and 1650, the functioning of the army in several countries was subjected to meticulous scrutiny. And what a transformation this led to!
The military revolution set in motion a process of rationalizing warfare and military
management, and gave to military organization the basic features which it still has
today. Loose military groupings were reshaped into well-structured, clearly hierarchical units. The various changes indicated a clear break, both with the tradition of
the knights, as well as that of the Swiss footsoldiers. The knights had been no more
than a loose grouping of individual fighting horsemen. The Swiss had never been
much more than an undifferentiated and uncoordinated mass of footsoldiers.

It all began in Holland where under the strict leadership of Prince Maurits experiments in new forms of military action were carried out.[1] One of the foundations
of the new system was a thorough analysis of the use of weapons. How thorough
this analysis was is illustrated by the fact that no less than 23 movements for the use
of the pike were distinguished. For handling the musket, on the other hand, there
were 43 officially recognized operations involved. All these distinct manoeuvers required separate training.

A second basic principle consisted of positioning troops in more effective formations. Crucial in this regard was Maurits' attempt to deploy his men in a less deep
line. Thereby the units were not only less vulnerable to enemy fire but in this way a
far greater portion of their weapons could actually be employed. These reforms
were completed by the mastery of certain tactical movements such as changing
from marching formation to battle array, and executing a countermarch.

Within this new system the soldier did no more than perform a subordinate task
within the greater whole. His actions had to be accurately coordinated with those of
the other military personnel. In this context hierarchy and discipline were the key
concepts. The army was conceived of as a kind of machine in which the soldiers,
without taking initiative, merely reacted like robots to orders from above. This machine model was an attempt to combine weapons and manpower in as efficient a
way as possible. It was also an attempt to make the whole become greater than the
sum of its parts. This was something neither the knights nor the Swiss had been able
to achieve.

The Republic of the Seven United Provinces, as mentioned, played a key role in
the process of military reform. This is not at all surprising in view of the fact that
around the year 1600 circumstances in the Republic were particularly favorable in
this regard. There existed a unique combination of theoretical and practical leadership, while, at the same time, the financial position of the Republic was strong.

The practical leadership came from Prince Maurits and from Willem Lodewijk.
Theoretical knowledge was provided by Leiden University. This institution was

characterized, among other things, by a genuine striving to introduce science into the social community. Intellectual circles in Leiden took a great interest in topical issues, and during the war with Spain military matters comprised one such important issue.

The work of the eminent humanist, Justus Lipsius, demonstrated what learning in combination with a strong pragmatic disposition could accomplish. Lipsius' exceptional knowledge of the classics laid the foundation for the reforms of the army in the Netherlands.

Alongside knowledge and leadership, money played an important role in the reform process. The success of reforms depended entirely on the introduction of drills and exercises. Among the soldiers themselves these activities were extemely unpopular. Nevertheless, Maurits was ultimately able to impose these activities because the Republic could mete out good and regular pay. The same could not be said of many other would-be contractors. This meant that Maurits was in a position to make demands. The soldiers were more or less obliged to put up with drilling.

It was also of importance that Maurits could hire his troops for a longer period of time. This made it possible to improve any acquired skills and to maintain them over the long term. With an army that had to be recruited anew for each campaign, professional standards of this kind would naturally be more difficult to introduce. Around 1600 the first initiatives were undertaken to create permanent standing armies which at a later time became general practice.

The experiments of Maurits were followed very closely by many foreign rulers and military men. Scores of foreign officers learned their trade in the army of the Dutch Republic. Once they returned home, they were eager to undertake their own forms of experiment with military reform. This was the case first in Brandenburg and then later in Sweden where Jacob Delagardie informed his king Gustav Adolphus about the work of Maurits. From Sweden the new concepts concerning warfare and army organization found their way to England where Oliver Cromwell was pleased to make use of them.

Gustav Adolphus and Cromwell carried forward the work of Maurits and while doing so brought in other emphases. For instance, in the case of Gustav Adolphus the officers' corps received greater attention. Cromwell, for his part, caused a sensation with his reorganization of the cavalry. The basic principles, however, were the same everywhere. In all cases it was a question of creating rationally structured, efficient organizations. Moreover, it is striking that, to begin with, the spread of the rational model of organization remained limited to the Protestant countries of North-West Europe. In the southern Catholic countries this mentality of rationality, sobriety and self-control which formed the basis of the new model did not exercise an appeal, at least not for the time being.

These reforms that have been briefly sketched gave the military an enormous advantage over other sectors of society. Outside the army, the modern principles of rational organization still found almost no application. In this respect the armed forces were virtually operating in a social vacuum. This meant that whatever the armed forces thought out and set down in manuals and regulations was by no means faithfully carried out in practice. For quite some time there remained a great gap between the blueprints that Maurits, Gustav Adolphus and Cromwell drew up, on the one hand, and the day-to-day running of army affairs, on the other. For none of the three founding fathers did the army function as a violence-producing machine that could be turned off and on at will from one central point. Nevertheless, the foundation had been laid. A military organization had come into being with the help of which warfare could be waged more or less systematically. Within this framework it was now possible for a professional officers' corps to emerge, and in parallel herewith a science of warfare developed.

The seventeenth and eighteenth centuries succeeded in further bridging the gap between the blueprint and reality. Fredrick the Great of Prussia brought these developments to their culmination.[2] This monarch commanded expertly drilled troop units that remained controlable even during the peak of a pitched battle. With Fredrick the machine model was no longer an ideal to be striven for but something that to a great extent had already been achieved.

From the viewpoint of the central aim of military organization, i.e. the production of massive violence, it can be confirmed that during the period that began with Maurits and ended with Fredrick the Great there was indeed an increased efficiency achieved in military organization. The production of violence had not only become greater, but it was becoming steadily more controlable. If we take a look at other aspects of the military, however, it must be said that since the time of the military revolution scarcely any progress had been made. This is true for logistics (the provisioning of men and animals), as well as for military medical provision in the broadest sense of the word. Similarly, in the case of many soldiers personal commitment to efficient organization left much to be desired. It would still take centuries before these factors were brought under control.

Logistics

In the model army that was created in the Dutch Republic under the inspiring leadership of Prince Maurits, the logistical services were still regulated in the most traditional manner.[3] Private entrepreneurs, for a fixed daily fee, provided ships and wagons for transport, as well as horses to move artillery. While on campaign the army would be accompanied by a large host of merchants and dealers who provided the necessary provisions. In addition, looting and plundering were carried out on a large scale, all the more readily if the troops were a certain distance from home.

This looting and plundering, also referred to as living well from the land, was the general practice in the seventeenth century. During the Thirty Years' War (1618–1648), the population of North-West Europe was heavily afflicted by the massive troop movements which were occasioned by this conflict. When a village was visited by an army unit, everything that was eatable for man or beast disappeared. Cattle, hay, winter stocks, seed – the army had a use for all of it. In planning their campaigns, generals were concerned not to have to pass through an area which had already been visited a short time before by other troops. That would cause supply problems of a very serious nature for when the land had no more to offer, the fighting simply had to stop.

In the eighteenth century, the logistical aspect of an army received greater attention from the generals. This was especially the case in France. There the state was steadily becoming more successful at getting a grip on the provisioning of uniforms, weapons and food stuffs, thanks to a bureaucratic apparatus, the *Intendance*, which had been especially set up for this purpose. This system not only led to cutting costs but also resulted in a clear improvement in the quality of the goods provided.

To make it possible to spare the civilian population in time of war and to minimize theft and requisitioning, during this same period supplies that were needed by the army were stored in various locations. The construction of these storehouses can be seen as an attempt to make the army less dependent for supplies on the area in which it had to operate at any given moment.[4]

The system of storehouses accorded with the manner of practicing warfare at that moment, a warfare that was characterized by the tendency to keep armed conflicts short and limited. The eighteenth century was the heyday of manoeuvering. It was the era when much time was spent meticulously planning campaigns in advance. Everything was done to avoid exposing to unnecessary risks the costly military apparatus which rulers had invested their wealth in. In warfare of this kind a certain degree of logistical mastery was possible.

Martin van Creveld has shown that the storehouse system only offered a very limited solution to the problem of logistics. In the eighteenth century as well, large military formations remained to a certain extent dependent on what the area of operations could supply them with. The system was too rigid and too vulnerable to be able to meet the needs of an army advancing on the march. This was especially true with regard to the Napoleonic Wars. Napoleon fully appreciated the importance of stockpiling supplies and constructing storehouses, but the strategy he followed, in which fast forced marches were a crucial element, could not be combined with a static logistics system. Once again, Napoleon's troops were generally obliged to live off the land. If the land in question had little to offer, as was the case in Spain or in Russia during the retreat of the Grande Armée, then his armies experienced great difficulties.

Only with the arrival of the railroads did a new age for logistical organization begin to dawn. By means of that transport system armies acquired not only unprecedented mobility, but an impressive ability to remain in the field for protracted lengths of time.

The first country where the railroads were used for military purposes was Russia. There in 1846, 14,500 men were transported by rail over a distance of 200 miles. In 1850, Austria transported no less than 75,000 men in the same manner from Vienna to Bohemia. A few years later, the French surprised the world by transporting 604,138 men and 129,227 horses. These were shipped from France to Italy between April 16th and July 15th.

However, the large-scale expansion of the railroad network had not really begun yet. In 1870 there were 65,000 miles of track in Europe. When the First World War broke out, 180,000 miles of track existed which represents an increase of almost 200 percent. At the same time stronger locomotives were added to the picture and the organization of the railroads became more efficient. Improvements of one kind or another resulted in an enormous boost to transport capacity. Whereas in 1870 a single line could handle eight trains a day, by 1914 this capacity had increased to forty.

In Prussia the military importance of the new transport system was not immediately appreciated. This is not surprising since the railroads in Prussia could not match those of France. Only after 1860 was there a gradual change in this respect. It was then namely that Prussia would demonstrate that the railroad had changed warfare once and for all. The course of Prussia's war with Austria (1866) and the Franco-Prussian War appeared to be dictated by the railroad network. In the famous Schlieffen-Plan (1905) there was a key role assigned to the railroad as well. In the American Civil War the Northerners owed the victory they managed to win over the Southerners in no small measure to the better use they had made of the railway network.

Nevertheless, there was one particular weakness inherent in the military use of railroads, a weakness which would continue to exert an influence up into the Second World War. The weak link was the connection between the last railroad station and the troops in the field. Even in the case of the excellently organized Prussian army, problems arose in delivering supplies to the troop units in the field. This occurred in the conflict with Austria, as well as during the war with France. When the German troops had forged a path through France, long lines of supply trains came to a standstill between Frankfurt and Cologne. It turned out that the railroad terminals were unable to process the mass of goods quickly. Newly arrived trains could not be unloaded because of the encumbered platforms. The connection with the army in the field was maintained by means of horses and wagons. Clearly the speed of the latter was scanty compared with the train. Consequently, new delays took place.

With the arrival of the railroad, therefore, armies did not so much come to dispose over a completely new transport system, but rather a new facility was added to the traditional transport network. For quite a long time the coordination of both elements remained far from optimal. In fact in the autumn of 1870, once again the Prussian soldiers lived off what the enemy territory could provide. Since it was a rich, fertile area, there were no insurmountable problems concerning food supplies. In the First World War the same situation arose during the German advance through Belgium. Again the connections between the large train stations and the army in the field bogged down. Again the troops had to live from what they could confiscate or plunder on the spot. When in the course of the Second World War horses and wagons were increasingly replaced by trucks, the problem of maintaining contact with an army in the field disappeared from logistical organization. This ideal situation was particularly the case when the American armed forces, after their landings in Normandy, began to operate on the continent. In the German army that launched its attack against Russia in 1941 the logistical organization was far less effective. Only the tank divisions had the disposal of motorized transport columns. The seventy-seven infantry divisions involved depended on horses and wagons to transport their supplies from the railroad yards.[5]

Furthermore, all the divisions were expected to look after their own sustenance, i.e. to live off the enemy's land. As for the tanks, supply trucks were absolutely necessary to transport fuel, ammunition and stocks of spare parts. Every division had special officers who were in charge of requisitioning the required foodstuffs. On the whole no account was taken of the needs of the population in the area in question. Particularly impressive was, for examle, the shopping list of the 12th infantry division. Between July 24th and August 1st, the following was demanded of the population: 112 tons of grain, 760 tons of hay, 32 head of cattle, 65 sheep, 94 pigs, 2 tons of potatoes, 350 kg. of butter, 2,350 eggs, and 2,200 liters of milk.[6] From this example, it emerges that one of the most advanced war machines of the twentieth century, i.e. the German Wehrmacht, when it came to logistics operated in pretty much the same way as the mercenaries employed by Gustav Adolphus in the seventeenth century.

These critical remarks do not, however, change the fact that the importance of the railroad for the logistics of warfare can scarcely be overestimated. Napoleon once observed that in the end the biggest battalions win the battle. By means of the railroad network and its corresponding organization, the biggest battalions can be delivered and supplied.

Since the Second World War the functions of the railroads have been more and more replaced by motorized transport. Without a doubt the flexibility of logistical organization has thereby been increased. Nonetheless, in this regard one cannot speak of a linear development. For one thing, it is a fact that the consumption needs of an army have risen enormously over the last hundred years. In the Franco-Prussian War a division consumed about 50 tons of provisions a day. The greatest part of this was food for the soldiers and fodder for the horses. Midway into the First World War this figure had risen to 150 tons, of which an increasingly more important constituent was ammunition. In 1944, before its advance into Europe the American army reckoned on consuming 650 tons per division. Martin van Creveld has calculated that over the decades that have followed the end of that war a doubling and even a trebling of consumption has occurred.[7] Modern armies are thus increasingly more dependent on extensive, complicated logistics systems which leaves much to be desired in terms of flexibility. What was true of the railroads is equally applicable to motorized transport. But despite all this, the implications for improving logistics have been enormous.

Maintaining the troops in the field was facilitated still further by important innovations that took place during the nineteenth century in the foodstuffs industry. Examples that come to mind include canned meat, powdered milk, as well as margarine, which brought about a revolution in the dietary pattern in the army.[8]

As far as diet is concerned, American servicemen, ever since the Second World War, have occupied a unique position. Their English allies used to refer to them as 'overfed, oversexed and overpaid'. This description is certainly true regarding the first and the third characterization for the post-war period. During NATO manoeuvers, American rations have for years been the most popular with the participating troops. The Americans' partners often react to this 'luxury' with a mixture of aversion and jealousy. That the lesser degree of luxury among their own servicemen can chiefly be attributed to the far more limited logistical organization at the disposal of the European armies, is too easily forgotten.

Sickness and Death

Despite the limited size of the seventeenth-century armies and the scanty willingness to fight on the part of the mercenaries, battles and sieges nonetheless took a heavy toll on human lives.[9] In the big battles and sieges of the Thirty Years War the total number of dead and wounded came to almost 350,000.

In the eighteenth century things remained more calm and peaceful from a military point of view. In comparison with the previous period the size of armies did in fact increase – there were fighting forces of more than 100,000 men put in the field – but the tendency actually to use these expensive apparatuses was not that great among most rulers. When this did happen, however, the losses could be gigantic. During the Spanish War of Succession, there were 36,000 casualties at the battle of Malplaquet, which amounted to 20 percent of the forces that took part in the fighting. During the Austrian War of Succession (1741–1748), losses of around 15,000 men per battle were normal. In fact every ruler risked losing his entire military potential in a single battle. This was the reason for the cautiousness we referred to.

And yet, these were not the losses that preoccupied military commanders and medical men. Battles, in any case, could almost always be avoided. Whoever did not wish to fight was not obliged to do so. In reality, the losses in actual battle, however high they might turn out in the seventeenth and eighteenth centuries, were always much lower than the losses which occurred due to all sorts of epidemics. Typhus, typhoid fever, the plague and other contagious diseases represented the greatest enemy of pre-industrial armies. This enemy could not be eluded by simply refusing to join battle.

Concerning the exact size of the losses that resulted from disease, there is a considerable divergence of opinion in the relevant literature. The German doctor Robert Koch, one of the founders of bacteriology, calculated that between 1733 and 1865 1.5 million men died in military action, whereas 6.5 million died due to disease. The Russian researcher Boris Zesarewitch Urlanis believes that this ratio is too high and estimates the losses due to disease in the seventeenth and eighteenth centuries to be two to three times greater than those in battle. Even this conservative estimate makes it clear that epidemics represented an enormous problem for military organization.

In 1636, over a period of little more than two weeks, Gustav Adolphus witnessed the strength of his army decrease from 26,000 to 12,000 men. This time the great culprit was dysentery. Epidemics of plague and typhus saw to it, moreover, that during the Thirty Years' War the mortality rate as a result of disease far outstripped losses in battle.

During the eighteenth century, an improvement in military medical care occurred in various countries. The epidemics, however, could still not be brought under control. During the Seven Years War (1756–1763), the Austrian army lost 6,000 men in 16 days as a result of infectious disease. The total number of fatal casualties due to disease in that army came to 83,000 men. That was two and a half times more than those who had perished in battle.

During the Napoleonic Wars, the situation had still not changed fundamentally. Of the 400,000 French soldiers who lost their life in Spain, 'only' 100,000 died as a result of action in battle. Napoleon's adversary, Wellington, did not fare any better. He too lost almost three times as many soldiers to disease as he lost in battle.

From a health perspective, the troops were the most vulnerable during a siege. This was true both for the besiegers and for those under siege. In the case of the former, a combination of bad weather conditions and defective food supplies provided an excellent breeding ground for the spread of infectious disease. The garrisons were generally more comfortably quartered. During long-term sieges, however, here as well something could go wrong with provisioning and lead to a drastic decrease in resistance to disease. Moreover, a garrison found itself in a very thorny position once an epidemic did break out. A well-known example in this respect was the siege of Saragozza by the French in 1808. The Spanish garrison, which was 30,000 strong, lost 18,000 men during the siege due to typhoid fever. During the sieges of Dantzig, Torgau, and Mainz, cities which Napoleon had provided with powerful garrisons, the French lost 67,000 soldiers to epidemic diseases in 1813 and 1814. This figure is considerably higher than all the fatal casualties sustained in large battles of those same years. Thus, from the medical point of view, it can be said that Gustav Adolphus and Napoleon operated in a comparable situation. As far as disease was concerned, they had to deal with the same enemy and were both equally powerless.

Only in the course of the nineteenth century did a change in this situation gradually take place. Although it cannot be said that the outbreak of epidemics could finally be prevented, it may nonetheless be noted that the most notorious culprits were to some extent brought under control. Increased medical knowledge and improvement of the military medical organization played an important role in this process.[10]

Medical science had gone through a transforming development in the previous century. After the discoveries of Pasteur (1878) and Koch (1879) bacteriology entered a flourishing phase. Growing knowledge of the role micro-organisms played in the spread of infectious disease was naturally of great importance for military medicine. These new insights could be used, among other things, for setting up prevention programs.

The emergence of antiseptic surgery, which was first employed by Lister in 1866, was also of great importance. The post-operative mortality rate decreased sharply as a direct result of this development. The last group of medical innovations introduced in this period had to do with the use of anaesthetics. By adequately anaesthetizing a patient, first by means of ether (1846), and then with chloroform (1847), surgeons acquired greater possibilities for carrying out operations. Complicated operations, which had previously belonged to the realm of the impossible, now became medically feasible. Advances in the field of communication and transport allowed medical innovations to spread over the whole developed world with unprecedented speed. Medical men visited each other's laboratories and could learn of one another's findings by other means as well, for example through books, newspapers and scientific journals. This process continued unabated even during times of war, as we shall see below in the section on military psychiatry.

As far as the military is concerned, medical insights are only of value if a good level of organization exists which is responsible for their concrete application. The nineteenth century was also an important period for the military medical services. Two factors in particular saw to it that the army leadership began to take these services seriously. To begin with, there was the establishment of armies made up of conscripts. These men were making an important sacrifice on behalf of their homeland and it was only reasonable that something should be done in recognition of this. One such thing would be to assure that the wounded received good medical care. Secondly, the development of weapons technology had its role to play. Over the last decades of the previous century, the ability to sow death and destruction had increased on a terrifying scale. It became increasingly more difficult for a nation to go on endlessly absorbing losses in battle. A good medical service was considered absolutely indispensable for maintaining an army's fighting power.

If we now take a look at the wars during the period concerned and the losses sustained in them, we find ourselves confronted with a very heterogeneous picture. The Crimean War (1854–1855), as far as the rate of casualties involved, represents one of the deepest abysses of military history. Measuring with a scale of 1,000 men per year, the Russians suffered the greatest battle losses recorded in the whole of history up to that time. The French army achieved the highest score for losses due to disease. A completely new record was set during the American Civil War. Viewed statistically, the latter was the most life-threatening war of all times. A soldier's chance of coming through the conflict alive was one out of four.

This sad reality was the result of a combination of circumstances. For one thing tactical principles had not yet been adapted to the level of weapons technology.[11] Many casualties occurred for this reason alone. In addition, relatively soft, lead bullets were in use. The wounds caused by these projectiles were far more serious and difficult to treat than those occasioned by the bullets that came to be used later. It is also worth mentioning that many recruits already displayed physical defects and were often undernourished at the time they were conscripted. A considerable portion of them came from isolated agricultural areas where they had not built up sufficient immunity to current infectious diseases. These vulnerable and weakened soldiers turned out to be a welcome prey to the classic enemies of the military: typhus, typhoid fever, and dysentery.

As we stated above, the study of war in the nineteenth century reveals a hetero-geneous state of affairs. Consequently, there were conflicts which displayed a quite different countenance. The most striking example in this respect is the Franco-Prussian War. During the expedition against Paris, the German army enjoyed all the benefits of an efficiently functioning medical service. Similarly, from a medical point of view Von Moltke's troops were well prepared. The soldiers had been sys-tematically vaccinated and there was adequately trained medical personnel on hand to treat the wounded. After 1871, German military organization, from the medical standpoint as well, became a leading example for the rest of the world.

We meet with the absolute high point of medical provision in the Russo-Japanese War (1904–1905). The Japanese here made it clear that they were not only able to appreciate the full value of Western innovations, but that they were capable of making extraordinarily effective use of them.[12] This was the first large-scale war in which, at least on the Japanese side, the relation between losses sustained in action and losses as a result of disease was reversed. The Japanese army lost 8 percent of its manpower in combat with the enemy, whereas only 2 percent of its force suc-cumbed to disease. This transformation can rightly be considered an event of his-torical import.

Naturally, it was a great advantage that the Japanese soldiers maintained a high degree of personal hygiene due to their upbringing. They were accustomed to bathe regularly and to shave every day. The customary practice of cremating the dead on the spot instead of burying them also had a positive effect on the hygienic circumstances in which the army operated. Nonetheless, these customs and prac-tices on their own would not have been of significance. During the war with China (1894), it appeared that the Japanese army was very vulnerable to dysentery, chol-era, and malaria. After these painful experiences the army decided to carry out a logical application of the medical know-how which had already been available for quite some time. This knowledge originated in Germany where Japanese students attended the renowned medical faculties. Similarly, German professors came to Ja-pan to give instruction in the medical field.

An essential element of the Japanese army's medical service consisted of system-atically informing every Japanese soldier about a certain range of health questions. Every officer was obliged to follow a course on hygiene in the field. All the non-commissioned officers were responsible for passing on instruction to the lower ranks. Of course, information by itself was not sufficient and other factors played a role. And in this respect as well, the Japanese were good at organizing their affairs. Adequate supplies of medicine and dressing materials were provided. The army also had at its disposal an ambulance system which functioned humanely and with speed. And, last but not least, an adequate number of well-trained doctors was on hand.

The Japanese achievements are all the more impressive if we compare them with the performance of the British army during the same period in the Boer War (1899–1902). In particular, the preventive measures adopted by the British left much to be desired.[13] Ultimately, they lost 16,000 men as a result of typhus and dysentery. That was two and a half times more than the number of casualties caused by the Boers (6,000). Yet on paper everything appeared to be in order. An official medical service existed and all manner of sanitary regulations had been issued. But the problem was that no one took any of it seriously. The health officer was generally looked upon as the most useless figure in the army. The men in the ranks and most of the officers did not concern themselves in the least about the most crucial regulations, such as obligatory boiling of water before consumption.

The Boer War once again made it clear that medical knowledge alone is not sufficient. Without a well-organized medical service this knowledge remains ineffective. Although there were and still are big differences regarding this point within the armed forces of the industrialized nations, it can be stated that from the beginning of the twentieth century the creation of military medical services was taken seriously everywhere.

Desertion

A ruler in the sixteenth century, who wished to settle a religious or a political conflict with arms, naturally had to dispose of the necessary financial means. Nor was that an end to the matter. For many rulers their real problems only began the moment they availed themselves of the services of a military entrepreneur. Indeed, the risk that one might end up the proud owner of an army and yet find one had very limited real authority over this instrument, was far from being purely hypothetical. To the mercenaries the general was their real employer. The ruler, who ultimately paid for everything, resided far beyond the immediate horizon. The military was in fact run by the generals and their subcontractors. Should they find that it was better to conclude peace or that a campaign should be brought to an end, they did just that. If need be, they would act against the will of their paymaster. The great German military entrepreneur *par excellence*, Wallenstein, is one of the best known examples of this behavior.

From the end of the seventeenth century, the grip of rulers on the army became greater. Both in France and in Prussia standing armies were created in which the nobility fulfilled the function of officers. By this means the absolute rulers acquired a firmer grip on their military apparatuses.[14]

Yet these armies, which were now more tightly bound to the state, still proved difficult to control. Mutinies, individual or collective desertion, and a generally low willingness to fight were as a rule characteristic of armies in the pre-industrial period. Geoffrey Parker has described how the continuous mutinies among the Spanish troops assured the final victory of the Dutch Republic in the Eighty Years' War. Even the army of the Republic, despite its favorable pay arrangements, was so plagued by desertions that the reforms of Maurits were seriously endangered.[15]

In the years that followed, the situation in this regard scarcely changed at all. Even in Fredrick the Great's Prussia where everything was done to prevent desertion, many a soldier would suddenly decide his contract was up and disappear in thin air. For example, a regiment of guards quartered in Potsdam between the years

1740 and 1800 lost as a result of desertion: 2 officers, 93 non-commissioned officers, 1,525 men of the ranks, and 32 musicians. This amounts to half the regiment's
normal strength.[16] During the Napoleonic Wars, the losses due to desertion and
their consequences, were regularly greater than the losses resulting from engaging
with the enemy.

Generally speaking, in the pre-industrial period it was relatively simple to desert.
The faulty logistics system, as described above, made it necessary for troop units to
go off on their own to find their sustenance by plundering and robbery. These expe-
ditions offered unique opportunities to escape from the military organization. Intelligent generals like Wellington took the trouble to ensure that the continued existence of the army did not depend on practices of this kind. For instance, in Spain
by accepting to pay high prices he created a local market where peasants and craftsmen willingly came to sell their wares and services.

During pitched battles, there were frequently opportunities for individuals or
groups to withdraw from the fighting. On the whole, the military medical services
were so faulty that the transport of wounded had to be carried out by troops taken
out of the battle. Once these had arrived in the rear, it was generally difficult to get
them to return to their fighting positions. This is why commanders in the field often
forbade transporting the wounded or giving them treatment while the fighting was
going on. Due to the presence of large quantities of smoke, the battlefield was
sometimes so obscured that soldiers could easily withdraw from the action for
shorter or longer periods. The situation was facilitated by the fact that the actual
battlefields were often so restricted in size that the distance to a safe area could be
crossed very quickly. During the Battle of Waterloo, for instance, a few Belgian
units found safe refuge by simply withdrawing into the nearby woods. In many armies, therefore, the cavalry had a double task: to destroy the enemy forces, and to
be on the look-out for desertion among their own troops.

On the whole, it can be said that the average general or officer did not have a
high opinion of his own troops. In this connection, Teitler has remarked that the
model of organization which developed during the time of the military revolution
underwent a change of function in the eighteenth century.[17] The model of a social
machine which originally was an attempt to combine manpower and weapons as rationally as possible, gradually acquired a different content. This model now became
the expression of the social distance that existed within the armed forces. On the
one side was the nobility that occupied all the officer functions. On the other side
stood the lowest social strata from which the men in the ranks were recruited. The
subordination and discipline of the lower strata became the main function of the
machine model. Hierarchy and discipline thus took on another meaning. During
the *ancien régime*, neither in France nor in Prussia was it in the first instance a question of forming an effective fighting machine. What was more important was the
creation of an organization in which the nobility felt at home and which caused a
minimum of disturbance to the rest of the community.

Obedience was enforced by means of fines and a wide range of corporal punish-
ments. Branding, flogging and running the gauntlet belonged to the normal folk-

lore of military life. For more serious offenses, such as deserting the colors during battle, there was the death penalty, carried out with the noose or the bullet. The central thought underlying this package of disciplinary measures was clearly expressed by Fredrick the Great. He stated that the ordinary soldier must feel greater fear before his own officers than before the enemy. This statement, which was subscribed to by many contemporaries without hesitation, illustrates how low the average soldier's motivation to fight was estimated by his superiors.

In the European military tradition there existed one alternative to the mercenaries who were deemed untrustworthy. This was the militia, a variant that had already been adopted by the Greek city-state. In Florence Macchiavelli attempted to escape from the plague of mercenaries by establishing a militia. During the first phase of the French Revolution, the well-to-do citizens of Paris formed a national guard which once again gave shape to the ideal of a militia. This institution, which had moreover been adopted several times in history, had one important drawback, however. The area of recruitment was limited to the well-off strata of the community who were in possession of political rights. Therefore, large armies could not be fielded in this manner. A better alternative, it appeared, was a conscript army. Bringing in conscription, first in France in 1793, and later in the nineteenth century in the other continental countries, laid the basis for the formation of armies that were both large and trustworthy.

Conclusion

The military revolution provided the army with an effective form of organization by means of which violence could be produced in a rational manner. However, a military force for quite some time thereafter remained a rather precarious possession. Desertion, disease, and hunger presented perpetual threats to the continued existence of the military organization. The industrial revolution brought about a change in this respect. In the course of the nineteenth century it became steadily more easy to constitute large armies and to maintain them over long periods in the field. In addition, by bringing in conscription the required basic loyalty was obtained. Thus the opportunity was gradually created to give attention to other matters that were of importance for the continuity of the military. It was in this context that military psychiatry took shape.

On the other hand, these developments had by no means reached their final stage. We cannot simply say that the classic threats had been brought under control and that attention could now be directed to new matters. In fact every war brought with it new medical questions, including new kinds of wounds and other forms of contagion. At the same time, illnesses ranging from simple flu to syphilis have remained a continual threat to the effective use of an army's full potential. The newly acquired loyalty also turned out not to be an invariable factor which could be counted on at all times. In the summer of 1917, after the bloody misfortunes of the previous months, the French soldier's loyalty had almost completely disappeared. Desertion and mutinies were once again the order of the day. In the autumn of

1917, the Russian army did not fare much better. Even in Germany the army collapsed in 1918 and the soldiers appeared to be receptive to revolutionary slogans. During the Normandy invasion of the Second World War, the British conscripts who had previously fought in North Africa and Italy were tired of war. After the successful landings, it was clear that a considerable portion of Montgomery's army was exhausted and suffered from a low level of motivation.[18] Desertion and self-inflicted wounds were becoming more and more common. Psychiatry was only one of the refuges to which soldiers had recourse, even if unintentionally, to get themselves removed from the fighting.

The following quotations, taken from a report drafted by the commander of the 6th Duke of Wellington Regiment, present a vivid picture of the psychological state this fighting unit was in in June 1944:

3 State of Men
  a) 75% of the men react adversely to enemy shelling and are 'jumpy'.
  b) 5 cases in 3 days of self-inflicted wounds – more possible cases.
  c) Each time men are killed or wounded a number of men become casualties through shell shock or hysteria.
  d) In addition to genuine hysteria a large number of men have left their positions after shelling on one pretext or another and gone to the rear until sent back by the M.O. or myself.
  e) The new drafts have been affected, and 3 young soldiers became casualties with hysteria after hearing our own guns.
  f) The situation has got worse each day as more key personnel have become casualties.

4 Discipline and Leadership
  a) State of discipline is bad, although the men are a cheerful, pleasant type normally.
  b) NCOs do not wear stripes and some officers have no badges of rank. This makes the situation impossible when 50% of the battalion do not know each other.
  c) NCO leadership is weak in most cases and the newly drafted officers are in consequence having to expose themselves unduly to try to get anything done. It is difficult for the new officers (60%) to lead the men under fire as they do not know them.

Conclusion
  a) 6 DWR is not fit to take its place in the line.
  b) Even excluding the question of nerves and morale 6 DWR will not be fit to go back into the line until it is remobilised, reorganised, and to an extent retrained. It is no longer a battalion but a collection of individuals. There is naturally no *esprit de corps* for those who are frightened (as we all are to one degree or another) to fall back on. I have twice had to stand at the end of a track and draw my revolver on retreating men.[19]

When this report reached Montgomery, he gave the order to disband the regiment, which ceased to be an independent fighting unit.

The loyalty of the American conscripts in Vietnam proved to be a constant problem to the very end.[20] Especially after 1968, the soldiers made it increasingly clear that they were unwilling to expose themeselves to personal danger in that war. In 1971 alone, 254 cases of refusal to take part in combat were officially registered. It may be assumed that the real number was much higher since by no means every commander was concerned to report cases of this sort.

Thus the changes ushered in by the industrial revolution were no final solution to the age-old problems of the military but in fact no more than a precarious balance. To be sure, military psychiatry had acquired a place within this balance, but what its exact position was in each ensuing conflict will be the object of discussion below.

III- The Psychologically Wounded Soldier: An Actor with a Lead Role among the Wounded

Introduction

The fruits of the industrial revolution have in many respects led to an improvement in the quality of daily life. This is true for the military sector as well. The modern soldier is on the whole far better off than his pre-industrial counterpart with regard to clothing, nutrition, housing and health care. In the previous chapter we saw how modern improvements made it possible to pay attention to questions of a psychological nature.

Attention of this kind was in fact necessary because modernization not only solved old problems but created new ones as well. In this chapter we will show that modern warfare has generated an enormous psychiatric problem. Of course, changes did not come about willingly nor did they take place from one day to the next, but in the end all Western armies were obliged to recognize the reality of the problem. What factors shaped the situation? Why was it precisely in the twentieth century that so many soldiers could come to be designated as psychologically wounded. Edward A. Strecker, who was the military psychiatrist attached to the American expeditionary army in Europe, makes the following statement in his description of American military psychiatry at the time of the First World War:

...in World War I the terrorizing and lethal properties of machines of war for the first time approached the saturation level of human nervous resistance.[1]

In Strecker's view it was primarily the new weapon systems, such as the improved artillery, which made modern warfare unbearable.

Thomas W. Salmon, a man who was among the first to formulate the fundamental principles of military psychiatry, had a somewhat broader vision. In his opinion it was not only the new weapons that were responsible but, more generally speaking, the new circumstances in which war was waged:

The present war is the first in which the functional nervous diseases ('shell shock') have constituted a major medico-military problem. As every nation and race engaged is suffering from the symptoms, it is apparent that new conditions of war are chiefly responsible for their prevalence.[2]

In the present chapter these new circumstances will be examined with a view to their psychological significance. We will limit our focus to the most crucial factors in this respect, i.e. massive volume, fire power and the combat situation.

Massive Volume
Napoleon was a military genius. He forged the achievements of the French Revolution into a sword with the help of which he forced Europe to its knees. Only in Russia and Spain did things go wrong. One of the chief achievements the emperor had at his disposal was an enormous army built up from conscripts.

Later in the century the improved administrative and logistical infrastructure enabled the great European powers to outshine by far Bonaparte's capacities.[3] In 1870, 1 out of 74 Frenchmen and 1 out of 34 Germans were available to the army. Toward 1914 the figures had become 1 out of 10 and 1 out of 13, respectively. According to statistics, on the eve of the First World War the following numbers of men were available to armies: 3,200,000 in France, 2,700,000 in Germany, 3,900,000 in Russia, and 2,300,000 in the Austro-Hungarian Empire.

Conscription also made it possible for the powers involved to suffer enormous losses. On New Year's Day 1917, the Allied Powers still had around 4 million men concentrated in the trenches on the western front. They were there to face up to a half million Germans. At the end of the Second World War, Russia and the United States each had about 15 million people (men and women) on active service in their armed forces. The vast majority of them were conscripts. One of the most impressive examples of what an efficient mobilization system can deliver is provided by the state of Israel. In 1990 the total population was four and a half million. On the basis of this Israel was able to put together an army of 646,000.

Obviously, due to economic and organizational considerations it was not advisable to maintain these armies on permanent active duty. Most of the soldiers, after having received their basic training, returned home again. In time of crisis they could then be called up and added to the forces of the standing army.

Seen in these terms, bringing in conscription gave the states in question access to what appeared to be an almost inexhaustible reservoir of manpower. Nevertheless, there are certain inherent weaknesses that one can point to in a conscript army. One of these weaknesses has to do with the great difference that has existed in every country from time immemorial between the military and the civilian sector. Military life comprises a separate world with its own values, its own rituals, and a specific work atmosphere all its own. Entering into that world can entail an intense and often painful adjustment for the average citizen. Of course, there are great differences to be noted in this respect. After all, the army includes a great number of functions which are current in the civilian world as well. This means that for the average cook or chauffeur the transition is much smoother than for someone with a profession that has no equivalent in the army. But the big problem is that for real combat functions there are no comparable functions in the civilian community. In this area, therefore, the transition is the most demanding. And these are precisely the servicemen who will be confronted with the greatest psychological stress during a war.

Another disadvantage of a conscript army has to do with training. When an army of this kind engages in combat, there will always be soldiers on hand who received their training years ago and since then have become rooted in civilian society again. Nor can one always assume that the training they received was up to standard. In democratic West-European civilian society the length of military service has always been under pressure. Shortening time spent in military training is a well-known method for making cuts in the defense budget. The state of Israel has never been able to allow itself such a luxury. Israel requires conscripts to spend three years in active service (officers four years). In addition, demobilized servicemen are called up on manoeuvers for one month every year. Despite all this, there is a certain scepticism among the professional army personnel *vis-à-vis* the capabilities of the reservists.

The Anglo-Saxon countries are in a particularly vulnerable position. England and the United States have made do with small professional armies in peace-time. During the great wars the armies have then become filled up with volunteers and conscripts. For the military authorities involved, this situation presented a gigantic problem. It meant that within a short period of time – in some cases extremely short – large numbers of recruits had to be housed, trained, and provided with weapons. Indeed, in England the outbreak of the Great War was accompanied by a stampede on the army's recruiting offices. During the first week of the war about 1,600 volunteers were signing up daily.[4] This meant that within one week 11,000 men had joined the army. And this was only the beginning. When the British expeditionary force took a beating at Mons – it was even described as a heroic retreat – the enthusiasm to be sent to the front increased still further. On August 25th, the flood of new recruits already amounted to 10,000 men. During the week that followed, the recruiting offices accepted a total of 63,000 recruits. The likelihood that such large numbers of men would receive adequate training was not great, as events on the battlefield were to show. On the eve of the Second World War there was a similar situation in the United States. America ranked eighteenth on the list of the world's military powers, directly behind Portugal. This meant that millions of soldiers had to be inducted and put through a rapid course of training over a brief period of time. When they then got their first taste of combat, as in 1942 in North Africa, they were still not properly prepared.

With Erwin Rommel as an opponent, the American army learned what the hard reality of war meant. Before the North African campaign was over countless numbers of soldiers experienced breakdowns because they were unable to adjust to the tough conditions of desert warfare. By way of summing up, it may be said that industrialized societies did come to dispose over enormous armies, but these formations, potentially at least, were especially vulnerable from a psychological viewpoint.

Fire Power

In pre-industrial Europe craftsmen as well as technically minded military men occasionally made attempts to improve on existing weapons or to invent new ones.
But both the contemporary system of production and the rigid military organization that had emerged during the military revolution hampered the rapid development of weapons technology. During the last decades of the previous century a
change took place in that respect. New weapons and weapon systems found their
way into the military domain at a rapid pace.

The extent to which fire power increased during the nineteenth century can be illustrated by a comparison of the situation at the time of the Napoleonic Wars with
that on the eve of the First World War.[5] Napoleon's army had at its disposal three
pieces of artillery for every thousand men. The armies in 1914 not only disposed
over double that number but the rate of fire of their cannons had increased twenty-
fold. As for the weapons used by the infantry, these had on the whole increased
their rate of fire eightfold and their range fourteenfold. Through one improvement
or another an infantry brigade of 3,000 men in 1914 could muster the same fire
power as an army of 60,000 under the Duke of Wellington.

In *The Face of Battle* John Keegan has given a good example of what the effect
could be of these differences in fire power on an infantry unit.[6] During the Battle of
Waterloo a battalion of the celebrated Innis Killing Fusiliers was exposed to intensive fire from the French side for three hours. The result was devastating. No less
than 61 percent of the battalion's strength, i.e. 427 men, was put out of commission.
During the first day of the Somme offensive in 1916, the same battalion suffered
losses of 70 percent of its fighting force, i.e. 568 men. Only this time it happened
within the first half-hour of the battle.

The example Keegan gives is both enlightening and misleading. Without a doubt
the capacity to sow death and destruction had greatly increased during the period
in question. The casualty figures of the British battalion aptly illustrate this point.
What is misleading, however, is that the existence of some sort of direct relationship is suggested between fire power and the number of casualties. But in fact the
relationship between these two variables is not that simple. Before going further
into this question, we will first consider in greater detail the innovations which had
taken place with regard to means of producing violence.[7]

What was most striking was the improvement in artillery. Both the explosive
force of the shells and the distances over which they could be delivered increased at
a rapid pace. The repercussions of this development are particularly evident in the
history of fortification techniques. Many shellproof forts, almost immediately after
their completion, proved to be extremely vulnerable to artillery bombardments.
Moreover, these fortifications had to be constructed at increasingly greater distances from population centers. Equally spectacular was the increased efficacity of
field artillery. During the American Civil War, the shells that were fired into the
midst of the enemy troops burst into five splinters. After 1886, thanks to charges of
high explosive, upward of a thousand fragments were produced. The capacity to
put the enemy out of commission thereby increased enormously.

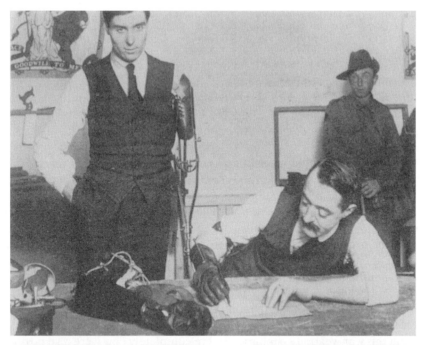

Some effects of shell bursts

Somewhat less striking, but of no less importance, were the improvements effected in the weapons employed by the infantry. New type rifles with a more rapid rate of fire and a greater range came into use. The introduction of smokeless gunpowder made it possible for a rifleman to keep his target in sight, with the result that continuous fire could be maintained. It was also of great significance that the handling of standard weapons was becoming easier. Consequently, by the end of the previous century a soldier could fire his weapon in every possible position – standing, lying down or running. An important development in the arsenal of the infantryman was the machine-gun.[8] During the American Civil War, protoypes of the machine-gun were first used, but without much success. The French army had the *mitrailleuse* at its disposal in the Franco-Prussian War. Bitter feuding that had broken out between different subdivisions of the army resulted in the new weapon being consigned to the artillery stationed behind the front. Thus the German army suffered no serious problems because of it. The machine-gun caused a sensation for the first time in colonial wars. By means of this weapon a relatively small European force had been able to drive off large hosts of native warriors. The weapon was judged less suitable for the European battlefield. Thus when war broke out in 1914, all the sides involved were unprepared in this respect. But they were quick to make up for their neglect when it was demonstrated that white troops too were highly vulnerable to machine-gun fire.

During this war weapon systems that were completely new were also introduced, such as the tank and the airplane. Both these weapons were further developed during the interwar years and deployed again with great success from 1939 onwards. The Second World War brought with it new weaponry as well. For our study mention may be made of rockets such as the Russian *Katyusha* and the German *Nebelwerfer*. One salvo from these weapons was capable of saturating whole areas with explosives. The modern American variant can neutralize a terrain the size of six football fields with a single blast. As for the most spectacular of weapons, the atom bomb, there is no need to expatiate. Nuclear weapons have only ever been used on Hiroshima and Nagasaki. For the treatment of our subject it is not necessary to go into details about the development of nuclear arsenals. Indeed, the further expansion of conventional weapons is sufficiently impressive by itself. After 1945 an intense arms race began which has ultimately led to almost all weapons, from the simple rifle to the strategic bomber, undergoing wide-ranging improvements in efficacity.

In 1980 the American army estimated that thanks to technological advances conventional warfare had become 400 to 700 times more deadly and intensive than it was at the time of the Second World War. At Fort Irwin in California, where the army regularly carries out realistic combat exercises, simulated casualties, both among those attacking and those on the defensive, reach above 90 percent.[9]

Chemical weapons, which were first used systematically and on a massive scale in the First World War, comprise a separate chapter on their own. These weapons have a devastating effect when used against troops that have no protection. With the arrival of gas masks and protective clothing the deadly gases used in warfare lost much of their original capability. However, to this day their psychological significance has remained great.

The psychological effect weapons may have is to a great extent independent of the real damage they are capable of inflicting. The sound that airplanes and tanks produce can make a more disturbing impression than the actual bombs they drop and the shells they fire. When modern weapon systems are being built, these secondary effects are duly taken into account. One of the most striking examples of this phenomenon is the German *Stuka* which the Luftwaffe used in May 1940 to achieve big successes. And yet this airplane could only carry a very small load of bombs. The sirens mounted on its wings, however, produced such a terrifying noise when it went into a dive, that panic regularly broke out among the Allied troops. By sending in B-52 bombers both in Vietnam and in Iraq, the Americans intended above all to break the morale of the enemy, while the actual material damage caused was of secondary importance. Whatever may be the intended effects of developing and using weapon systems, one thing is certain: in modern warfare the combined effect of massive volume and fire power has attained bewildering proportions.

Death and Destruction

The American Civil War marked the beginning of a new era in the history of warfare. During that conflict the combined effect of massive volume and fire power was made manifest for the first time. The war was waged with exceptional intensity and included no less than 48 confrontations which can be characterized as 'major battles'.[10] During these violent clashes, such as Antietam, Gettysburg and Cold Harbour, losses commonly exceeded 25 percent of the fighting forces. Among the Union's troops a total of 110,000 men lost their life during the four-year period that the war lasted. On the side of the Southerners, 94,000 soldiers perished. In addition to these casualties in battle, another 400,000 people died as a result of privation, exhaustion and disease. The total population of the United States in 1860 was approximately 32 million. Thus the losses involved were quite large in relative terms as well.

Broadly speaking, the First World War presents the same picture.[11] Only in this case the major battles were larger and extended over longer periods of time. For the French, the campaign at Verdun (1916) has come to symbolize the war. Their losses (dead and wounded) amounted to half a million men. The opposing side suffered 400,000 casualties. In the case of the British, the Somme offensive has to this day remained engraved in their collective memory. The 400,000 casualties they sustained exceeded any losses they had previously experienced in the whole of their military history.

The First World War, at least as far as Western Europe was concerned, can be classified as a soldier's war. The number of civilian casualties was small. During the Second World War a change took place in this respect. Many millions of civilians lost their lives in the years 1939–1945. Table 1 gives an idea of these losses.

Table 1. *Estimated losses in the Second World War (Pacific included)*

Countries	Total	Soldiers including prisoners of war	Civilians
USSR (1941-45)	20,600,000	13,600,000	7,000,000
Germany	6,850,000	3,250,000	3,600,000
Great Britain	388,000	326,000	62,000
France	810,000	340,000	470,000
Poland	6,123,000	123,000	6,000,000
Yugoslavia	1,706,000	300,000	1,400,000
Hungary	420,000	-	-
Greece	520,000	-	-
Rumania	460,000	-	-
Austria	480,000	-	-
Italy	410,000	330,000	80,000
Czechoslovakia	400,000	-	-
Other European countries	425,000	-	-
Total losses all European countries	±40,000,000		
USA (1941-45)(Pacific included)	295,000		

A large part of the civilian casualties was the result of the policy of extermination which the Nazi regime pursued. Many civilians also died because both sides attempted to knock out one another's industrial centers by means of bombardment. Finally, in Yugoslavia the harsh guerilla war exacted a heavy toll from the population.

In the beginning the war was relatively mild for the military participants. The *Blitzkrieg*, a form of warfare that avoids large-scale confrontation, was accompanied by low casualties on the part of both aggressor and defender. Only from the summer of 1941 onwards, when Operation Barbarossa, the attack against Russia, went into effect, did a change set in. This offensive cost Hitler a loss of three-quarters of a million men, and the great battle for Moscow had still not begun. Operation Barbarossa made it clear that even mobile warfare was capable of exacting a heavy toll. This was certainly the case if one's opponent was willing and able to fight back. It is important to bear in mind that behind the dry statistics given above a world of emotions is hidden. Perhaps it is appropriate at this point to consider more closely what a soldier's direct experiences are in war.

Combat is an emotional experience *par excellence* although the feelings aroused by war are not always uniform in their nature and intensity. To begin with, there is the fear of failure, of letting down your comrades at the decisive moment and as a result being branded with the label 'coward'. After a while this threatening feeling decreases and a new anxiety takes its place, that of assuring your own survival.

The realization that you can die or be wounded gradually assumes more concrete forms. On the battlefield confrontation with death takes numerous forms. Almost every veteran still remembers the first dead person he saw. Generally speaking, one is not only able, years later, to say precisely when it was but one can even describe in detail what the dead person looked like. But with the passage of time one seems to go through a process of habituation. The dead now form part of war and one comes to see death as something that to a certain extent is 'all in the game'. At least so it seems when death occurs in a neat and tidy manner, for example because of a tiny hole in the head. One has far more difficulty in accustoming oneself to cases of extreme disfigurement – a torn open abdomen, severed limbs, and smashed skulls. In confrontations with death one's sense of smell also plays a role. A soldier not only comes across those recently killed on the battlefield but meets with corpses that are at various stages of decomposition. Because of this the battlefield acquires a distinctive odor which after a number of days turns into an unbearable stench. Most veterans can give a detailed description of these special sensations as well.

Along with the dead there are the wounded. The variety in this domain, if such a thing is possible, appears to be even greater. Broadly speaking, wounds can be subdivided into desirable and undesirable injuries. The former group comprises light wounds which make a soldier exempt from further active service but do not entail long-term consequences. Undesirable wounds, on the other hand, do result in such consequences. Here one has in mind permanent disability or serious disfigurement, such as burns to the face for example.

During protracted heavy fighting, many soldiers experience the desire for a neat, light wound. The desire is sometimes so strong that the soldier decides to take matters into his own hands and inflicts an injury on himself. One of the chief tasks of military medicine has always been to determine whether a wound is due to this specific form of initiative, and if such is the case, to report it. In dealing with more serious wounds, the military doctor is less on his guard since the average soldier will do everything in his power to avoid these. After all, who wants to go through the rest of his life blind or a cripple? From time immemorial protecting the genitals has occupied a special place in the thoughts of a soldier. Concern for preserving these vital organs has always been reckoned a top priority of a warrior. The weapons industry has contrived to exploit this fact. For instance, after the Second World War mines were developed which were not immediately triggered when tread upon, but only exploded at the appropriate height. In designing the device, it was assumed quite rightly that the psychological effect of this kind of explosion was greater than that of the classic situation in which only a foot would be blown off. As in the case of the dead, with the wounded too there is an additional dimension. The dead give off an odor and the wounded let out unimaginable shrieks and moaning. Descriptions of the wailing of wounded soldiers form some of the most terrifying accounts of war ever written. In the trench warfare of 1914–1918, the shrieks and wailing of the wounded in no man's land at times provoked such emotions that the most hazardous rescue operations were mounted to provide help. A British officer has given a vivid description of what he heard one night on the war-stricken fields of Passchendaele:

From the darkness on all sides came the groans and wails of wounded men; faint, long, sobbing moans of agony, and despairing shrieks. It was too horribly obvious to me that dozens of men with serious wounds must have crawled for safety into shell holes, and now the water was rising above them and, powerless to move, they were slowly drowning.[12]

However, not every casualty wanted to be rescued at any price. Lieutenant Guerin, who had been wounded in both legs during the battle of Dien Bien Phu, shot himself in the head when he perceived that his men had begun to mount a rescue operation. The French officer in question obviously felt that his life was not worth this kind of dangerous undertaking.[13]

Unequal Chances

Bigger armies, better weapons and increasing casualty figures, that is how one might characterize the history of modern industrial warfare. But the relationship between the increased efficacity in fire power and the greater number of casualties is more complicated than what the above description might suggest. Thus in this connection it is appropriate to add two marginal observations.

First of all, the damage caused by a weapon does not depend exclusively on the characteristics of the weapon itself. What is also important is the manner in which the weapon is used, as well as how the opponent reacts to it. Thus in the relationship between fire power and final effect tactical principles and military doctrines play a significant role. Particularly informative in this regard are the various studies treating this subject which Colonel Trevor Dupuy has published.[14] Dupuy estimates that, from ancient times up to the October War in 1973, the average fire power of a 100,000 man army has increased by a factor of 2,000. On the other hand, we can observe that, certainly since the period of the military revolution, armies have reacted to this development in a definite manner. Put in the simplest terms, armies have made themselves less vulnerable by deploying their troops in more scattered formations. Square formations gave way to battle lines and these lines became steadily thinner. The final extension or thinning of the line, according to Dupuy's calculations, has increased by a factor of 4,000. The end result of this parallel development was a decrease in the number of casualties, viewed as a percentage of the total number of troops put in the field. The diagram in figure 1. shows that military organization, at least in the long run, has reacted in a rational manner to the innovations which took place in the area of weaponry. It has been possible to neutralize the more deadly efficacy of weapons by applying new tactical principles. The same diagram also makes it clear that there have been exceptions to this general tendency.

The most striking exceptons in this regard are provided by the Napoleonic Wars. The campaigns waged by the French emperor were accompanied by enormous losses. The cause of this was the tactic used by Bonaparte in which hordes of French troops in concentrated columns rushed upon the enemy. These formations were very vulnerable to rifle and artillery fire. Nevertheless, the French commander-in-chief could allow himself to use this tactic, which had an element of surprise that led to success, because by now he disposed over an army of enormous size. In his overall strategy he took account of sustaining heavy losses. None of Napoleon's op-

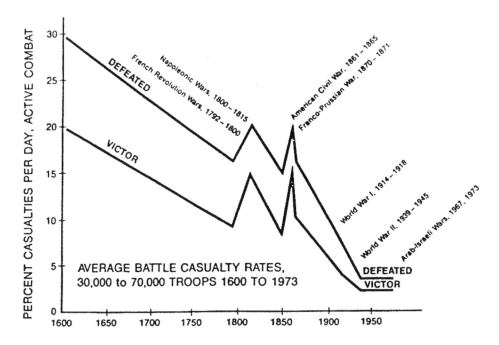

Figure 1. Battle Casualties, 1600-1973 (Source: T.N. Dupuy, The Evolution of Weapons and Warfare, p. 314)

ponents could afford to squander manpower on such a scale. In this respect as well the French emperor was quite unique.

After the period of Napoleon the relative decrease of casualties in battle proceeded at a rapid pace, but there were still notable exceptions. The two major examples of this kind of exception occurred in the American Civil War and the First World War. The carnage that took place in these armed conflicts was, for the most part, due to the methods of warfare employed. Both during the American Civil War and the War of 1914–1918, the mode of attack was almost the same as in the pre-industrial period: thick, heavily concentrated formations advanced against the enemy at a walking pace. Today it appears unimaginable to us but this is what happened. Before these tragedies took place there had been fierce discussion within the military establishment. During the second half of the previous century, the military had been inundated with a flood of new possibilities. Accommodation required time. This was certainly true concerning the new situation that was dawning with regard to fire power. The French colonel Charles Ardent du Picq, one of the greatest military thinkers of the nineteenth century, was well aware of the dilemmas brought about by innovations in the area of weaponry. We find the following observations in a letter he wrote in 1870:

In the last century, after the improvements of the rifle and field artillery... improvements to which the recent Prussian successes in war in part are due – we find all thinking men in the army asking themselves the question: 'How shall we fight tomorrow?' We have no combat doctrine. And the various contradictory methods [that are suggested] confuse the intelligence of military men.[15]

In those cases where tactics did not adjust properly to technology great catastrophes occurred. The first day of the Somme offensive was a catastrophe of this kind. Thus Keegan's example of the increased destructive effects of new weapons, which we cited toward the beginning of the section on fire power, applies to a particular kind of situation. It illustrates what modern weapons are capable of if an opponent refuses to take account of their efficacity. Consequently, the risks a soldier runs depend on the particular moment in history that he is serving in the military. Those risks are the greatest in periods when military organization has not yet worked out a tactical response to an increase in fire power.

Chances of being killed or wounded also depend to a great extent on the function one fulfills in the army. A modern army is a small-scale version of the greater society that surrounds it. It consists for the most part of mechanics, truck drivers, telegraph operators, cooks and other maintenance personnel. The actual combat troops are a minority. Already by the Second World War 50 to 70 percent of servicemen belonged to non-combatant personnel. Of course, in modern warfare these servicemen are also in danger, but the risks are significantly lower than those which confront the combat troops. Sy M. Kahn kept an informative diary during the Second World War which has recently been published under the evocative title *Between Tedium and Terror*. Reading this work attentively, one realizes that in fact there was no question of tedium or of terror. Kahn was on duty in the Pacific working with a company that unloaded ships carrying supplies destined for the marines who were fighting to recover various islands from the Japanese. It was hard, strenuous work but there are no life-threatening situations described in the book.

The New Context
The size of armies and their powerful arsenals are not the only features which distinguish industrial warfare from the conflicts which were fought out in earlier times. Increased fire power, improvements in the field of transportation and other technological achievements have resulted in far-reaching changes in the combat situation. In general, it can be said that these changes, which will be briefly described in what follows, have led to an increase in the psychological pressures the soldier experiences.

Time and Space
In the pre-industrial period, mounting a military campaign, as well as engaging in battle, were limited by natural factors. Only springtime and summer were suitable

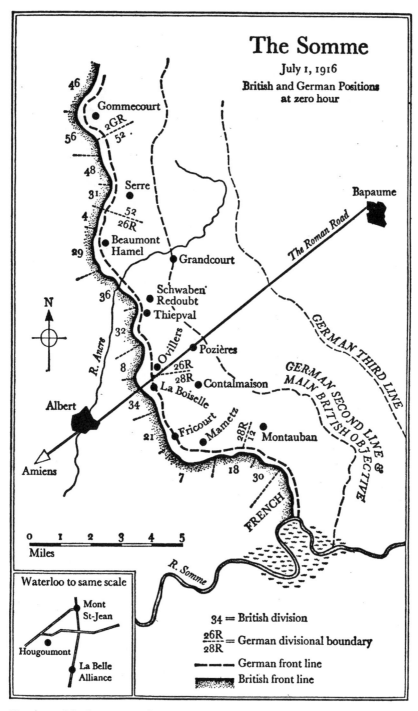

Waterloo and the Somme on scale

for launching an offensive. For the rest of the year the condition of roads made large-scale movements of an army impossible. Combat itself was carried out during the day. Battle could not be engaged during the nocturnal hours. This was not only due to the fact that the arrival of darkness made it impossible to coordinate military action, but it also had to do with the nature of the pre-industrial mercenary's motivation. A dark battlefield afforded too many opportunities to desert. If we bear in mind that most battles in the seventeenth and eighteenth centuries only lasted one day and that a considerable part of that time was spent on the deployment of the troops, it will be clear that the actual fighting took place during a very short timespan.

In the industrial period the seasons lose their meaning and the difference between day and night has less importance. Naturally, the break with the pre-industrial situation is not absolute. Winter has remained a bad time for waging war in certain regions and nocturnal operations are still more difficult to carry out than actions during the daytime. None the less, the point being made here is that, to a great extent, technology has been successful in surmounting natural limitations which had confronted the military thoughout the centuries. Thus thanks to modern means of communication and transport a different combat situation was created, a situation in which the duration of battles could be enormously increased.

The big battles at Ypres, Verdun and on the Somme each lasted more than a hundred hours. The invasion of Normandy went on for two months during which time there was intense fighting almost daily. In both world wars it is clear that the seasons were of less importance. At Verdun the fighting began in February; the Somme offensive continued into November. On the eastern front there were spring, summer, autumn and winter offensives. The Russian counter-offensive at Moscow in December 1941 was carried out in temperatures of minus 36 degrees Celsius, while the roads were covered with a meter of snow. The last German attempt to push back the tide in the West by means of a big offensive in the Ardennes began in 1944 just before Christmas.

Another characteristic of the industrial combat situation has to do with the potential size of the battle terrain. We have already alluded to the fact that, in response to the development of weapons technology, military organization adopted the tactic of thinner troop deployment. Large concentrated formations were replaced by smaller groups that operated over widespread areas. The area of operations of a division or of an army corps has steadily become greater, as is shown in the following table.

Table 2. *Historical Army Dispersion Patterns (Army or Corps of 100,000 Troops)*

	Antiquity	Napoleonic Wars	American Civil War	World War I	World War II	October War
Area Occupied by Deployed Force 100,000 Strong (sq km)	1.00	20.12	25.75	248	2,750	4,000
Front (km)	6.67	8.05	8.58	14	48	57
Depth (km)	0.15	2.50	3.0	17	57	70
Men Per Sq Km	100,000	4,970	3,883	404	36	25
Square Meters/man	10.00	200	257.5	2,475	27,500	40,000

Source: T.N. Dupuy, *The Evolution of Weapons and Warfare*, p. 312.

Furthermore, armies have steadily become bigger and they contain a greater number of fighting divisions. Both these tendencies combined led to the result that battlefields steadily grew in size.

In addition, it may be noted that the demarcation between the battlefield and the hinterland has become more vague. Heavy and medium field artillery were capable of shelling soldiers located several kilometers from the front. Later, airplanes, helicopters and rockets were responsible for a still further extension of the zone of danger.

Numerous factors have brought about a situation which is in sharp contrast with conditions during the Napoleonic Wars. Earlier it had been possible for soldiers, individually or in groups, to withdraw from the fighting and its concomitant dangers by simply moving one or two kilometers away from their assigned positions. Withdrawing from the battlefield in this manner is nowadays far less effective for the reasons sketched above. During the offensive at Ypres, British soldiers ran a considerable risk of being killed or wounded even when they were on leave in Poperingen, a town located 10 km. from the front. Because of the size and the structure of industrial armies, which leads to the hinterland being more heavily manned than the front line, this form of 'escape' has become increasingly more difficult.

The Lonely Soldier

To the unsuspecting civilian the battlefield can have a surprising appearance. In an interview the American actress Shirley McLaine once recounted how one evening in the early 1970s she switched on the television and landed in the middle of a war film. The film was uninteresting. There was not enough action, not enough excitement, in short it was clearly the work of a bad director. After a while, however, she realized that she was not watching an ordinary feature film but an in-depth news program dealing with the Vietnam War. The American film maker David W. Griffith had a similar experience in 1917. Quite exceptionally, he was granted permission by the British authorities to film at the front. After all, what could be more exciting than the reality of war? But Griffith was unable to record the gripping images he was after. In the end he decided to transfer his film team to a studio in England and he shot his film there, far from the violence of war.

The unspectacular character of the modern combat zone is due to the fact that the area in question appears to be empty. The opposing forces are virtually invisible. During basic training every infantryman learns the golden rule that you are to see what you can without being seen. From the following examples it is clear how well this lesson can be learned. In May 1953, the American Eighth Army was occupying the extended position which was later to become the line of demarcation between North and South Korea. One day during that month official reports register that along the whole breadth of that front a total of 37 enemy troops were observed. Admittedly, this is an extreme case, but there are stories from the Vietnam War that tell of soldiers who after a full year of active duty had not seen a single Vietcong or Vietnamese from close up.[16]

Of course, these are rather uncommon examples but their status as exceptions should not be overestimated. The modern battlefield does indeed present the appearance of being empty. One way or the other this is the result of the increased efficacity of infantry weapons. Approaching within sight of one another has become too risky a business. Nor is it any longer necessary to be within sight since the precision use of weapons has become so much greater that they can be loaded and fired from every imaginable position. Staying out of sight in this way is not only relevant with regard to the enemy but, to a lesser extent, has an effect on one's own troops. Let us try to picture an infantry platoon advancing into enemy territory. The soldiers are walking along both sides of the road with their rifles poised. Naturally, they do not walk closely bunched together but make sure to keep the necessary distance between themselves. Then suddenly the group comes under fire. From that moment the unit takes on a completely different aspect. Everyone seeks cover on his own initiative as quickly as possible. Within a few seconds what was previously an orderly formation breaks up into 40 separately reacting individuals.

The French colonel Ardent du Picq, whom we have referred to earlier, dwelt at great length on the consequences of this situation. He pointed out that in such cases another form of discipline is required. Now that the individual soldiers cannot be easily supervised by their officers, everything comes to depend on an internalized discipline. A soldier must be prepared to carry out his task even when he is temporarily no longer under the direct control of his commanding officer.[17]

When the group breaks up under enemy fire and comrades withdraw from one another's sight, either partially or completely, this can have further consequences. It means that at the moment of danger the soldier comes to stand on his own and is thrown back on his own resources. Naturally, breaking up like this is fully justified from a tactical point of view and offers the individual soldier the greatest chance of survival. However, the psychological effects work in a wholly different direction. In fact, in time of extreme danger all people, including soldiers, tend to have a different pattern of reaction. They want to huddle as close as possible to one another. They derive a sense of strength and support from being together. Being on one's own leads to feelings of loneliness and insecurity. In particular, inexperienced troops, but there are known cases of this among experienced units as well, have the tendency to bunch together. Men have frequently paid for this comfort with their lives. A grim example of this behavior is provided by the fate that befell about 80 Americans who were taken prisoner by the SS on December 18th, 1944, during the Ardennes offensive and then met their death in circumstances that have never been made clear. The soldiers in question were members of an artillery unit that had the misfortune of crossing the path of the SS Kampfgruppe Peiper just south of the small village of Malmédy. The German tanks immediately opened fire and the American trucks went up in flames. The Americans did not run away although the grey winter's morning and the nature of the landscape offered suitable cover. They remained standing alongside one another. It was then a simple matter to take them prisoner. They were held in a field near the crossroads where the fighting took place, and left behind under guard. How they ultimately came to die has never been clarified. They may have been shot by the SS because prisoners were a burden to look after, or perhaps they were killed by a second wave of German troops who were advancing in the tracks of Peiper. To the present day this mass execution near Malmédy has not be explained due to lack of witnesses. We have mentioned this event in order to show how difficult it can be to act rationally and to seek solitude in an hour of danger. Real security demands a degree of psychological discipline.

Conclusion

Military organization and methods of warfare were profoundly influenced by the industrial revolution and the changes it brought in its wake. What immediately strikes one is the enormous increase in potential for violence which modern states came to dispose over. Armies in the post-industrial era are not only bigger and better armed than their pre-industrial predecessors, but they can be maintained in the field for longer periods of time.

These changes have had consequences for the psychological pressure which soldiers undergo. Modern warfare has confronted them with death and destruction on a hitherto unknown scale. Similarly, they face weapon systems that have consciously been designed to exploit their fears and insecurities. Technological advances have seen to it that the natural rest periods which were available to the military throughout the centuries have come to be of less significance. Campaigns are no longer limited to particular seasons and even the difference between day and night is no longer as absolute as in previous times. Finally, the combat situation has changed from the social viewpoint as well. Combat in massive closed formations has given way to individual action and fighting in small open groups. The modern battlefield is inhabited by 'lonely' soldiers who frequently are unable to see their enemies but merely feel an anonymous threat.

Naturally, it is difficult to disagree with Napoleon who remarked that in the end it is the biggest battalions that win the battle. Nevertheless, massive volume also has certain drawbacks. Moreover, the French emperor himself was perfectly aware of this. The large armies of industrial societies were put together by means of conscription. The vast majority of their troops were civilians in uniform. Provisions for offering these millions of conscripts a suitable preparation for what awaited them at the front were, due to lack of time for instance, far from optimal. Summarizing, one may say that over the last hundred years the potential for violence has increased tremendously, whereas by contrast the capacity for resistance on the part of its victims has decreased. This concludes our description of one important aspect of the general background to the emergence of psychiatric problems in modern warfare.

IV - Victims, Perpetrators and Witnesses

Introduction

In the previous chapter we presented an overview of the most important characteristics of modern post-industrial warfare. Perhaps in so doing we appeared to be suggesting that there is, by definition, such a thing as a modern war, whereas nothing could be further from the truth. Recent history displays a wide spectrum of armed conflicts with great diversity in character, scale and intensity. For example, during the first half of this century the great European powers were engaged in total, all-encompassing wars. Subsequently, they waged war on a much more limited scale in their colonial territories where independence movements contested European hegemony. Some conflicts such as the First World War, in which armies consisting of more than a million men bombarded each other from trenches, possessed a static character. Later, the German Wehrmacht, followed by the Israeli armed forces, demonstrated the offensive capacities of modern military organization.

Similarly, any particular war may be made up of widely divergent combat situations.[1] In May 1940 the Germans surprised the Allies with the *Blitzkrieg*. This same tactic turned out to be less effective against the Soviet Union. Consequently, on the eastern front the German offensive was quickly transformed into a defensive campaign. Meanwhile, behind this front the Germans were engaged in a completely different kind of war against the partisans. Chaotic retreat proved to be the costly counterpart to the *Blitzkrieg*. The British expeditionary army on its way to Dunkirk and the American forces at the beginning of the Ardennes Offensive are examples of the same situation. During the Second World War the American marines effected numerous amphibious landings on heavily defended beaches. Operation Overlord, or the Normandy landings, still represents the most spectacular example of this kind of combat situation. Finally, one can mention attacks carried out against strongly fortified positions. These actions require the employment of well-trained elite units. Examples that come to mind include the surprise attack against Eben Emael by the German pioneers and the storming of Point du Hoc by the American Rangers. Thus the Second World War was definitely not uniform but displayed a variegated range of military actions.

To a certain extent the same can be said about the far more limited war that the Americans fought in Vietnam. In this case it was in reality a question of three different forms of military intervention. There was the guerrilla war with the Vietcong, as well as the more or less regulated struggle against the North-Vietnamese army that had infiltrated the South, and then finally the bombing raids directed against North Vietnam. In short, industrialized warfare has many faces. This also means that we may expect that the psychological pressures experienced by servicemen will exhibit quite some variation. To illustrate this point more effectively, in what follows we will analyze three different combat situations. They represent ideal type cases in which the three roles of soldiers with regard to the use of force will be discussed. The situations in question are trench warfare, fighting against guerrillas and the task of the UN observer. The roles that correspond to these situations are that of victim, perpetrator and witness.

The Trenches

The choice of a more dispersed deployment of troops and the replacement of closed formations by more open ones were logical reactions to increased fire power. Digging into the ground was another way to cope with the lethal effects of modern firearms. The shovel became an essential component of an infantryman's standard equipment.

Digging in can assume different forms depending on the amount of time one intends to remain in a particular spot. If armies come to take up positions opposite one another for somewhat longer periods, the original foxholes and ditches that were temporary arrangements become transformed into impressive networks of trenches. Trenches, which were already employed in pre-industrial siege tactics, appear from the time of the American Civil War right up to the recent conflict in the Persian Gulf. Thus although trenches are not specific to any particular conflict, it must be said that the First World War can rightly be characterized as the epitome of trench warfare, at least on the western front. Consequently, our examples will be taken from that particular struggle.

Alistair Horne, in his deservedly praised book on the fighting at Verdun, has also given some attention to day-to-day life in the trenches.[2] He notes that among those who actually experienced trench warfare the memory of its hardships has softened with the passage of time. Nonetheless, from the plethora of first-person documents that have been preserved concerning the First World War it is clear that life in the trenches was indeed a bewildering experience. It was a dangerous existence, as well as an extremely uncomfortable one.

Naturally there were differences. After all, the network of trenches formed a labyrinth that stretched from the English Channel to the Vosges. Over so wide an area differences existed in the circumstances under which men had to fight. There were dangerous and less dangerous sectors. In some areas life was exceedingly uncomfortable and in others it was more bearable. The surroundings of Ypres were notorious and feared. The fighting there was almost permanent, and the cold and ubiquitous mud made life into a hell. In the area around the Somme life was a bit more pleasant, at least up until the summer of 1916 when the British began their first big offensive there.

Despite the differences referred to, life in the trenches can be characterized as dangerous, uncomfortable and, with the passage of time, depressing and hopeless.

Danger was omnipresent. A major threat was the activity of snipers who were employed by both sides. These elite soldiers, who were issued with special rifles, constantly kept watch over the invisible enemy in the hope that someone would expose himself to fire. It is no coincidence that in Erich Maria Remarque's *All Quiet on the Western Front*, the best-known war novel of the twentieth century, or more appropriately put, anti-war novel, the protagonist is finally killed by a sniper.

A second danger came from artillery shelling which sometimes occurred without any warning at all. Intensive bombardment could lead to the total collapse of a trench network, with the result that the occupants were all killed or buried alive. Artillery shelling also provided the highest likelihood of becoming badly mutilated. Lord Moran, who was later to become Winston Churchill's personal physician, took part in the First World War as a regimental doctor and has described the effects of an artillery bombardment.

At the time of this bombardment I was not too much frightened. I was too stunned to think, but it took its toll later. I was to go through it many times in my sleep. I used to hear all at once the sound of a shell coming. Perhaps it was only the wind in the trees to remind me that war had exacted its tribute and that my little capital was less than it had been. There were men in France who were ready to go out but who could not meet death in that shape. They were prepared for it if it came cleanly and swiftly, but that shattering, crudely bloody end by a big shell was too much for them. All their plans for meeting death with decency and credit were suddenly battered down. Self-respect had gone out of their hands. They were no longer certain of what they would do. It frightened more men away from the trenches than anything else.[3]

Artillery shelling was not only feared because of its horrifying results. It afforded the best illustration of the powerlessness with which the soldier in the battlefield was confronted. An infantryman could not do anything in response to enemy fire. He had to wait and hope that the artillery would miss its target. Airplanes and helicopters can have the same paralyzing effect. Firing back by troops who are being bombarded, even when these units do not possess effective weapons, can have an important psychological significance. From that moment on the soldier is no longer a passive victim but becomes an actively engaged fighter. This is one of the many illusions that provide support to a soldier in modern warfare.

Especially dreaded were chemical weapons which were used for the first time in April 1915. Even when adequate gas masks and protective clothing were available, and as a result the chemical weapons lost much of their lethal power, fear of them continued to exist.

With men trained to believe that a light sniff of gas might mean death, and with nerves highly strung by being shelled for long periods and with the presence of not a few who really had been gassed, it is no wonder that a gas alarm went beyond all bounds. It was remarked as a joke that if someone yelled 'Gas', everyone in France would put on a mask. At any rate, the alarm often spread over miles. A stray shell would fall near a group at night. The alarm would be given. Gas horns would be honked, empty brass shell-cases beaten, rifles emptied and the mad cry would be taken up. It sounded like the Chinese trying to chase off an eclipse. For miles around, scared soldiers woke up in the midst of frightful pandemonium and put on their masks, only to hear a few minutes later the cry 'All safe'. Then they would take them off again amidst oaths and laughter. Two or three alarms a night were common. Gas shock was as frequent as shellshock.[4]

Although chemical weapons were not used during the following world war, their development and production continued throughout the Cold War. Chemical weapons also became popular in countries which, for technological or financial reasons, were unable to acquire a nuclear arsenal. Libya and Iraq are examples of such a situation. During the Gulf War of 1991 the central questions which were posed in the media concerning the conflict were connected with Iraq's willingness and ability to wage chemical warfare. Thus the psychological significance of chemical weapons has not greatly diminished since the First World War.

Besides being full of risks, life in the trenches was also physically harsh and uncomfortable.[5] One of the big culprits was vermin. Rats were always on hand, as well as lice. The latter not only caused itching but were responsible for all sorts of painful infections. Besides affecting the health of the troops, this could also be damaging to their morale.

Similarly, food supplies were far from satisfactory, in particular when actual fighting was going on. At first glance this might appear strange. From the point of view of logistics, waging a static war like this would almost seem to be ideal. One knows exactly where one's fighting units are and where they will be tomorrow and the next day. In theory, therefore, every supply delivery can be planned and organized with precision. But the problem had to do with the final link in the logistical chain. The terrain at the front and directly behind it was often so difficult to traverse that endless delays were inevitable. When in December 1915 the section of French headquarters dealing with propaganda proudly announced that the French troops were excellently fed and that at least twice a day two sumptuous meals were served, 200,000 angry letters arrived from the front which gave a different version of the situation.[6]

Vermin, cold and damp, and with a certain degree of regularity, hunger: these were the chief ingredients of day-to-day life in the trenches. These 'inconveniences', as they are euphemistically referred to by sociologists of labor, were shared on brotherly terms by the men in the ranks and the lower officers. What these social categories also had in common was a total lack of information, at least of official information. All leadership echelons of the army treated their front line troops like robots that could be set in motion or halted whenever the high command wished. The grand plans to win the war that were drawn up far behind the front line were kept hidden from the men in the forward ranks. For one reason or another it was extremely difficult for the individual soldier to confer any sense and meaning on his own action. The immediate result was an atmosphere of mistrust, in particular mistrust of everything that was taking place to the rear of the front. Indeed, with regard to the staff officers, especially those of the army command and the army corps who

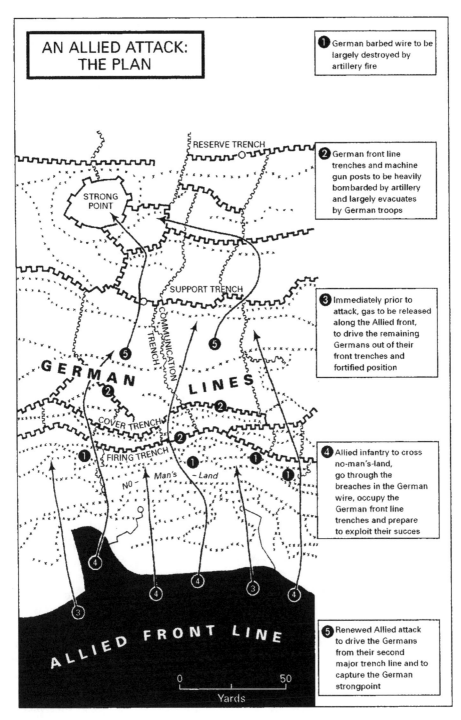

AN ALLIED ATTACK: THE PLAN

1 German barbed wire to be largely destroyed by artillery fire

2 German front line trenches and machine gun posts to be heavily bombarded by artillery and largely evacuates by German troops

3 Immediately prior to attack, gas to be released along the Allied front, to drive the remaining Germans out of their front trenches and fortified position

4 Allied infantry to cross no-man's-land, go through the breaches in the German wire, occupy the German front line trenches and prepare to exploit their succes

5 Renewed Allied attack to drive the Germans from their second major trench line and to capture the German strongpoint

RESERVE TRENCH

STRONG POINT

SUPPORT TRENCH

COMMUNICATION TRENCH

GERMAN LINES

COVER TRENCH

FIRING TRENCH

NO – Man's – Land

ALLIED FRONT LINE

0   50
Yards

Trenches on the map

were housed in attractive country estates far from the danger zone, often enough there even arose feelings of hatred. Sometimes these emotions were stronger than those which had developed towards the enemy. With the passage of time it became easy to consider oneself and one's opponents as victims of the same system. In certain sectors of the front this feeling of solidarity led to all sorts of informal arrangements and practices which were aimed at making life for both parties as bearable as possible. Any such developments went against the express wish of the leadership whose greatest fear was that the agressivity on both sides might disappear. If that were to happen, the whole system would collapse – according to this not wholly unfounded fear.

This trench warfare was not completely static in character. There were also times when it actually took on a dynamic dimension. Small, tactical campaigns were constantly being carried out. These had as their goal the achievement of small corrections in the front line, for example occupying a particular hill or cutting off a salient (a bulge in the line of defense). And then there were the big offensives aimed at achieving a strategic breakthrough after which the mobile war could be resumed.

These latter actions were especially accompanied by enormous casualty figures. The figures are shocking and bewildering. What is shocking is not only the numbers in absolute terms, as great as these were. Equally amazing to the observer is the manifest senselessness of the sacrifices offered up. Until shortly before the armistice, none of the armies involved succeeded in forcing a breakthrough. During the big costly campaigns of the First World War, the participants did not even manage to advance over a distance exceeding fifteen to twenty kilometers. This meant that for every meter of terrain won an absurd price in human lives had to be paid. This fact has been indelibly stamped upon the image of the First World War. The efforts which the generals nonetheless undertook to portray their campaigns as a success have not been able to change this impression. These efforts consisted in claiming successes, despite the absence of territiorial gain, by comparing the ratio of casualties sustained in combat. Thus the winner was the side that had suffered 100,000 casualties, for example, whereas the loser had suffered losses in excess of that figure. One cannot deny that there is a certain military logic to this mode of reasoning but it is not capable of offsetting the image of absurdity and madness associated with the situation. For many people it will remain difficult to locate a war of attrition within a framework of normal, rational behavior. The same will also have been the case for the soldiers involved in the 1914–1918 war.

We have characterized the soldiers who manned the trenches as the victims of modern warfare. However, it is rare that people are merely passive victims who sit back and allow everything to happen to them. The same holds true for the soldiers on the Western front. Tony Ashworth has convincingly shown that some British units succeeded in making their lives more bearable and increasing their chances of survival by means of a subtle complex of informal arrangements with the enemy.[7] The actual arrangements of this 'live and let live system' varied according to time and place. Occasionally, especially at the beginning of the war, this would include openly agreed upon truces. Later, more refined variants came into use such as establishing pauses in combat and the production of ritual violence when one fired over the enemy's head on purpose.

Naturally, a system of this kind, based on mutual trust, can only emerge under very specific circumstances. For instance, the troop formations involved would have to have been positioned opposite one another for a longer period of time. And it would be necessary for the soldiers not to belong to fanatic elite units. In the case of the guard regiments, for example, the tendency to enter into an accord with the enemy was not great – one might say totally absent. One of the chief concerns of the high-ranking officers and generals in the First World War had to do with the alertness and aggressivity of the front line soldiers. From Ashworth's study it is clear that the British military leadership in the end was quite successful in eradicating the 'live and let live' attitude. The consequences which this had for the front line soldier are easy to imagine.

Guerrilla Warfare

For the weapons industry Operation Desert Storm, which began in January 1991, was a gift from heaven. With undisguised pride the parties concerned demonstrated the advanced armaments they had in stock and what could be done with them. Millions of viewers were able to watch on television what a modern conventional war could mean. But this enormous show was in no way representative of the armed conflicts that have taken place since 1945. Warfare in the post-war period has had a totally different countenance. Well-known examples include the British in Malacca, the Dutch in Indonesia, the French in Indochina and Algeria, as well as the Americans in Vietnam and the Russians in Afghanistan. A large number of specific terms were introduced to categorize these conflicts, such as 'civil war', 'guerrilla war', 'subconventional warfare', and most recently, 'low intensity conflict'.[8]

Characteristic of these forms of armed struggle is the disparity between the parties involved. In fact, one observes something like a David and Goliath relationship in which large, heavily armed armies confront small, lightly armed opponents.[9] At the height of the Vietnam War the strength of the American intervention forces numbered half a million. Some decades before that the British had stationed 300,000 security troops in Malacca. Russia installed 100,000 soldiers in Afghanistan who were equipped with the heaviest weapons available in the world at that moment.

In all these cases war was waged against opponents who were numerically far inferior and who moreover scarcely disposed over modern weapon systems. However, in reality this quantitative and qualitative superiority for the most part proved to have an unexpected outcome. Generally speaking, it can be said that the military superpowers were not able to realize their ambitions. In this sort of conflict modern military organization has come up against its limits. How then is this to be explained?

Let us first take a look at the question of numerical superiority. France was able to deploy 200,000 soldiers in Algeria, whereas the rebels of the FLN did not dispose over more than 30,000 men. This was the case for the period from 1956 to 1962. France thus enjoyed a great numerical superiority. But these figures are only of significance if the two parties come to confront one another along a clearly delineated front. Then numerical superiority can be exploited to the full. In a guerrilla war waged across the whole country, and in which no fixed front exits, the situation is completely different. In fact the government troops only have two possible paths of action. Either they spread themselves evenly over the whole region, or they concentrate themselves in the most important population centers. Should they follow the first option, the rebels, at least if they are able to concentrate their forces, can build up a local superiority. Adopting the second option means simply surrendering a part of the country to the guerrillas. Thus quantitative superiority offers no absolute guarantee of success.

The asymmetry characteristic of this sort of war also has implications for the weapons being used. Here as well, the stronger countries ought to benefit, at least theoretically, from the enormous development that weapon technology has undergone in the post-war years. However, it is possible to interpret the historical significance of advanced weapon systems quite differently. Martin van Creveld, in his recent book *The Transformation of War*, has drawn very explicit conclusions in this respect.

If countless instances from Vietnam to Nicaragua and from Lebanon to Afghanistan have any lesson to offer, surely it is that the most advanced weapons have simply not been relevant to them. This is because, as experience shows, any good they can do is more than balanced by the damage inflicted on the environment, and their own insatiable demands for supply and maintenance.[10]

Now what Van Creveld is out to prove in this polemically oriented book is that a modern-day army deserves to be compared to a dinosaur and as such is doomed to extinction. His pronouncements can be described as rather bold, or one might say, one-sided. The thesis he advances should be toned down to some extent. Both in Afghanistan and in Vietnam advanced weapon systems certainly played a significant role. For example, in January 1968 the North-Vietnamese attacked the most important American base Khe Sanh. In the Western press parallels were immediately drawn with Dien Bien Phu where in fact the French did suffer a definitive defeat. But in 1968 the conflict was to have a completely different outcome.[11] Within twenty-four hours after the attack began, the American airforce launched an enormous offensive under the code-name Niagara. A large variety of bombers, including Skyhawks, Skyraiders and B-52s, took part and flew 300 flights a day. By the end of the offensive, it was estimated that between six and eight thousand North-Vietnamese troops had been annihilated in the bombing. Similarly, during smaller battles American patrols were time and again rescued by air support.

In Afghanistan the Russian combat helicopters inflicted enormous losses on the rebels. Therefore the modern weapon systems were surely not without significance.

On the other hand, they were not able, as Van Creveld rightly observes, to achieve final victory, either in Afghanistan or in Vietnam.

Numbers and weapons are indeed important elements in an armed conflict but in the final analysis morale and psychological attitude are the decisive factors. This is especially true of the combat situations described in this section. As with the other aspects of guerrilla warfare, there is also a manifest asymmetry regarding the psychological dimension. Here, however, the scales are tipped in favor of the weaker party. This is not necessarily the case right from the beginning, but if the conflict continues, David will eventually end up as the winner over Goliath.

How does this process actually operate? We may assume that the first guerrillas who have decided to take up arms are quite strongly motivated. Indeed, in most cases the undertaking presents very great risks at the beginning and a good outcome, from the point of view of the individual involved, is by no means certain. As for the government troops, their morale can also be high at the outset of the conflict. Many tens of thousands of Dutch servicemen sincerely believed that they had come to restore peace and order in the Dutch Indies and that due to their actions prosperity would once again be on the increase in the Netherlands. We may also assume that many French, American and British soldiers were strongly motivated and with the best intentions set out for distant lands to carry out their task there. But then gradually a discrepancy emerges with regard to the motivation of the opponents.

For the guerrillas every victory, however small it may be, is a positive stimulus to morale. Fidel Castro, for example, was perfectly aware of this and continually saw to it that his men experienced small-scale successes in their struggle against Batista. He did this by attacking with superior force out-of-the-way police stations. Such operations were of slight military importance but they gave a great boost to morale. Even battles that are lost can acquire a similar significance. Indeed, where a part of the guerrilla forces manage to escape, the whole operation can be presented as a victory. In this case, then, the enemy did not succeed in annihilating the rebels. As for the government troops, the situation is precisely the other way round. A partial success is no success at all because the struggle will simply continue. Even a series of resounding victories can have a negative effect on morale, if despite this the situation still cannot be brought under definitive control. In the soldier's experience earlier successes are thus reduced to nothing more than a sequence of meaningless events. In this sort of warfare maintaining morale is an exceptionally big problem.

Guerrilla warfare occurs in circumstances that deviate greatly from what was usual up until 1945. Most notable is the intermittent character of the new conflicts. Generally speaking, guerrilla fighters are not capable of beleaguering their opponents continuously. They wait for a favorable moment and then launch their attack. The opposing party is often caught unawares by the attack. As for the soldiers of the regular army who carry out the military response, they lead a life full of contrasts. While they remain on their big base, their life is generally safe, even pleasant and comfortable. This was certainly true of the Americans in Vietnam, where the soldiers in the base camps were not lacking anything. Coca-cola, hamburgers and cheap-priced prostitutes, everything was on hand in abundance. In sharp contrast to this, there was the life on patrols in the jungle. This sort of action was always strenuous and rarely without risks. However, the danger on this kind of patrol was different than in previous wars. There was scarcely any fear of artillery shelling or bombardment from the air. The threat came from firearms, mines and booby-traps. The psychological stress caused by the last mentioned can be enormous. In her book about Vietnam veterans Myra MacPherson sketches a vivid portrait of the atmosphere characteristic of guerrilla warfare.

The patrol picked its way through jungle so thick that by moon it was dark. A dead, midnight kind of darkness. Fifty men threaded their way. The first ten began to cross a river. The soldier walking point touched something with his boot. It was not a twig, not a root, not a rock. It was a trip wire to oblivion. In an instant the wire triggered a huge, fifty-pound Chinese mine. There was an enormous roar, like the afterburner of a jet, as it exploded, instantly ripping the point man apart. Shrapnel flew for yards.

Tom, six feet tall and slim, at nineteen already developing a characteristic slouch, froze, hunched his shoulders, and, in a flash, caught the scene forever in his mind: the face of one buddy disintegrating from the explosion; others walking their last steps and falling, bones sticking white out of flesh sheared off at the hips. Some bled to death, coating the ground and mud and leaves with their last moments of blood, before the medevac choppers could come. Some were caught in the river. Tom always remembers the river, running red 'like Campbell's tomato soup'. Those that weren't hit screamed in panic. Those that were screamed in pain...

There was no time for anything but frantic, adrenaline-charged action. The jungle growth was so thick that they had to hack fiercely at the bamboo, its sharp ridges ripping their skin, before the medevac helicopters could come in. The choppers took the seriously wounded – the ones with no legs, the ones with gaping chests. And the dead. More than fifteen of the men were dead or seriously wounded.[12]

In contrast to this spectacular, devastating action, there then followed four or five patrols during which absolutely nothing happened. In short, in this kind of a war there are enormous contrasts, not only between rest and military action but even when one is carrying out a military action.

A second characteristic is the vagueness of this sort of warfare. For instance, as we mentioned earlier, there is no clearly defined front. In principle the fighting takes place within the whole region. Friend and foe cannot be localized within a given space. At best one can only speak of regions that have been more or less brought under control. Similarly, the enemy is often not recognizable as such. Generally, guerrillas and partisans do not wear uniforms. Consequently, they cannot be distinguished from the civilian population. Sometimes they are also an integral component of the population for a great part of the time. Being a guerrilla does not have to be a full-time job but can be restricted to the nocturnal hours or to specific periods of the year. It is also not always possible to determine whether certain persons really form part of a resistance movement or whether they may simply have been forced to lend a helping hand.

When an army feels itself forced onto the defensive, the tendency will be to draw a very wide boundary and to consider every peasant an enemy until he is proved otherwise. This brings us to the third characteristic of this type conflict, the numerous violations of the norms of the current law of war.

Guerrilla wars are cruel and barbaric. The excesses which take place can assume various forms. Justin Wintle maintains that the Americans in Vietnam became caught up in 'hi-tech barbarism'.[13] This appears to be an accurate characterization in my view. Among other things chemical weapons were used to cause defoliation in forests. Likewise, the use of napalm increased the longer the war went on. Another barbaric practice was declaring certain areas to be 'free fire zones' in which one could shoot at anything that moved, without restriction. In general, lapses of this kind represent attempts to bring the war to a conclusion by deployment without any moral norms of the superior technology that one of the sides has at its disposal. Technological barbarism is based on contempt for one's opponent. Once it is put into operation, the door is opened for all kinds of excesses including the plundering and burning of villages, and the random killing of civilians. Naturally, technological barbarism is not a necessary pre-condition for the appearance of these kinds of lapses, but it establishes a climate in which the norms concerning acceptable behavior towards the other camp take on a different content.

One of the most notorious excesses of the post-war period occurred on April 16th 1968. On that day in a small Vietnamese village named My-Lai approximately 500 women, children and old men were killed by a unit of GIs under the leadership of Lieutenant William Calley. A year and a half before that a South-Korean unit had done almost exactly the same thing in Binh Hoa, located in an adjacent district. For reasons that remain obscure information about the event was only made public in 1991.[14]

The British media has with a certain regularity given attention to the action of a patrol of Scots Guards who in 1948 in the forests of Malaysia shot dead twenty-five Chinese workers from a rubber plantation. In these three cases it was a question of the arbitrary use of violence. There was a dubious level of discipline and a low morale in Calley's platoon when it was sent out on 'a search and destroy operation'. When they did not manage to find any Vietcong, the soldiers took out their frustrations on the villagers. In Malaysia it was a case of badly prepared, scarcely trained conscripts who were assigned a task for which they were not suited. The massacre of the Chinese was due to fear and insecurity. It was not so much a question of sadism or resentment – the women and children were in fact left alone – but a complete lack of professionalism.

Among the Dutch units that were sent in against the young Republic of Indonesia lapses of this kind also took place. The example that follows, taken from *De Excessennota* (*Memorandum on Excesses*), illustrates what can go wrong when frightened, unsure soldiers have to confront a threatening situation.

On the evening of August 1st 1949, the Information Officer who was on duty at Tjilatjap, a (reserve) 1st lieutenant in the Royal Infantry, received a report from an informant that in the *desa* Goenoeng Simping in the house of a certain Somodihardjo about fifty members of the T.N.L. had gathered, being partially armed and in uniform. The lieutenant then decided to investigate the situation with a patrol.

Around 20:00 hours the lieutenant set out, at first with two trucks and then on foot. After he had left both drivers behind and two soldiers as cover, his patrol consisted of fifteen men, including himself and the informant who was acting as his guide.

Before setting out the lieutenant also informed the *wedono* of Tjilatjap. The latter, as it emerged later, was unaware that an assistant *wedono* had accorded Somodihardjo permission to give a party for the wedding of a family member on the condition that he observed the curfew, i.e. that the party come to an end by 19:00 hours. This last condition, however, had not been communicated to Somodihardjo.

When the patrol arrived near the house in question, they found a crowd of several hundred people – men, women and children – who were seated on an open, poorly lit veranda watching a *wajang* performance with *gamelon* music. The lieutenant had not reckoned on this situation. He had the premises surrounded and after whispering an order to the nearest soldier not to shoot, he went off with drawn revolver to reconnoitre the situation. But the soldier who was ordered to hold his fire did not pass on the order, as he assumed the others had already been informed by the lieutenant.

When the lieutenant reached the premises at the outer edge of the circle formed by the public, a shot was fired. Next, several Dutch soldiers opened fire, including with a bren gun. The firing quickly ended because the lieutenant, who had fallen to the ground, immediately gave the order to stop shooting. According to the account of the local administration, due to this burst of fire fourteen men, eleven women and one child lost their lives, while thirty-three other persons were wounded.[15]

Not all excesses of violence are arbitrary or undirected. Van Doorn and Hendriks have pointed out that we should be careful in postulating a simple connection between lapses in the use of violence and the existence of frustrations among particular troop units.[16] Indeed, it is tempting to explain a massacre of civilians by the fact that a short while before the patrol involved had been caught in an ambush in which the popular sergeant Smith had been killed. But in their analysis of the function of the Dutch army in Indonesia they show that the acts of violence often were not the work of enraged soldiers but were carried out by special forces who, for example, belonged to the intelligence services. It was often a question of directed, organized violence which to a large extent was independent of the psychological state the group was in at that moment. The mopping-up operations that were carried out by special elite forces under the leadership of Captain Raymond Westerling in 1947 in the Celebes also fit into this category.

Likewise, the Vietnam War offers numerous well-documented examples of directed and planned excesses of violence. During the Tet-offensive of 1968 the Communists succeeded in occupying the city of Hué for some time. They made use of this opportunity to liquidate three to five thousand supporters of the Saigon regime. These killings were carried out on the basis of a list with names and addresses drawn up by the Vietcong. It was a perfectly organized massacre.[17] To a certain extent the same can be said of the 'Phoenix' program that was devised by the CIA in 1967. In accordance with this plan agents infiltrated the farming communities in the Mekong Delta on a large scale. These specialists attempted to unmask Vietcong members and subsequently to liquidate them. In 1969 the Americans claimed that the program had been very successful and that about six thousand Vietcong fighters had been summarily executed.[18]

In our description of trench warfare we noted how, with varying success, soldiers attempted to make their life more bearable by creating a 'live and let live' system. Guerrilla wars, waged with small groups in huge uncontrolable areas, have afforded far more possibilities to pursue the conflict in a less dangerous manner. Indeed, it is quite easy to avoid meeting the enemy at all. If it does come down to shooting contact, scrub and woodlands still provide abundant opportunity for an individual to avoid combat. On the basis of a study carried out by the American Defense Department in 1970, it can be concluded that the official patrol tactics in Vietnam of *search and destroy the enemy* had become replaced by a tactic of *search and evade him*.[19] Many commissioned and petty officers paid with their life for attempting to force their men to engage in combat with the enemy. Although no official figures regarding the phenomenon exist, it is generally accepted that *fragging*, i.e. liquidating one's own commanding officer, regularly occurred – certainly during the final phase of the war in Vietnam.[20] In the short term action of this kind can naturally increase a soldier's individual safety. It is highly doubtful, however, that the well-being of the perpetrators can be served this way in the long run.

UN Operations
Servicemen who have taken part in the so-called peace-keeping operations of the United Nations have in their own way also come in contact with war. With respect to some points their experiences correspond to those of soldiers who have directly participated in the conflict. On the other hand, their involvement with the violence has been different with regard to certain crucial points. To be sure, their life was not without risks. Let us consider the example of the former Yugoslavia. Every UN soldier learned before he was sent out that if he left the road, he would run the risk of stepping on a mine. In addition, the observation posts, sometimes on purpose, sometimes unintentionally, were fired upon. The greatest danger was due to the ever active snipers. Many soldiers who tried to protect civilians from these elusive murderers paid for their intervention with their life. Finally, in the summer of 1995 large groups of blue-helmets were also taken hostage for the first time.

Nevertheless, the risks undergone by these UN soldiers are limited compared with a 'real' war. The casualty figures have thus remained low, at least up until now. It can also be said that the deprivations have pretty much remained at an acceptable level. Food and drink have always been available, even if it was often necessary to fall back on emergency rations. In short, danger and deprivation are not the foremost elements in the daily life of an observer. Rather, what is characteristic is the fact that these soldiers have been witnesses of large-scale devastation and atrocities. Formally it was expected that they would prevent precisely these kinds of situations, but the resources and authority to do this have been denied them. Civil wars are always brutal. This is especially true of the Balkan states where there is a centuries-old tradition in this regard. Similarly, the fact that the fighting in Bosnia is to a large extent carried out by militias and bands that operate independently of one another is an absolute guarantee for the occurrence of excesses of violence. The Dutchman Gerard Wondergem, who in 1992 served as a UN observer in several places in former Yugoslavia, has described a number of such lapses. One of his accounts is as follows:

During the current week events in Bosinska Dubica take a sad turn. Before our meeting with the authorities in Bosinska Dubica, the Serbian interpreter, Vera, tells us that last night in the Muslim quarter a drama had unfolded. We inform Krnjajic, the vice-president of the town council, that we first wish to visit the Muslim quarter. Eriksen and Ahmad remain in the town hall, while Jose and I go to the house in the Muslim quarter. The substitute commander of Bravo Company will act as interpreter for us.

Before we reach the house we are confronted by an angry crowd. It is not difficult to figure out what has happened here. The facts are shouted at us. In the course of the night a group of about ten drunken Serbian soldiers entered the quarter to work off their frustrations after having served at the front. Totally drunk, they forced their way into a house and raped the three women on the premises, whose age ranged from 18 to 68 years. The husband of the middle woman was badly beaten up and thrown out of the house. Totally confused and upset, he alerted the neighbors. Because at the beginning of the war all firearms had to be turned in, they had nothing at their disposal but clubs and stones. Naturally, there is not much one can do in that situation. So they alerted the militia. Not that they expected them to do anything – still you never know. Meanwhile, events inside the house got completely out of hand. The women were raped and abused by the whole group. The oldest woman was shot in the leg. Then a soldier took out his revolver and shot at the youngest woman. She was frightened for her life and tried to tear herself away. The soldier made a notch with his knife in a bullet and fired again. Half the young woman's face was blown off. The shots had a sobering effect on the men and they ran out of the house. Outside they came up against the militia patrol and a fire fight resulted. The murderer of the girl was killed in the exchange of fire. The young woman herself lay dead on the kitchen floor at the back.

We find her body covered with a sheet. We take down the facts and I go to see the father of the victim. I cannot do anything more than shake his hand. Every word is trivial and meaningless. Together with Jose and the provisional interpreter we return to the town hall.[21]

This same officer was present when a mortar-shell exploded in the middle of a waiting group of people. When all these experiences are added to the impressions that devastated and burned out villages make, it is easy to imagine that an enormous alteration in the psychological stability of the involved servicemen takes place.

Confrontation with the misery that arises from a civil war is only one side of the coin. The other side consists of a soldier's powerlessness to intervene effectively in the situation. He is only allowed to make use of weapons if his own life is in danger and then only if he has no other way of assuring his safety. This causes frustrations. This dilemma is a pre-eminent characteristic of the psychological state the UN soldier finds himself in. The frustrations involved stem from various underlying causes. The way Unprofor functions inevitably leads to innumberable misunderstandings and breakdowns in communication. Many observers only learn at the very last moment where they will be deployed and with whom they are to cooperate. The limited mandate and light weaponry further contribute to a soldier's feeling of being reduced to the position of a powerless on-looker.

Added to this powerlessness there is not infrequently a sense of the complete meaninglessness of the whole operation. Any soldier who is regularly fired upon by both sides and who is booed by the civilian population he is meant to be protecting will eventually doubt the purpose of his presence. In Sisal (Croatia) the blue-helmets are given the Hitler salute by young people on the street. In Zagreb the same soldiers are greeted with texts like 'UN go home!' Well-intentioned actions in the mother country can also stir up doubts among the UN soldiers about their mission. Wondergem refers to a good example of this.

On Saturday we heard on the BBC that the world is beginning to talk about peace-enforcing. One commentator said that it will not be without risks to the participating troops. He's right. It's too crazy for words that the world has to send troops to enforce peace here. On the other hand, the Netherlands is receiving part of the 1500 deserters: people from Bosnia who refuse to fight for their own cause and nation. If you stop and try to understand what's behind it all, it's enough to drive you around the bend.[22]

Powerlessness, Guilt and Frustration

The combat situations we have described above can to a great extent be seen as highly extreme cases. In the trenches the soldier is confronted with the full potential of violence that can be mustered in a total war. In face of this orgy of violence the individual soldier is powerless. He looks on while his comrades are killed, wounded or buried alive. These events fill him with fears that are manifestly real and concrete. Added to these threats are exhaustion and deprivation which in combination with one another will lead to the impairment of his mental stability. Thus the soldier in the trenches can be characterized as the victim of modern warfare *par excellence*.

Among this category of servicemen the phenomenon of the psychologically wounded soldier manifests itself in the most visible manner. Robert Gaupp, a high-ranking German military psychiatrist, came to a similar conclusion in a lecture he gave in 1917.

When the wards filled up with sick and wounded from the end of August [1914], there were many patients among them with neurological and cerebral injuries, but almost no mental patients [i.e. mentally ill]. It remained like this until Christmas 1914. Only when the big artillery battles in Champagne began in December 1914 and the artillery superiority of our Western opponents swelled into a devastating uninterrupted barrage, did the hospital trains bring us a large number of uninjured mentally ill officers and soldiers. From then on their number increased with an ever more rapid pace. Initially, one made do by placing the mental patients in with the other sick and wounded, but the unsuitability of this procedure was soon evident. Special field hospitals had to be created for the mentally ill. Ever since then their numbers have been growing; a hospital for mental disorders is scarcely set up, when it becomes full and further space must be sought. We have now reached the point where, numerically, the mentally ill represent by far the most important category of patients in our army and the field hospitals for mental patients in our country are the only hospitals which are always full...

In any case, taken together the mental patients in Germany today amount to several army corps which have been removed from serving at the front or on garrison duty.

The primary causes are terror and fear occasioned by exploding shells and mines, witnessing their comrades being maimed and killed, the collapse of defense shelters and seeing their own wounds or physical injuries inflicted by brute force. The consequences are the cases you are familiar with where there occurs a sudden loss of speech, hearing or both, general trembling, the inability to stand and to walk, and fits of fainting and cramps...[23]

It can also be said regarding the Second World War that the war of position, and everything connected with it, was responsible for generating psychologically wounded soldiers on a large scale. That was true of the Eastern front as well as of Normandy.[24]

The soldier who is deployed in fighting against guerrillas finds himself in the opposite position. He belongs to the side that has at its disposal weapons of mass destruction. He is a component of what, on paper at least, is the stronger party. To begin with, he is not a victim of violence, but a producer of violence. The feelings that normally go with such a role are those of guilt. This is especially the case when the use of violence is not regulated and civilians also become casualties. The latter is virtually unavoidable in a guerrilla war. Naturally, a soldier in this situation also experiences all sorts of fears. He is afraid of ambushes, traps and attacks. He is also confronted with inevitable deprivations during operations. But these fears and deprivations are generally of short duration. Dangerous and strenuous patrols are followed by periods of rest and relaxation. In contrast to the situation of trench warfare, the soldier employed against guerrillas is, as a rule, not subjected to continuous stress until he becomes burned out. Consequently, conflicts of this kind are not known to produce high numbers of psychiatric cases. In Vietnam, for example, the American army had significantly lower scores in this respect than in the two world wars and in Korea.[25]

To avoid any misunderstandings it should be noted that this statement only concerns soldiers who break down during fighting. The fact that in a guerrilla war only a small number of troops are taken out of combat for psychological reasons does not mean that this type of conflict has no psychological effects on those involved. It is perfectly conceivable that the effects may become manifest at a later time. A striking statistic in this regard is that more than a million American Vietnam veterans had serious psychological problems after the war. We will come back to the subject of delayed reactions to stress in Chapter X.

The position of the UN observer is the most similar to that of the soldier in a guerrilla war. The deprivations that he is obliged to put up with are not usually so great. Similarly, the personal risks are relatively limited. The life of the witness is undeniably safer than that of the perpetrator or the victim. Operations carried out by the UN, at least up until now, have not been characterized by a large percentage of casualties consisting of psychological disorders. Nevertheless, the witnesses do have one thing in common with the victims, namely an overwhelming sense of powerlessness. This sense of powerlessness of the witness does not arise from an inability to defend himself but from the impossibility of carrying out his assigned task in a proper manner. The UN observer is not merely reduced to doing only a little; he can actually do nothing. The soldier in question will at times certainly experience fear or become filled with feelings of revulsion. But what characterizes his role *par excellence* are the frustrations he undergoes. These emotions in particular are responsible for a soldier 'coming home a different person', as Wondergem put it.

Conclusion
Modern warfare has many faces. The *Blitzkrieg* and trench warfare comprise two of the most extreme. In the first case it is a matter of tank units that can easily advance tens of kilometers a day. In the second case one may be dealing with fixed positions where neither side makes any gains in territory over a period of several years. Between these two extremes there are innumerable other combat situations, a few of which we have briefly described.

The sketched situations vary with regard to the intensity of psychological stress which they entail. Amphibious operations have always stirred up enormous feelings of anxiety. Likewise, storming fortified positions has given rise to disconcerting emotions. On the other hand, tensions associated with participating in a *Blitzkrieg* are not as extreme as those encountered in the other two examples.

The psychological pressures vary not only according to intensity but according to content as well. In this chapter three ideal type positions have been sketched in which soldiers can be involved in using violence, namely as victim, perpetrator and witness. The predominating feeling in the case of the victims is powerlessness. The perpetrators are primarily troubled by feelings of guilt. In the case of the witnesses a sense of frustration dominates.

Naturally, in describing these positions we are employing a schematized representation of reality. Specific emotions do not have to be exclusively coupled with particular positions. In practice all kinds of hybrid forms of emotion may be experienced. The soldier fighting against guerrillas, for instance, may at times feel extremely powerless. A soldier in the trenches can become overwhelmed by feelings of guilt if it turns out that he is the only person in his platoon to survive a bombardment. Nonetheless, these ideal types of emotional response can have a function.

They can be helpful in analyzing the extremely complex phenomenon which can generally be designated as the emotional effects of war.

.

V - Civilian Psychiatry

Introduction

Industrial warfare begins with the American Civil War. The winner, as it turned out, was not the party with the best generals at its disposal, i.e. the Southern states. On the contrary, after five years of intensive fighting the war was won by the Northern states. The industrial and logistical potential of the North proved to be decisive in the end. In the fighting the classic bladed weapons, the sword and the bayonet, played a subordinate role. Almost all the casualties were due to rifle or artillery fire.[1]

Among the wounded there was also a group of psychologically wounded which was by no means negligible in size. The Northerners, for example, found themselves obliged to withdraw from combat five to seven thousand men a year who suffered from psychological problems. The main diagnosis given in these cases was *nostalgia* (homesickness). Although the head of the military medical service of the Northern armed forces, William Hammond, had a great personal interest in this category of patients, a military psychiatric service was never set up.

Various factors were responsible for this shortcoming in military organization. One such factor was undoubtedly the continued presence of two traditional enemies of the army: epidemics and desertion. During the Civil War the losses as a result of all kinds of illness were in fact five times as great as losses in battle. Likewise, after the first year of the war desertion certainly posed a problem that ought not to be underestimated. Moreover, it should be pointed out that when war broke out, the US army had scarcely any medical service at its disposal. On the basis of talented improvisation a make-shift medical service was thrown together in great haste. Viewed in this context, it is to some extent understandable why psychiatric patients did not receive the attention which they should have had a right to according to our contemporary standards.

However, there was a still broader background to the low level of activity regarding care for the psychologically wounded soldier. This shortcoming was the direct consequence of the state of psychiatry at that time. Within the ranks of the American psychiatric establishment there was almost no interest in the Civil War. Indeed, this lack of attention was no coincidence. It can be stated that, not only in the United States but throughout the Western world, psychiatry was simply not equipped, either in a theoretical or in a social sense, to offer help to victims of war, at least not in the 1860s. In contrast to medicine in general, where the Civil War provided a dynamic impulse to the development of specializations such as neurology, plastic surgery and dentistry, psychiatry was scarcely affected by this conflict.

The explanation for this state of affairs is to be found in the history of that specialized discipline. That history is the subject of the present chapter, which will follow a chronological framework. The theoretical principles of psychiatry, as well as the practical therapies it applied, will be discussed. Similarly, attention will be given to the important role which the mental asylum has played in psychiatry's development. We will begin our survey at the end of the eighteenth and the beginning of the nineteenth century. This was pre-eminently the period when psychiatry began to take shape as a specialized discipline. It was also the time when people began to change their views about the mentally disturbed, which change was accompanied by efforts to apply treatment to the latter. Out of the new experiments that were undertaken in this field in different countries, modern mental health care emerged.

The Golden Age of Psychiatric Asylums
The reorganization of care for the mentally disturbed was certainly not a separate, self-contained phenomenon, but formed a subordinate part of a large reform movement which manifested itself in a wide range of social sectors.[2] It can be characterized as a large-scale process of rationalization that stemmed from positive, ideologically grounded expectations regarding what could be achieved by man through social cooperation and education. The imprisoned, according to this way of thinking, must not only be punished but they must be rehabilitated. The poor should not only be given support but they should learn to overcome their idleness. And there was also hope for the mentally disturbed. It was quickly discovered that a sizeable number of them could be cured if they were treated in an appropriate manner. The treatment in question, which was first experimented with in England, became known under the name of 'moral treatment'. This moral treatment was not a fully thought-out therapeutic system. It was, as Kathleen Jones has put it, based on common sense and on Christianity. Moral treatment meant, first of all, the humanization of care for the mentally disturbed. Chains and other instruments of coercion, which were thought to be inhuman, were abolished and replaced by other specially designed means of coercion. Restraint in the use of these means was vigorously propagated. Similarly, the comfort of the mentally disturbed received due attention. A healthy diet and sound accommodation were deemed to be absolutely indispensable.

As far as the actual treatment was concerned, moral treatment broke with the classical medical approach. The latter, which had chiefly consisted of administering medicines, was replaced by a psychological-pedagogical perspective. Mental illness was viewed as a deficiency of the will. By means of a process of re-education, the weak will had to be strenthened. To stimulate self-control, undertaking systematic labor and receiving instruction were prescribed. Moral treatment was first applied in England. In this connection two well-known personalities deserve to be mentioned. The first of these is Francis Willis (1718–1807), a Protestant minister who ran a private asylum for the mentally disturbed in Greatford in Lincolnshire. The second is William Tuke (1732–1827), a coffee and tea merchant from York and a prominent member of the Quaker community in that city.

Willis achieved national celebrity when he was summoned to the royal court in 1788 to treat King George III who was incorrectly thought to be insane. The treatment employed by Willis caused quite a sensation, in particular because he allowed the king a degree of freedom which many found to be incomprehensible. For example, every now and then Willis allowed George III to shave himself with a razor. Willis justified his actions before an investigatory commission from Parliament. He especially referred to the great importance of his personal authority with regard to his patient. Personal authority, he maintained, could in certain cases be a substitute for mechanical instruments of coercion such as shackles and chains. By means of this personal authority the patient was subjugated to the practitioner and then the actual therapy could begin. As to the precise content of these therapies we are not very well informed because Willis never set them down in writing. Numerous contemporaries found that his treatment clearly worked and before long Willis was able to count among his clientele a wide range of prominent people, including many from outside England.

We are much better informed about the activities of William Tuke. In 1792 he managed to convince the Quaker community in York to set up a home for the mentally ill. The immediate cause for taking this step was the mysterious death of a patient in a mental asylum which the city of York had established in 1777. The death in question made Tuke (and others as well) suspect that abuses prevailed in the asylum, but it seemed that no one was capable of inciting the authorities to carry out an official inquiry into the case.

In order to offer members of his own Quaker community better accommodations and to demonstrate that humane care of the mentally ill was perfectly possible, Tuke founded his famous Retreat. This name was deliberately chosen. In view of the abuses in York's asylum, Tuke wished to avoid using the term 'asylum'. Tuke also had objections to the term 'hospital' because of his deeply rooted mistrust of the medical profession. Consequently, the Retreat was also not conceived as a hospital. It was, in fact, a home for members of the Quaker community or for those recommended by that community.

In the same period experiments in this field were also carried out at the local level in France and Germany. Medical men as well as laymen took part in these experiments. In France the physician Philipe Pinel (1745–1826) quickly came to occupy the central position. He developed the French variant of moral treatment: *le traitment moral*. In Germany J.C. Reil (1759–1813), a professor of medical science originally from Halle, formulated the German version which he called the *psychische Curmethode*.

Although the content of moral treatment varied to some extent in different countries, it was of great significance everywhere for the further development of care for the mentally disturbed. Indeed, all the prominent representatives of this therapeutic method were agreed that its benefits could best be achieved in an asylum. Various reasons were given in justification. In the first place, admission to an asylum made it possible to islolate the patient from the immediate environment, an environment which in many cases was the cause of the illness. In addition, confinement of the patient offered optimal possibilities for exerting systematic psychological influence. In principle the desired isolation could be brought about in any asylum but the ideal was to achieve this in asylums that were located in a rural setting outside the city.

The ideas of Tuke, Pinel and others were well received by various national governments. Philanthropic as well as financial reasons made it seem that an alternative system of care was necessary. It could not be denied that the mentally ill were also human beings and thus they deserved to be treated as such. Moreover, if mental illness could be cured, the costs involved in the curative process would be earned back in the long run because patients would once again become healthy, productive citizens.

The chief way in which these national governments gave evidence of their real interest was through legislation. In most European countries around 1840 so-called mental-health laws were promulgated. These laws gave prominence to three matters. In the first palce, regulations were prescribed to deal with procedures concerning admission and discharge. Secondly, requirements as to quality were defined and inspection systems were established. And thirdly, obligations were imposed on lower levels of government (provinces and regions) to create adequate asylum facilities in their area of authority.

After the enactment of these laws an enormous expansion of mental institutions took place. Hundreds of new asylums were built. Most of the new institutions were situated in the countryside in full compliance with the plan. By around 1850 the mentally disturbed had been banished to the spatial and social periphery of the community. The psychiatrists, the doctors specialized in treating the mentally ill, also departed with them. To this group was entrusted the running of the mental institutions. The important position of the psychiatrists was not a logical consequence of moral treatment as sketched above and thus a certain explanation seems appropriate in this regard.

Moral treatment in the beginning period had a strong anti-elitist, populist coloring to it. Resistance to the traditional medical approach was not only motivated by therapeutic considerations but by political factors too, such as aversion to the powerful medical corporations. In France the corporations were even abolished in 1751. The physician Pinel's great esteem for the contribution of non-medical persons such as the guardian Pussin and the monk Poution fits into this conceptual framework. Nevertheless, Pinel felt that the insights of these laymen had to be accompanied by statistical evidence and grounded in philosophical ideas. Empiricism and philosophy had to be combined. For this purpose it would be necessary to develop a new, broadly conceived medical science. Thus Pinel from the very start claimed a central position for the doctor in the treatment of mental illness. The revolutionary government in France supported this claim. The dominant position of the doctor symbolized two attitudes: it was an expression of the supremacy of science over belief and, likewise, the superior qualification of the medical civil servant with regard to the clergy. In England the doctors by means of good internal organization and clever political manoeuvring, with specific reference to the French model, gradually managed to monopolize the new field of work. Other countries followed the French and English example in this respect.

In this way the social solution to the question of mental illness became established. To begin with there were high expectations. The new asylums vied with one another on the basis of percentages of cures. In the United States, where the European development was closely imitated, there emerged what Deutsch has dubbed 'the cult of curability'. In Europe therapeutic optimism was generally of a somewhat lower order but here as well expectations ran high.

A beautiful future shone on the horizon. Factual developments, however, turned out to be different. The moment that psychiatric institutions began to become a fixed element in the social landscape, two particular problems made their appearance. The first problem had to do with the functioning of the asylum as a therapeutic institution. It soon became evident that the hopes raised by reformers regarding therapeutic capabilities had been set too high. By no means could everyone in a mental asylum be cured. By the middle of the nineteenth century this insight based on reality led to the result that the therapeutic pretensions of asylums were subjected to more and more criticism.

Therapeutic optimism gradually gave way to more pessimistic ideas. In the United States, where 'the cult of curability' had assumed the most extreme form, the shift in attitude can be most clearly traced. Precise statistical investigation, in particular carried out by Pliny Earle, one of the founders of American psychiatry, revealed that the cult in question was to a large degree based on statistical errors and deception.

The high increase in the number of the mentally ill during the latter half of the nineteenth century represented a second problem. In England, the country that had played a pioneering role in the reform of care for the mentally ill, this tendency was especially evident.

Likewise, in other European countries and in the United States the same tendency manifested itself. Percentagewise the number of mental patients grew faster than the total population. Time and again it turned out that estimates by the provincial and regional authorities – estimates on the basis of which the capacity of asylums was expanded – fell short of actual demands. The number of mentally ill applicants for admission continually turned out to be greater than the most conscientiously carried out research had led the authorities to believe. The planned capacity of asylums, therefore, continued to be insufficient to take in all prospective patients.

The changes which came about in the patient population after 1850 were of a qualitative as well as a quantitative nature.

In early nineteenth-century asylums a distinction was generally made between acute and chronic mental illness. Broadly speaking, the division between curable and incurable patients corresponded with this distinction. The flood of patients that confronted the asylums from the middle of the previous century was not equally distributed between these two categories. In particular, chronic patients were being presented to the asylums in an increasing degree. Grob and Deutsch have pointed out that many of these patients had first spent years in all sorts of social institutions such as poorhouses and workhouses. During their stay in these institutions, which were totally unsuited to their needs, their physical and mental state had often deteriorated to such an extent that they necessarily had to be characterized as incurable. The chronic patients formed a heterogeneous category.

In the United States immigrants who had fallen into pauperdom and suffered a multiplicity of illnesses made up an important subcategory. What we would nowadays designate as elderly people suffering from dementia formed a second group for whom admission to mental asylums was requested. Finally, syphilis patients and those suffering from other somatic illnesses were likewise put forward for admission. The reservoir of incurable patients who were already present around 1850, i.e. in the public asylums, was increased to a considerable degree by this new influx. This qualitative change in the patient population not only occurred in America. Scull and Kathleen Jones have sketched a similar picture for English asylums. Certainly the patients who were pouring into the County Asylums fulfilled two criteria. They were poor and they were incurable.

The rising stream after 1850 was not only met by building new asylums but the capacity of existing institutions was expanded. The latter then changed in character as a result of such modifications. The typical late nineteenth-century asylum for the mentally ill was fundamentally different in structure and function from its early nineteenth-century variant. The small, surveyable, home-like Retreat gave way to the colossal, complex, impersonal Asylum that was characteristic of the new period in which the mammoth institution made its appearance. The architecture of this type institution made it clear that the so-called romantic period of the first years of moral treatment belonged to the past. High walls encircling huge buildings, where large rooms were linked together by endless corridors, were the material components of a rigid organization within which hundreds of mental patients were locked up.

This transformation was accompanied by a change in the public assessment of psychiatric asylums. In the last decades of the nineteenth century an extremely negative image of institutional psychiatry emerged. The psychiatrist was portrayed as a kind of prison guard. Patients appeared as pitiful victims of the machinations of their families or the government. Once again the psychiatric asylum became the subject of a public debate. Only now it was no longer an issue of improving patient care as had been the case a half century earlier. Now it was primarily a question of providing better guarantees against improper application of the mental-health laws. The citizen must be better protected against the possibility of involuntary confinement. Admission to an asylum was no longer seen as a great therapeutic benefit but as an occurrence of a highly dubious nature against which the citizen must be as well protected as is possible. Representative in this respect is an article that appeared in 1881 in the *North American Review*. The author, among other things, launched a fierce attack on the trustees in charge of American psychiatric asylums and pleaded for the creation of an efficient system under central supervision. His greatest outrage, however, he vented on the boards of medical directors.

But the authority of the asylum superintendent is, if possible, more dangerous and unchecked than that of the trustees. He is an autocrat – absolutely unique in this republic – supreme and irresistible alike in the domain of medicine, in the domain of business, and in the domain of discipline and punishment. He is the monarch of all he surveys, from the great palace to the hencoops, from pills to muffs and handcuffs, from music in the parlors to confinement in the prison rooms; from the hour he receives his prisoner to the hour when his advice restores him to liberty...

This unparalleled despotism – extending to all conduct, to all food, to all medicine, to all conditions of happiness, to all connection with the outer world, to all possibilities of regaining liberty – awaits those whose commitments may easily be unjust if not fraudulent, whose life is shrouded in a secrecy and seclusion unknown beyond the walls of an insane asylum.[3]

The positive reception which this article met with in the United States makes it perfectly clear that in the second half of the nineteenth century psychiatry had not only manoeuvered itself into a position of isolation, but that it now found itself with its back to the wall.

From this defensive position the asylums began a counter-offensive. Measures were taken to improve the therapeutic climate and attempts were also made to compensate for the earlier loss in status. An important step was the creation of low-priced institutions which were specifically intended for looking after the more or less hopeless, chronic patients. The asylums could then concentrate more on treating the acute cases.

By bringing in the 'cottage system' a further attempt was made to offset the notorious massiveness of asylums. By means of architectural innovations it was possible to restore some of the older feeling of a small-scale operation. Changes also took place in the area of therapy. The most striking of these includes the introduction of bed nursing and bath therapy. In bed nursing absolute rest is prescribed for the patients. For this purpose the asylums were equipped with so-called bed wards where inmates sometimes remained for months on end. In this way, according to the underlying principle, a patient's overwrought nerves could calm down. In bath therapy, or more accurately put, in prolonged bath therapy, agitated patients were kept for long periods in a lukewarm bath. By means of a sheet fastened over the top attempts to stand up were hindered. This facility was no luxury as the duration of the 'baths' could vary from a few hours to a few weeks.

Bringing in these new methods of treatment gave the asylums a different appearance. Thanks to the wards of beds and the bathtubs, asylums acquired a resemblance to normal hospitals which could give a certain boost to their status.

Of great significance were the attempts made, notably in the decades before 1900, to overcome the isolation that psychiatry had come to find itself in. Successfully breaking out of this position was accompanied by an expansion of psychiatry's sphere of activity. But this process did not proceed in the same manner everywhere.

In what follows, the chief bridges that were erected between psychiatry and society will be examined in greater detail.

Breaking Out of Isolation

In the final decades of the nineteenth century medical science went through a developmental boom. This development was made possible by the fact that medicine clearly became increasingly linked with natural sciences such as chemistry, physiology and biology. It is not really so unusual that psychiatrists, being doctors themselves, should try to become associated with this new trend. The result was the emergence of an organic-somatic approach according to which behavioral disturbances were related to anatomical defects and to disturbances in the nervous system. The German psychiatrist Griesinger expressed this new perspective concisely when he stated: 'Mental illnesses are illnesses of the brain.'

This re-orientation of psychiatry, in which its original psychological principles were steadily pushed further into the background, was greatly promoted by the situation that the psychiatric asylums found themselves in. Within the mammoth asylums there were simply no longer any possibilities for applying moral treatment and that approach ceased to have any significance. Similarly, a framework based on somatic interpretation appeared to be more suitable for dealing with the patient population in a mammoth asylum. The sick and debilitated pauper patients often ended up in such bad physical condition that one could not assume they would be able to recover solely by means of pure will-power. Moreover, it was becoming increasingly clear that for a certain category of patient there was a definite connection between mental and physical disturbances. This was the case with those suffering from dementia paralytica. In the course of the nineteenth century it became increasingly obvious that this disease was the result of syphilis infection. The hope that other mental illnesses would come to be explained in an identical way appeared to be justified. Between researchers and clinicians a division of labor came about. The former went to work in their laboratories to search for the biological mechanisms of disease which were responsible for the existence of mental illness. The latter concentrated their efforts on classifying disease entities. Germany was the original home of this development which was rapidly followed in other countries. One indication of the scientification of psychiatry is provided by the number of professorial chairs that were created in this discipline in the German universities (Berlin, 1864; Göttingen, 1866; Heidelberg, 1871; Leipzig, 1882; and Bonn, 1882).

From an institutional point of view this process of scientification had an important consequence, namely the emergence of a *Universitäts Psychiatrie* alongside the existing *Anstalts Psychiatrie*. After 1860 it was in fact the *Universitäts Psychiatrie*, where the coupling of psychiatry and science had occurred, which was to determine the face of German psychiatry. Within the university clinics a high level of research was developed in histology, biochemistry and the anatomy of the brain. The more descriptive and classificatory work of the clinicians followed a parallel course.

Through the growth of university psychiatry a part of psychiatry was liberated from the social isolation it had come to be in because of its exclusive link with the psychiatric asylum. For psychiatry as practiced in asylums, however, this breaking out of isolation was of little significance. Asylum psychiatrists were, generally speaking, not interested in scientific research. Moreover, in most asylums the necessary facilities for carrying out research were lacking. Providing care and science went their own separate ways. For psychiatry in the asylums scientification meant the arrival of a new opponent. Psychiatrists with an orientation toward the natural sciences, and neurologists, began increasingly to participate in the debate on psychiatric asylums. They rehearsed every possible criticism regarding the lack of scientific merits on the part of asylum psychiatry. A good illustration of the situation is provided in the early period of 'the mental hygiene movement' in the United States. The existence of this movement, which was later to create a sensation in the Netherlands too as a movement concerned with public mental health care, in the first instance owed much to the activities of the American Clifford Beers.[4] In 1908 he published his autobiography *A Mind That Found Itself* which was to achieve world-wide fame. Beers, who had himself been a patient in a psychiatric asylum for some years, voiced sharp criticism of mental health care in the United States and at the same time made all kinds of proposals for improvement. Among other things he pleaded for smaller asylums, better educational establishments for nurses and the founding of out-patient clinics. It was also quite important that Beers put forward the idea of prevention. Thus 'mental hygiene', besides striving after better treatment for the mentally disturbed, also meant attempting to remove the causes of mental illness that lay inside and outside the individual.

The fundamental principles that Beers formulated were not new. We find the same ideas being promoted by the National Association for the Protection of the Insane and the Prevention of Insanity (NAPIPI) which was founded in 1880. This association, in which neurologists and social workers played the chief role, became the bastion from which established asylum psychiatry was attacked. It was in part due to the activity of this association that psychiatry in the United States took its first step on the road to breaking out of its social isolation. The transformation in 1892 of the Association of Medical Superintendents of American Institutions for the Insane into the American Medico-Psychological Association was more than just a change of name. It was an expression of the broader base which this professional association had acquired and of the greater interest which had arisen in psychiatry for study and research. The NAPIPI had in the meantime been abolished due to internal strife. Nevertheless, its fundamental core of ideas was kept alive by individual neurologists, psychiatrists and social workers. Thus when the above-mentioned book of Beers appeared, the necessary groundwork had already been carried out.

In advocating prevention with regard to mental illness, Beers drew his inspiration from the results that had been achieved in the field of prevention against the great epidemic diseases of the nineteenth century. In his autobiography he took the campaign against tuberculosis as an example and advocated the creation of a similar organization to fight against mental illnesses. Thus, in the United States as well, reference was made to the successes of a medical science oriented toward the natural sciences, though in this case it was primarily a question of setting up an adequate system of prevention.

In the United States the fundamental principles of 'mental hygiene' were, generally speaking, well received. A national movement arose which was coordinated by the National Committee of Mental Hygiene (1909). On this committee there were eminent leaders from the fields of psychiatry, neurology, social work, religion and philanthropy. 'Mental hygiene' won respectability for psychiatry. Once again psychiatrists became serious participants in discussions on what was deemed to be necessary social change in the United States.

In France psychiatrists had already succeeded in attaining the same recognition a few decades before.[5] The soirées that were organized by the celebrated Jean-Martin Charcot in the 1870s were visited by representatives of the whole cultural and scientific elite of Paris. What is particularly pertinent to our present concern is that Charcot, who was attached to the Salpêtrière, endowed psychiatry with a new prestige and at the same time considerably broadened its field of activity. Whereas psychiatry had previously been limited to what we would nowadays describe as psychotic behavior, he succeeded in extending its area of competence to include the domain of neurotic disorders. Along with the classic *aliéné*, the *demi-fou* now became a legitimate subject for psychiatric research and practice. Neurasthenia and hysteria were the best known disease entities which were distinguished in this approach. Neurasthenia was described for the first time at the end of the 1870s by the American physician-neurologist George M. Beard. This discoverer was of the opinion that it was a typically American disease belonging to the middle classes in his country. Charcot was soon to learn differently; neurasthenia was universal and had existed at all times. Headaches, nausea and dizziness were the chief symptoms of this milder variant of mental illness. As for hysteria, here it was a question of more serious cases. Attacks of hysteria were accompanied, among other things, by convulsions and symptoms of paralysis.

Hysteria was already known in Greek antiquity. For centuries it had been considered a disorder which particularly affected women in the highest social circles. There was a lack of clarity concerning its exact symptoms. In the nineteenth century hysteria was a kind of residual category in which were accommodated all manner of borderline cases of mental illness that were difficult to diagnose. On the basis of a detailed photographic study, Charcot presented a penetrating discription of the symptoms and the different phases that an attack of hysteria could display. He made hysteria scientifically acceptable. His demonstrations that involved patients were famous and made a strong impression on young up and coming scientists such as Sigmund Freud. Similarly, the phenomenon of hysteria was widely commented on in the medical-scientific literature. In the 1870s Charcot's influence extended over the whole of the Western world. At Charcot's instigation the Salpêtrière also began to create facilities for out-patients and part-time patients. These were the first steps on the road to offering treatment to out-patients. To begin with, two categories profited from this form of care. Among the patients, this included the so-called middle groups. They were not capable of paying for treatment in a private clinic and yet they were unwilling to have themselves admitted to a public asylum. For them private practice offered an affordable alternative. Among the doctors, private practice offered great opportunities to those psychiatrists who were less well-off financially and would otherwise be obliged to pursue a bureaucratic career in one of the asylums. Starting up a private clinic required large capital investment and was therefore only viable for a small minority.

The elevated scientific status of hysteria was accompanied by an enormous increase in the number of diagnosed cases. In the last decades of the previous century, hysteria spread like a real epidemic over the whole of the Western world. Yet the illness was nowhere so popular as in France where the illness not only crossed the boundaries of gender but appeared no longer to care about social stratification either. Anyone, man or woman, rich or poor, could fall prey to hysteria.

It was perfectly self-evident that the *demi-fou* must also receive treatment. In this regard the psychiatrists could choose from a variety of therapies. Therapies could be aimed at the body as well as at the mind. The Institute for Physical Therapy established in Amsterdam had on offer at the beginning of this century the following methods of treatment:

...hydrotherapy in various forms and applications, with showers, semi-baths, moist wrappings and rub-downs, and douche massages in the manner of Vichy, Aachen, Aix-les-Bains; various forms of balneotherapy, with baths of suphur, tar, bran and pine-needle extract, as well as carbonate baths; electrotherapy; pneumatotherapy, with various kinds of inhaling apparatus; thermotherapy, with electrical light-apparatuses and hot baths in sealed body-chambers.[6]

Among the interventions aimed at the mind, one may especially mention hypnosis. According to this method, an attempt is made to put the patient in a trance after which it is suggested to the subject that upon his or her waking up the disturbance will have disappeared. Most of the therapies may rightly be described as covering up the symptoms of illness or offering support. They did not address the cause of the disorders. This was certainly true of the treatment of hysterical patients. Even the great Charcot had been unable to indicate the origin of hysterical manifestations. It was Joseph Babinski and Sigmund Freud who, in their divergent ways, attempted to fill in this gap. Babinski, who replaced Charcot at the Sorbonne after the latter's death in 1893, came to discover that the patients Charcot had used in his demonstrations had acted out a kind of role playing. They had done exactly what the famous doctor had expected of them. The conclusion that Babinski drew was rigorous: hysterical manifestations were based on suggestion. It was the psychiatrist himself who evoked the symptoms in a patient. The pyramid-like hierarchical structure of the French medical establishment guaranteed that Babinski's views would dominate thought in the world of French psychiatry, just as had previously been the case with the ideas of Charcot. The popularity of the illness underwent an enor-

mous decline. By the eve of the First World War hysteria had clearly fallen out of favor.

A completely different vision of the cause of hysterical syptoms was propagated
by Sigmund Freud. To begin with, Freud, like most of his contemporaries, was also
primarily interested in the anatomy of the nervous system.[7] His orientation was
therefore of a bio-medical nature. After having studied with Charcot (1885),
Freud's interest in the function of psychological mechanisms grew. During this
process of development the Vienese psychiatrist increasingly came to distance himself from the psychiatric establishment. He stopped employing electrotherapy and
also became more restrained in his use of hypnosis. The crucial instrument in his
office came to be the couch, rather than any complex scientific equipment. During
therapy the patient was encouraged to give his or her thoughts free play. Freud was
there to listen, to listen meticulously, and then to give meaning to the words of the
patient. In making his interpretation, he based himself on a psychoanalytical theory
he had formulated himself. According to this theory, physical disorders could be
traced back to repressed conflicts within the psyche. In this connection Freud attributed great significance to conflicts with a sexual background. His treatment,
psychoanalytic discussion, aimed at restoring to the consciousness of the patient
problems that had been repressed. Once consciousness of the problems had been
achieved, the physical disorders would disappear. Thus, put briefly, what it came
down to is that Freud tried to explain hysterical manifestations by pursuing the psychological, not the somatic, path. In this way Freud, in contrast to Babinski, sought
the cause of the manifestations in the patient himself and not in the process of in-
teraction between the doctor and the patient.

From this survey it should be clear that in the years around the turn of the century the development of psychiatry was gaining momentum. The main thrust was
toward scientification, a growing involvement with social issues and an extension of
its professional domain. These tendencies did not manifest themselves in every
country in the same manner and with the same intensity. Thus, to begin with, university clinics flourished in Germany. An interest in the less extreme cases, the neurotic patients, appeared particularly in France and later in Austria-Hungary. Finally, it was in the United States that social involvement succeeded in taking shape
on an impressive scale.

The position which England came to occupy in this period is rather unusual. English psychiatry, in comparison with that in the other Western countries, remained
more or less unchanged. Naturally, there were individual psychiatrists who were informed about what was going on abroad, but they were not capable of influencing
the existing system of mental health care. It was the First World War which would
force the psychiatric establishment in Albion to adopt another course. We will
come back to this development in Chapter VI.

If we leave England out of the picture for the moment, we can confirm that, as a
result of the processes of change we have described, the structure of mental health
care had been transformed in a number of significant ways. The psychiatric asylums
lost their unique position. Sanatoriums for those suffering from nervous disorders

appeared, while all kinds of out-patient facilities were vigorously promoted. Nonetheless, until well after the Second World War the asylum remained the cornerstone in the edifice of mental health care. In most countries the number of patients admitted to asylums continued to rise every year. By creating services for prevention and follow-up care these institutions also managed to play a role in the increasingly more important area of extramural care.

Within the asylum itself time did not stand still during the period we have been describing. Especially in the area of therapy quite spectacular developments occurred which drastically altered the face of the asylum.[8] In 1917 Wagner von Jauregg introduced the malaria-cure. In this treatment fever is induced in patients by artificial means, namely by injecting them with the blood of someone who is suffering from malaria. The malaria-cure became famous as the most effective method of treating dementia paralytica.

During the years 1934–1938 the international world of psychiatry saw the introduction of a trio of related methods for combatting schizophrenia: cardiozol-shock therapy, introduced by the German doctor Von Meduna in 1934; insulin-shock treatment, applied by the Vienese psychiatrist Sakel in the same year; and electroshock treatment, employed for the first time in 1938 by the Italians Cerletti and Bini.

Shock therapies, moreover, were based on a weak theoretical foundation. There is still little known 'about the physiological and biochemical working mechanisms' of electro-shock treatment which is the only one of these therapies being used today. They 'are supposed to exert influence on the activity of certain substances in the brain, which are meant to improve the vegetative functions, and therewith the mood'.

At that time the background to the use of shock therapy was the observation that the body type of sufferers from epilepsy was the opposite of that of the schizophrenic patient. Moreover, it was noted that epileptics got well more quickly in those cases where they displayed schizophrenic symptoms. The conclusion was that the reverse could also be the case, and therefore that recovery from schizophrenia could be promoted by artificially inducing an epileptic seizure. Heart-fortifying drugs, including especially cardiozol, were suitable for this purpose. The advantage of giving injections of this drug was the low labor-intensiveness involved. According to Von Meduna, during a single morning 60 to 80 patients could be injected. After five treatments over a period of two and a half weeks there followed 'an energetically carried out psychotherapeutic treatment'.

Insulin-shock therapy required much more attention. Over a period of 60 days insulin was injected in slowly increased doses, which at first induced drowsiness and perspiration. However, at a certain moment, which was different in the case of every patient, the blood sugar became so low that a shock set in which manifested itself chiefly in violent muscular spasms followed by a coma. The patient was then brought out of the coma by having glucose administered to him. After the cure had been completed, withdrawal symptoms were avoided by gradually administering smaller doses of insulin.

Electro-shocks were first used by Cerletti and Bini in experiments on animals. With this method epileptic attacks were induced by means of a surge of electric current. The patient had electrodes attached to the temples and was then very quickly rendered unconscious. To begin with, currents of 300 to 600 milli-amperes were employed with a charge of 80 to 130 volts. Since the therapy was clearly quite painful, some practitioners decided to administer the shock under an anaesthetic. Electro-shock remained exceptionally popular in the treatment of psychotic patients up until the 1960s.

Of an entirely different nature were the sleep-cures that were experimented with during the interbellum period, notably in England. In this case patients were put in a deep sleep for around twenty hours per day over a period of two weeks. These cures were not without danger because patients could sink into a coma or could suffocate. Mild forms of the sleep-cure remained in use up until the 1950s.

These new medical therapies were not of great significance in changing the look of the psychiatric asylum. Rather it was the latest variant of work therapy developed in the 1920s and 30s which was responsible for that. We are here referring to what the advocates of this therapy, not without some sense of irony, described as 'more active therapy'. This form of therapy is based on the assumption that the psychiatric patient in question is not so much in need of rest (bed nursing), but on the contrary that he must be kept physically occupied – during the daytime by means of labor, evenings through active relaxation (singing, dancing and music). In the 1920s the German psychiatrist Simon began experimenting with 'more active therapy' in the Provinzial-Heilanstalt in Gütersloh. The term 'more active therapy' in Simon's conception not only referred to keeping the patients busy but also meant an increased activity on the part of the medical practitioners. They were expected to try constantly to stimulate the patients to keep busy and to accept as much responsibility for themselves as possible.

By bringing in the new method of treatment the psychiatric asylum underwent a real transformation in appearance. The superficial resemblance to a hosptial that had formerly existed, for the most part disappeared. Instead the asylum now took on the appearance of a large-scale farm. Bringing in 'more active therapy' was in fact accompanied by the cultivation of fallow lands for the purpose of agriculture and market-gardening. In addition, parks, gardens and roads were laid out by the patients as a counterpart to the public works that were being undertaken in the community by the unemployed. The results of this form of work can still be seen today in numerous Dutch asylums for instance.

Bringing in 'more active therapy' increased the isolation of asylums. They became more than ever self-sufficient little islands set apart from an unknown, unloved outer world. This situation only began to undergo fundamental change in the 1960s. At that time asylums became the subject of public debate and once again found themselves in the limelight. On this occasion the discussion was instigated by the spokesmen for antipsychiatry. The form this discussion took and its consequences are the subject of the following section.

The Debate in the 1960s: Antipsychiatry on the Offensive
The term antipsychiatry refers to the theoretical and practical work of a group of critical, alternative psychiatrists who were active in various countries from the 1960s onward. The psychiatric establishment was subjected to an unprecedented degree of harsh criticism by these antipsychiatrists. The criticism they voiced was based on what they experienced in their own work, in particular when treating schizophrenic patients. They concluded that the current psychiatric modes of thought were inadequate and were in need of fundamental revision. Furthermore, they were influenced by the results of research in the social sciences, including historical research on the function and origin of mental health care.

Although antipsychiatry has never been a real social movement and cannot be compared with the psychoanalytic movement for example, the antipsychiatrists, despite their differences from one another, do have certain things in common.[9] To begin with, they are unanimous in their rejection of the medical model. They consider the medical model incomplete because it scarcely allows any room for social-psychological or sociological insights, or because they take it to be false. This last standpoint is held by Thomas Szasz, among others. The position of Szasz and of many other psychiatrists is that the use of the medical model leads to an obfuscation of the social, political and ethical problems which according to this model are reduced to somatic questions. Thus one of Szasz's most famous books is entitled *The Myth of Mental Illness*. A particular view of the psychiatric asylum is a second element which the antipsychiatrists have in common. With regard to this point they draw heavily on the studies of the sociologists Goffman and Scheff, studies which focus attention on the pernicious effects of residence in an asylum for the self-image of a patient. Existing psychiatric asylums, which only make patients sicker and more despondent, should be abolished according to the antipsychiatrists. Many antipsychiatrists such as Ronald Laing, David Cooper and Franco Basaglia were thus occupied with attempts to design new forms of communal living for psychiatric patients. Most of these experiments, however, ended in failure, not least of all because of the bitter resistance on the part of the psychiatric establishment.

In the search for alternatives to the psychiatric asylum, home nursing, which had existed a hundred years earlier, was rediscovered in Geel in Belgium. Home nursing had originated as a consequence of medieval pilgrimages. The system of Geel was investigated, among others, by a team of specialists from Columbia University in New York. A study published in conjunction with this research by the anthropologist Roosens drew due attention in the Netherlands as well.[10]

The accusation that the psychiatric establishment functions as an instrument of social control on behalf of the rulers in society is also something one finds among all the antipsychiatrists. In his book *The Manufacture of Madness* Thomas Szasz did not shrink from branding institutional psychiatry as the successor to the Inquisition.

Although the antipsychiatrists did not hesitate to explain their ideas in lectures and publications, antipsychiatry has none the less remained a small current within the world of psychiatry. Because of their polemical style of writing and the expressly ideological stance of much of their work, they have provoked an enormous resistance within the psychiatric establishment. Thus American psychiatrists were happy to subscribe to the idea that their Russian colleagues by declaring dissenters to be mentally ill functioned as an instrument of social control on behalf of the rulers. But that they themselves performed this very function by their willingness to apply the same label to people with deviant sexual morals or with a preference for using officially unrecognized drugs – this they found more difficult to go along with. Nonetheless, this was pecisely what antipsychiatry maintained.

The writings of the antipsychiatrists struck a sympathetic chord with the reading public in Western countries. Laing, Cooper and Szasz were each capable of attaining sales figures that ran into the hundreds of thousands. In this respect their ideological orientation proved to be a positive advantage. The 1960s were characterized, among other things, by sharp ideological contrasts and an increased political consciousness. It does not seem far-fetched to attribute this trend to an increase in the level of development of the population in the West, an increase which is related to the massive extension of secondary and higher education after the Second World War. As a result of this development, a public was created that was keenly interested in questions of a philosophical and ideological nature. Antipsychiatry here found a receptive breeding ground.

In view of the small response which antipsychiatry received within the world of its professional colleagues, one should not draw the conclusion that that world did not undergo change. Of course it is true, for example, that the medical model remained dominant, but it is equally true that alternative models were developed alongside it. It was certainly not the case that the whole of psychiatry had shut its eyes to the views of psychology, sociology and anthropology. Around 1970 the advocates of the various models and therapies combatted one another fiercely. The medical model had by then already lost its exclusivity.[11]

The importance of the psychiatric asylum was by that same year already significantly diminished in various countries. In the United States, for example, more psychiatric patients were by that time in the psychiatric sections of general hospitals than in psychiatric asylums.

Some changes were the result of alterations that took place in the course of the twentieth century in legislation concerning mental patients. The arrival of psychiatric drugs was also of great significance in this respect. To begin with the first point, laws from the previous century dealing with the mentally ill were based on the idea that compulsory admission to an asylum, even when this was in the patient's interest, signified a deprivation of liberty. Therefore, the intervention of a judge was also required. There was no provision for the possibility of a voluntary admission where an official juridical procedure could be omitted. Gradually, a change came about in this area, particularly because of the actions of psychiatrists who felt that the admission procedure had a stigmatizing effect. In the course of this century it has become possible almost everywhere to have oneself admitted to an asylum without the intervention of the lawcourts. A second change due to specific legislation concerns the place where the mental patient is admitted. In the original laws it was stipulated that only insane asylums could look after the mentally ill. This had been done to deter the old pre-industrial practice of locking up insane people together with criminals and vagrants. The new legislation now made it possible to treat psychiatric cases and somatic patients in the same institution. To begin with, this turned out to the advantage of the university clinics which had need of patients for teaching purposes. Later, ordinary hospitals began to create facilities for psychiatric patients. This meant a considerable loss of ground for the asylums.

The same tendency was reinforced by the arrival of psychiatric drugs. By means of these drugs it became possible to suppress agitation and aggression in patients and at the same time to preserve more or less intact their intellectual faculties. Thanks to these medicinal aids, patients became not only more tractable, but more approachable as well. It was chiefly a question of making use of the following drugs:
- Tranquilizers like librium and valium, which were used sporadically from 1961 in combination with anti-epileptic drugs.
- Psychotonics or stimulating drugs.
- Antidepressants such as the thymoleptics, tofranil and tryptizol. Already in 1946 the antidepressant pervitine was used but because of mediocre results its use was soon discontinued. Thymoleptic drugs, which were introduced in 1966 on a large scale, received a much better press because they contributed to the disappearance of electro-shocks.
- Neuroleptics, the first psychiatric drugs, reduced nervous tensions and resulting agitation and aggression.

The new wonder drugs could be sure of receiving a warm welcome from psychiatry. In the beginning expectations ran very high, as was usually the case with something new in this field. Some people even spoke of a new therapeutic revolution. It goes without saying that the pharmaceutical industry hastened to embrace this growth market with enthusiasm. A stream of new drugs, as well as variations on the existing ones, was unleashed on the field of mental health care. This overabundance evoked a range of deserved criticism. In antipsychiatry circles it became common to speak of chemical strait jackets that had replaced the older means of coercion.

Although discussion still continues about whether or not the use of psychiatric drugs is sensible, it can be said that the significance of these drugs has been enormous. Many patients have become so tractable that looking after them in an ordinary hospital is now within the realm of possibility. Out-patient care has also come to have new chances thanks to these drugs.

Naturally, any discussion of the structure of mental health care is never simply a question of medical issues alone. The financial dimension is also an important factor that must be considered. In this connection it is significant to note that the debate about psychiatric asylums took place in a period when governments everywhere were beginning to be concerned about costs in the welfare state.[12] In the 1970s it became clear that extensive cuts in the medical sector were unavoidable as well. The attack against the psychiatric asylum where long-term expensive care was provided fit well into a policy that aimed at making financial savings. Ideologically inspired reformers and cool, practical-minded accountants found themselves in the same camp. The result of their joint action is the present-day form of mental health care. Within this sector the psychiatric asylum is now only one of the building blocks.

Conclusion

The history of psychiatry was for a long time identical with that of the psychiatric asylum. The nineteenth century has rightly been designated as the golden age of asylum psychiatry. To begin with, expectations with regard to this institution ran high. By the middle of the previous century a close-knit network of insane asylums criss-crossed Europe.

Through this development the banishment of the mentally disturbed to the spatial and social periphery of society had become a fact. This banishment affected the patients as well as the practitioners. In the second half of the nineteenth century psychiatry found itself in a state of complete isolation from society. In this same period it became increasingly evident that the asylums could not fulfill the high expectations they had initially aroused. Several factors contributed to asylums coming into discredit and they were obliged to relinquish a large part of their recently gained status. It is quite clear that psychiatry, as it then was, and the American Civil War had little to offer each other. Consequently, there was no question of their exerting any mutual influence on one another.

In the decades leading up to 1900, the first changes began to be discernible. There was a trend toward scientification (Germany), expansion of the field of activity (France) and a breaking out of social isolation (United States). All this meant that mental health care came to have a much broader purpose. Supplementary facilities were made available at the same time that alternatives were created. Nonetheless, the asylum as an institution was successful in adapting, certainly from an overall perspective. Only in the 1960s did more fundamental changes occur in this respect. Antipsychiatry, sometimes with the support of the patients' movement, campaigned fiercely against what it took to be a pernicious institution. In some countries the government authorities, in their effort to limit the costs of the welfare state, appeared to be prepared to listen to these critical voices. Out-patient and semi-out-patient facilities are, after all, cheaper than institutional care. With the arrival of psychiatric drugs, for many patients the reason for admission to an asylum disappeared. As a result of these developments the psychiatric asylum has clearly lost some of its importance in the field of mental health care.

The discussions that have gone on over the last two hundred years in psychiatry have not only been concerned with the role of the asylum. There have been no fewer heated debates about the causes of behavioral disturbances. Various theories and perspectives have generated enthusiasm, only to come into discredit at a later time. At first psychology provided the dominant interpretative framework. Afterwards there followed the bio-medical model, and in the 1960s sociological and social-psychological viewpoints came to receive a lot of attention. These viewpoints were accompanied by widely divergent therapeutic strategies. Modern mental health care undoubtedly has much to offer. The neat and surveyable simplicity of the years of 'moral treatment' lies far behind us. However, as to whether increased therapeutic possibilities have led to greater efficacity in the treatment of psychiatric disorders, for the time being no definitive answer can be given.

PART TWO

MILITARY PSYCHIATRY

VI – From Shell Shock to Combat Stress

Introduction

What exactly were the soldiers suffering from who ended up in the safety nets of military psychiatry? What were their complaints, and how did those offering them treatment react to these complaints? In posing these questions, we find ourselves face to face with one of psychiatry's fundamental activities, the task of making a diagnosis. On the basis of analyzing exhibited symptoms, a specific underlying disease entity must be detected after which the patient can be assigned a particular label. Only after this process is completed – when it is clear what is wrong with a serviceman and how the disorder has come about – can the actual treatment begin. In this chapter we will see that military psychiatry first of all let itself be guided in the area of diagnosis by whatever theoretical and practical knowledge was available in civilian psychiatry. We will, therefore, be reviewing certain well-known concepts such as hysteria, neurasthenia, neurosis and stress. This association with civilian psychiatry was only logical since military psychiatrists received their education in regular universities; here they underwent their initial training which might later be supplemented by a more specifically military training, though this was by no means true in all cases. The knowledge thus acquired had to be adapted to a very particular organizational and circumstantial context, namely that of the army and warfare. This led to the creation of certain terms for specific occasions, terms that were unknown in civilian society. To begin with the context of warfare, some diagnostic categories were a direct result of the theater of war in which they first came into being. Shell shock is closely associated with the artillery shelling which was so characteristic of trench warfare in the 1914-1918 war. Combat exhaustion reflects something of the experiences of the infantry during the Second World War. And finally, in the concept *'stress'* something is expressed of the tension involved in the jungle fighting in the Vietnam War. In other words, military psychiatrists are repeatedly influenced by the characteristic nature of the particular war they have participated in and whose victims they have become familiar with. In addition, the army is an important part of the context. This means, among other things, that the military psychiatrist is situated within a hierarchical structure and that he is no longer free in making his diagnosis and proscribing methods of treatment. For instance, the army command can forbid a certain diagnosis, or simply steer things in such a way that certain complaints are not diagnosed at all. Consequently, military psychiatry has had to develop in this regard within more or less clear boundaries. These boundaries were not only organizational in nature, but cultural as well. When introduced into the military, psychiatrists were and still are confronted with a very specific pattern of norms and values, namely military morality. Within this culture where courage and unflinching resolve are primary virtues there is scarcely any room for soldiers who can no longer cope and who break down. These servicemen are simply seen as cowards and weaklings. What they deserve is not help but punishment. Thus in many armies military morality was the first hurdle that had to be cleared before a beginning could be made in giving assistance. In the section below on the forms of resistance to military psychiatry this subject will be dealt with further. We will begin this chapter, however, with a description of the symptoms that were manifested and the main diagnostic labels that were brought into use by military psychiatry.

Shell Shock

In October 1914 the war in the trenches began for the British army. After a series of confrontations with the German army and the notorious retreat from Mons, the horrors of trench warfare arrived. Not only was the number of casualties great, but they were varied in nature. There were quite a few casualties who could not be diagnosed by the doctors of the military medical service. Three examples will serve to illustrate the situation. At the end of October a twenty-year-old soldier who was on his way to a trench with his platoon suddenly came under German fire. The rest of the unit managed to reach the shelter of the trench but the soldier in question got himself entangled in barbed wire. Then three shells exploded directly behind him. According to eye-witnesses, it was a miracle that he survived. And yet he did survive and even succeeded in freeing himself from the barbed wire and joining his platoon again. Shaking and crying like a small child, he was brought to the first-aid area by two comrades. There it appeared that his vision had been affected. Since it did not seem like he would be fit for service in the short term, he was transported to the rear of the front line. The second example concerns a twenty-five-year-old corporal. At the beginning of December he happened to be in a trench which at a given moment sustained a series of direct hits from the German artillery. The trench collapsed and the corporal lay buried under sand and rubble for 18 hours before he was rescued. He too was sent on to a quiet safe place for further treatment. Our last example is that of a twenty-three-year-old soldier who was put out of commission in January 1915. He had been sitting on a high stone wall. Suddenly a shell went off in his immediate vicinity, and he was projected through the air. Later in the day he came to in the cellar of a church. He had no idea how he had come to be there.

The examples we have just given were not chosen at random. Ultimately, all three cases ended up in the military hospital Le Touquet where they were treated by Charles S. Myers, captain-doctor in the Royal Army Medical Corps. Myers, in an article that appeared in *The Lancet*, has given a detailed description of the symptoms manifested by these soldiers.[1] The faculty of sight was to a larger or lesser degree impaired in all three. Nor did their sense of taste function properly. But the most remarkable point was that two of the three soldiers involved could not at first remember anything of what had happened or how they had been transported to the hospital. As for the third soldier, he could only recall things in the vaguest terms. Moreover, they had in common the same cause of their disorder, namely an exploded artillery shell. With this feature in mind, Myers entitled his article 'Contribution to the Study of Shell Shock'.

Here we are confronted with the most famous special term to emerge from the history of military medicine. It is remarkable that no attmept was made to clarify the concept. The nonchalant manner in which the term was introduced leads one to speculate that Myers assumed the reader was familiar with shell shock. This assumption is probably correct: already by the autumn of 1914 articles describing the strange effects that exploding shells could have on casualties had begun to appear in scientific journals.[2] A more detailed explanation, therefore, was no longer required in February 1915.

This was not to be Myers' only contribution. During the second year of the war Myers was confronted with several hundred cases of shell shock. He reported on a selection of these in January 1916 in the same medical journal.[3] From this report it is clear that it was a matter of a multiplicity of disorders: memory loss, blindness, symptoms of paralysis, as well as hearing and speech disorders. Along with these more or less severe cases there were also complaints of a somewhat lighter nature, such as exhaustion, irritation and headache. The ordinary military doctors, trained to treat serious gunshot wounds and wounds from bayonets, were at a loss as to what to do in most of these cases. For the physicians who had had a psychiatric

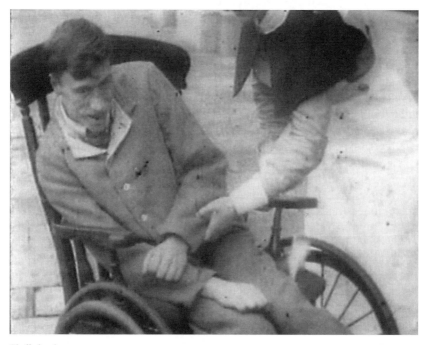

Shell shock

training it was a different matter. For them it was a question of symptoms that had long since been recognized in civilian society. If one adopts a simplified schematization, two important syndromes can be distinguished, a syndrome of hysteria and a syndrome of neurasthenia. What we characterized above in somewhat simple terms as the severer disorders were put in the category of hysteria, while the lighter complaints were categorized as neurasthenia.

Similarly, the social distribution of the symptoms corresponded in general outline with what was observable in civilian society.[4] There the majority of hysteria-patients originated from among the ordinary folk and, when they were confined, they resided in public institutions. Those suffering from neurasthenia were chiefly to be found within the better-off layer of the population. They received care in expensive private clinics. In the British army a similar distinction was perceptible. Symptoms of hysteria were mostly met with among the ordinary soldiers, whereas the officers exhibited complaints which were associated with neurasthenia. This difference in disorders was attributed to the difference with regard to responsibility that existed between officers and the troops. In the case of officers, it was assumed that they lived under constant pressure. Indeed, the lot of numerous individuals was in their hands. In the long run this unrelenting stress would lead to sleeplessness, irritability and headache. The troops found themselves in a different position and were therefore less susceptible to neurasthenia.

Regarding these two diagnostic categories there was widespread unanimity. The French, German and American military psychiatrists applied this distinction. For all the parties concerned, hysteria and neurasthenia formed the chief categories in which psychologically wounded servicemen were classified. The intense discussion which in fact continued throughout the whole period of the war had to do with the causes of these disorders. To begin with, an effort was made to adopt the bio-medical explanatory model which was dominant at the time. According to this intellectual framework, mental illness was conceived as a disease of the brain. The brain or the nerves had become wholly or partially defective due to physical injuries, which resulted in behavioral disorders. On the eve of the war, excessive use of alcohol and venereal diseases were seen as the main culprits. By applying the concept 'shell shock', Myers associated himself with this somatically oriented approach. The underlying assumption was that the senses and the brain could be injured by the explosion of artillery shells. These injuries might be so minuscule that they could not be directly observed. The behavioral disturbances that resulted from them, however, were no less real. And yet, from the outset, Myers had had doubts about this line of reasoning. Already in his first study of shell shock Myers had asked himself why in the affected soldiers the faculties of taste, smell and sight were damaged and their memory no longer functioned, whereas, by contrast, their capacity to hear was not appreciably injured. This question arose inevitably in view of the fact that the explosions were accompanied by an enormous production of noise, whereas the only gasses released were odorless. He therefore conjectured that there was a close relationship between the symptoms he observed and those associated with hysteria.

Thus Myers kept the possibility open for further psychologically oriented explanations.

With hindsight we can confirm that this was a wise decision. Indeed, as the war proceeded, the need for explanations other than the physical effects of shelling became ever greater. Soldiers who had not been exposed to artillery fire also began to display the same symptoms. Sometimes the symptoms of shell shock even occurred more or less spontaneously among soldiers who were on leave. In short, the explosion hypothesis became increasingly less credible. In the wake of these doubts new explanatory causes and new concepts were launched. Life in the trenches offered endless possibilities in this regard. One could refer to the deprivations soldiers were confronted with, the dangers they were exposed to such as attacks with poison gas, and the horrors they were forced to witness such as the killing and wounding of their comrades. These features of life in the trenches are reflected in the new names and diagnostic labels that were developed after shell shock: trench neurosis, gas neurosis, and burial-alive neurosis are the best known.

On the German side, after *Granatshock*, *Schreckneurosen* and traumatic neuroses came to the fore.[5] Half way through the war the more generic terms 'war neuroses' and '*Kriegsneurosen*' came into common use. However, the term shell shock became so established that it was employed in numerous studies. This was even the case with authors who were fully aware of the inadequacy of the term. When the British government set up a commission in 1920 to find out, among other things, what precisely had happened to psychologically wounded soldiers during the war, it was given the name The War Office Committee of Inquiry into Shell Shock. The concept had become so deeply rooted that even after the war there was no longer any way to avoid it.

The fact that many doctors were interested in other causes did not mean that the somatic explanatory model was jettisoned. The scientific aura that surrounded it was simply too great. Naturally, there were indications that it did not always hold true but, on the other hand, there were also many examples of soldiers where real brain damage could be demonstrated. And even when such was not the case, this did not have to lead to a complete rejection of the somatic hypothesis. Furthermore, psychiatry in civilian society had also reconciled itself to the fact that not everything can be explained in the short term. Why should not military psychiatry, just like its civilian variant, make do with a provisional hypothesis and postpone the burden of proof to some later date.

A very important element in the bio-medical thought of that time was the conception that anyone who became a casualty of shell shock must have been more or less predisposed to it. A person's hereditary temperament was meant to play a large role in his being predetermined in this way. Many military psychiatrists traced the disorders of their patients back to a weak constitution or nervousness in the structure of their personality. Wartime experiences were merely the final straw that broke the camel's back. To establish the real cause one had to go back to the soldier's past, or better yet the history of his family should be examined. If something could be found in the father's or the mother's side of the family that indicated the presence of mental illness, then the lot of the soldier in question was under-standable. Having this predisposition was not only true in the case of individual sol-diers but was applicable to larger categories of people. It should also be borne in mind that the bio-medical explanatory model was applied in anything but a consis-tent manner. Whereas one referred to the importance of physical factors with great conviction by way of explaining mental disorders, at the same time one felt no com-punction whatsoever in shifting the emphasis to the importance of immoral or anti-social behavior. In the case of virtually every single psychiatrist, whether he wore an army uniform or not, there was no consistently thought out argumentation. In prac-tice this system of thought was open to a wide range of racial and class-based stereotypes. Doctors who after the war testified before the above-mentioned War Committee expressed their doubts regarding the military capacities of the Jews and the Irish, for example. One of those who gave testimony was Captain J.C. Dunn, battalion doctor of the Royal Welsh Fusiliers and compiler of the fascinating book *The War the Infantry Knew*. This intelligent and above all brave doctor declared be-fore the commission that in the Boer War: '...the Jews weren't worth their salt. So far as I can determine.'[6] In the following section we will meet with Dunn again and then it will emerge that this highly decorated war hero did not think much of shell shock patients, either. To his way of thinking, it was wholly out of place to show sym-pathy, compassion or understanding for this group of patients. They were weak-lings who never should have been inducted into the army, or tricksters who de-served to be punished. In his view there was nothing in between. Dunn was certainly not the only doctor who thought this way. Military psychiatry from the be-ginning had to struggle against opposition from the non-specialized doctors. In the chapter that deals with the basic principles of military psychiatry we will examine the motives that led these medical practitioners to adopt their position.

What points of view then were developed from the psychological perspective?[7] We have seen that Myers, already at a very early stage of the war, had left the possi-bility for such an approach open. Indeed, he had talked about symptoms that were related to those of hysteria. Roughly speaking, three quite divergent viewpoints can be distinguished within this broad perspective. The first viewpoint attributed an im-portant function to traumatic experiences. Through traumatic experiences and the emotions that accompany them it was thought that behavioral disorders could arise. An experience of this kind occurs if a soldier sees the whole of his unit blown to pieces before his eyes. In the opinion of some psychiatrists an event like this was so overwhelming that it provided an adequate explanatory reason for the break-down of the soldier in question. Thus, according to this point of view, emotions could exert influence without having to be accompanied by damage to the nervous system.

We can most effectively describe the second variant of the psychological perspec-tive as the suggestion approach. The basic assumption here is the conviction that behavioral disorders have no real basis in the body or in the psyche of the casualty but are the result of suggestion. In the classic view of Babinski it is the doctor who consciously or unconsciously evokes the desired symptoms in the patient during the process of treatment. The hysterical soldier learns to play his role during treatment. If he adopts the role that the doctor has in his thoughts, the reward then follows in the form of a formal recognition that he is sick. The suggestion did not always have to come from the therapist himself. Auto-suggestion could also provide an important explanation for the presence of certain symptoms. An example by way of illustration will be useful. A soldier has just forced his way into an enemy position. In a state of extreme tension he awaits a reaction. Suddenly, someone springs out of a manhole, his hands in the air, ready to surrender. Our soldier had not reckoned on this. Before he realizes what has happened he shoots the defenseless opponent in the right arm. A few weeks later this too rapid shooter can no longer move his own right arm. In this case it is very plausible to explain these symptoms of hysterical paralysis as the result of auto-suggestion.

According to the third and last psychological approach, functional disorders can arise as the result of unresolved psychic conflicts in the mind of the soldier. A psychoanalytical perspective, such as the one elaborated by Freud, for instance, is the model *par excellence* of this viewpoint. Concerning *Kriegsneurosen*, Freud is perfectly clear:

The psychoanalytical school I brought into being has taught for 25 years that peace-time neuroses can be traced back to disturbances in a person's emotional life. The same explanation has now been generally applied to those suffering from war neuroses. Furthermore, we had maintained that those who are nervous suffer from psychic conflicts, and that the wishes and tendencies which are expressed in the symptoms of their illness are unknown to the patient himself, that is to say they are unconscious. Thus it was easy to conclude that the immediate cause of all war neuroses was a soldier's unconscious inclination to remove himself from the demands of military service that are dangerous or offensive to his feelings. Fear for his own life, resistance to the command to kill others, revolt against the total suppression of one's personality by superiors were the most important emotional sources that nourished the inclination to shun war.

A healthy soldier in whom these emotional motives were to become powerfully and clearly conscious would either desert or report himself sick. But only a small fraction of war neurotics were actually simulators: the emotional impulses against military service that arose in them and drove them to be sick operated in them without their being conscious of it. The impulses remained unconscious because other motives such as pride, self-esteem, patriotism, the habit of obedience and the example of others interfered at the outset, until for some adequate reason the latter were overwhelmed by the motives working at the unconscious level.[8]

Even military psychiatrists who definitely cannot be described as followers of Freud have often adopted a number of the central points of the above-mentioned line of thinking, such as the idea of conflicting motives and the significance of the unconscious mind. Thus Freud's influence has apparently been greater than one would expect in view of the limited number of his official adherents.

The explanatory models we have referred to functioned more or less alongside one another during the war. Of course, with time there were clear shifts in emphasis. Lieutenant-Colonel W.A. Turner stated in a lecture which he gave on 7 November 1918 before the Royal College of Physicians in London that at the beginning of the war most observers sought for the causes of shell shock in physical phenomena such as fatigue, gas poisoning and brain damage. The trend in modern psychopathology has been to swing in the opposite direction and to attribute all the deficiencies in a soldier to psychological causes.[9] In Germany also the psychological approach, and in particular the psychodynamic mode of explanation, acquired greater importance as the war proceeded. Nevertheless, no one model or intellectual framework managed to emerge from the war as the undisputed winner. In the August 1919 issue of *The Lancet* a report appeared concerning an experiment that had apparently been carried out immediately before the announcement of the armistice in November of the previous year. Two British military doctors attempted, by means of a series of tests involving human beings and animals, to gain a better understanding of the effects of physical and emotional factors. Explosives were detonated in an area where unprotected cages containing rats and mice had been placed at varying distances from the center of the explosion. The same procedure was carried out under water and fish were used as subjects in the experiment. After the explosions the dead animals, along with those that were still alive, were subjected to an intensive examination. Soldiers who worked in the explosives service were employed as human guinea pigs. They were placed in a bunker, with adequate protection of course, and then a selection of explosives was detonated outside at a certain distance. The experiment did not produce many new results. Behavioral disorders could be explained both by emotional and by physical causes. Which explanation deserved preference was only clear in the extreme cases. As for the broad middle ground, there was little that could be said. What the doctors involved did conclude at the end of the report was that in modern warfare soldiers are in fact increasingly confronted with both kinds of causes and that these variables could exert their influence in combination.[10] In short, in the area of the aetiology of war neuroses in 1918 a form of stalemate had emerged.

It is striking that in France no new concepts were formulated which gave expression to the specific image of the war. Soon after the first study on shell shock by Myers had appeared in *The Lancet*, *La Presse Médicale* published an article by the French professor Gustave Roussy who was at that time a doctor employed in the military hospital Val-de-Grâce. The title of his treatise was 'À propos de quelques troubles nerveux psychiques, observés à l'occasion de la guerre, hystérie – hystéro-traumatisme – simulation'.[11] In other French articles, as well, the usual psychiatric vocabulary was applied in describing the problems observed among soldiers. In my view this absence of new specific terms has to do with the special position that hysteria had acquired in the French medical world and abroad. It was in France that the modern concept of hysteria had developed. It was here that Charcot had carried out his famous demonstrations and, last but not least, it was here that Babinski had done his deflating work (see Chapter V). When soldiers presented themselves with forms of paralysis and other symptoms of hysteria, in France one immediately knew what was happening. Roussy, in the above-mentioned study, made sure there was no misunderstanding: 'Bien entendu, la guerre n'a rien créé de nouveau en matière d'hystérie...'[12] In fact, as far as the theoretical viewpoint was concerned, the war casualties were only interesting because they might offer the possibility of solving a few left over issues in the debate about hysteria. The French military psychiatrists were also aware of the aetiology of the psychological problems that they had to deal with. After all, the great Babinski had pointed to the important role that suggestion played in the whole affair. The pyramid-like hierarchical structure of the French medical system guaranteed that this conception would become commonly accepted among French doctors. Personally, I believe there was no other country where the change-over for civilian psychiatrists to the military setting involved so little mental adjustment as in France.

Symptom Displacement

From the German military standpoint, the First World War can be seen as a badly run general rehearsal for the Second World War. It cannot be denied that Hitler's *Wehrmacht* tried to learn from the mistakes that had been made earlier. One of the issues which aroused serious concern on the eve of the war was the phenomenon of war neuroses. German military psychiatrists, with great regularity, pointed to the enormous threat that such an eventuality represented for the fighting strength of the armed forces.[13] When the war finally did get under way, it appeared that all the concern had been exaggerated – at least in the beginning. In the first years of the war the dreaded *Kriegsneurosen* presented no more than a minor, almost negligible problem. Only in the summer of 1943 did the numbers begin to increase to such an extent that the alarm bell had to be sounded.

Different reasons can be given to account for the near-absence of combat neuroses during the first phase of the war. For instance, one can point to the fact that the *Blitzkrieg*, to begin with, led to rapid successes and was accompanied by small losses on the German side. The German troops enjoyed a high morale and their confidence in their weapons was great. In addition, the *Wehrmacht* made use of a shrewd system of personnel replacement. What the system boiled down to was that units that had suffered heavy losses were collectively withdrawn from the front line. During the subsequent rest period, the new replacements had enough time to prepare themselves for their new destinations and to become integrated in the groups they were to form part of. As a result of this, the German units acquired an enormous resilience and they proved to be extraordinarily capable of coping with setbacks and deprivations. The *Wehrmacht*, one could conclude, had given the necessary attention to prevention of combat neuroses. As part of this prevention one may also include the surveillance system that the army disposed over. In order to avoid a repetition of the outbursts of mass hysteria that had appeared during the First World War extensive measures were taken. These measures made it possible to isolate immediately any potential sources of panic that might appear and to remove them from the battlefield. Thus the lessons learned by German military psychiatry in the First World War had not been forgotten.

Yet there was a subdivision of the German war machine where neuroses did frequently occur right in the early phase of the fighting. This was the case with the so-called *Einsatzgruppen* that were active in Poland and Russia from 1941.[14] Murdering Jews and the extermination of partisans was part of the tasks carried out by these units. The notorious SS general Erich Von dem Bach-Zelewski was one of the best known commandants. It was he who kept the top Nazi echelons, and in particular Himmler, informed about the enormous psychological stress his SS troops experienced in murdering women and children. After some time, many members of *Einsatzgruppen* could not continue. They committed suicide, became insane, or only kept themselves going by excessive use of alcohol. Even the general himself had to undergo treatment by an SS psychiatrist due to psychological exhaustion. As far as we know, this form of breakdown was viewed with understanding. The only condition was that the patients must not question the meaningfulness of their work. If they did do that, they were dealt with in an entirely different way. The above-mentioned units represented an exception to the general picture which, to begin with, was characterized by a lack of combat neuroses.

The dramatic rise in the number of these neuroses in the last phase of the conflict can be associated with the shift in the fortunes of war. Optimism gave way to pessimism. In view of what had happened at Stalingrad and Kursk, the best that could be said was that Germany faced a dead-end situation. Because of the enormous need for manpower, military selection and training now came under pressure. One can interpret the abolishing of the psychological section of the army and the air force in 1942 as a manifestation of this situation. In the briefest terms, this meant that in the last years of the war stress on the German soldiers increased, while the quality of the troops during the same period decreased. On the basis of all this it can be said that chances of the occurrence of psychological problems increased appreciably. German authors have proposed an interesting alternative explanation for this striking pattern in the development of war neuroses. They indicate that in the first phase of the war there was indeed a far lower rate of neuroses than had been expected, but that during this period there was also a large increase in the number of organic disorders among German soldiers.[15] The soldiers affected did not become blind or deaf but suffered from stomach and intestinal complaints. On the basis of this the authors conclude that what happened was a *Symptomverschiebung* (a displacement of symptoms). By way of explaining this phenomenon, they draw attention to the wider context of the Nazi regime.

A further reason for the displacemnt of symptoms in the somatic realm during the first years of the war can also be sought in the political system of the time. Indeed, the Fascist regime suppressed the psychological protest of soldiers unwilling to fight not only with the more advanced psychiatric-psychotherapeutic methods but with open terror as well (prison, punishment battalions, concentration camps and execution). As far as the appearance of purely psychological symptoms was concerned, there was also the threat of being exterminated in the machinery of the Nazis' 'euthanasia' program for mental patients and 'psychopaths'. Only perfect simulation of physical illnesses or a form of self-mutilation that the doctors could not recognize as such offered someone who was conscious of his 'tendencies to avoid war' the possibility to escape from war. The military diagnosticians did still acknowledge the organic medical sphere. Illnesses and wounds of this kind were treated with medical methods and could, in appropriately grave cases, lead to dismissal from military service.[16]

This account does not, however, make clear why at a later phase combat neurosis once again became the most common form of manifestation. One possible explanation has to do with the change in the method of treatment which began to take effect from 1943. In brief, it comes down to the fact that organic disorders were met with increasingly less sympathy. The special *Magenbattalionen* that were formed in 1943 provide an illustration of this. It was expected that these *Speziellformationen* would have a deterrent effect and that the number of soldiers reporting in sick would drop. By the autumn of 1944 fourteen battalions of this kind had been created. The health service of the army calculated that there were enough sick fighting men to form seventy to eighty such battalions.[17] Thus, for one reason or another, being affected by organic disorders became steadily less rewarding for an individual soldier. For this reason as well – one might almost say for lack of a better alternative – combat neuroses were able to gain more ground. It would seem, however, that this situation did not represent a threat to the army's combat strength. Up to the final decisive battle for Berlin the *Wehrmacht* continued to dispose over a formidable fighting force. Only, belief in a good outcome steadily decreased.

Many German servicemen tried to get themselves removed from front line duty in the last years of the war or to get out of the army altogether. The military system attempted to prevent this at all costs.[18] In December 1943 the military courts were brought to their maximum strength. There were then 687 courts in operation with 1133 appointed judges. Most of the sentences handed down pertained to self-mutilation, undermining the armed forces and, last but not least, desertion. From June 1941 to November 1944 the number of death sentences increased eighteenfold. It would appear that for desertion alone 15,000 death penalties were carried out, the vast majority of which took place in the final phase of the war. Thus one might well conclude that seeking escape in combat neurosis presented an alternative to desertion or self-mutilation.

Combat Exhaustion

In sharp contrast to the course of events in Germany, on the eve of the war the British army command showed little concern about the existence of a future epidemic of combat neuroses. There was only fear among the authorities responsible for paying out benefits to the war casualties. Indeed, they were agonizing over the consequences that a new wave of shell shock patients would have. These financial concerns led to action. On the initiative of the Ministry of Pensions in July and November 1939 conferences were held during which measures were discussed on how to come to grips with such a situation.[19] Soon enough it was revealed that the

British had not been worried for no reason. Among the soldiers evacuated from Dunkirk there was a sizeable number of psychiatric cases.

William Sargant and Elliot Slater, who were attached to the neurological section of a military emergency hospital, reported on this group in *The Lancet*.[20] The soldiers in question exhibited symptoms of exhaustion, were obsessed with fear, complained of nightmares and had a range of other physical disorders. Sargant and Slater were not completely consistent in the terminology they employed. Whereas the title of their article is 'Acute War Neuroses', in the text of the article itself, at one point, they use the term 'shell shock' in parenthesis. I assume they chose to do this in order to make it clear quickly what sort of cases they were dealing with.

The symptoms recorded by these two authors are to be found again in almost every report or study that was published on this subject in connection with the Second World War. In their article they note four groups of symptoms:
1. Emotional problems: anxiety, insecurity, irritability, nightmares, and suchlike.
2. Cognitive disorders: loss of concentration, memory loss, etc.
3. Physical complaints: headache, stomach pain, trembling, sweating, etc.
4. Manifestations of hysteria: stuttering, blindness, symptoms of paralysis, etc.[21]

In fact this ordering of the symptoms is no more than a reworking of the dichotomy between neurasthenia and hysteria which is familiar from the First World War. In all probability, however, there was a significant difference between the two world wars. In fact, in almost all research studies it has been confirmed that during the last war the reactions of a hysterical kind were far less significant than in the previous one. The anxiety syndrome was the most frequently occurring neurotic pattern in the Second World War, not only in the British but in the American army as well. The manifestations that belong to this syndrome, such as restlessness, irritation, apathy and nightmares, correspond to those of neurasthenia. Thus what was previously seen as a typical disorder of an officer has now come back as a general disorder, unconnected with rank or class.

An interesting observation which should not be ignored was made by General Rees. This former Chief of the Military Psychiatric Service of the British Army stated that the soldiers in the Second World War were less apprehensive of showing their fear. During moments of distress, they made an open display of their anxieties.[22] They did not suppress these fears and therefore, as it appears, it was not necessary for them to have recourse to manifestations of hysteria. In a recent article in *Military Medicine* John R. Neill has made a similar statement:

With the coming of the Second World War, it would be fair to say that some greater degree of psychological sophistication was present among soldiers and the population in general, as well as the psychiatrists who were treating them. In the intervening three decades, through popular media and general education, social expectations of psychological distress had changed, admitting the notions that 'stress' and 'fatigue' nervous breakdowns could take place to 'ordinary people' without invoking the notion of major mental illness or insantiy.[23]

According to Neill, not only were the soldiers inclined to reveal their psychological problems quickly, but the psychiatrists as well were prepared to take direct action. The expression 'I can't take it anymore' was for the most part sufficient to set in motion the process of evacuation.

The British medical authorities did everything in their power, this time around, to stop the term shell shock from establishing itself. The official policy was not to assign any labels whatsoever but to confine oneself to the term NYD(N), which simply meant Not Yet Diagnosed (Nervous). In practice, however, there were various concepts that came into circulation from the outset, such as 'psychoneuroses', 'battle neuroses' and 'anxiety neuroses'. During the battles in the North African desert in 1942, it was common usage to diagnose 'exhaustion'. On the British side 'battle exhaustion' was the label employed for the psychologically wounded soldiers who were removed from action. The Canadians followed the British example. Only the recently arrived Americans preferred 'combat exhaustion'. The concept *exhaustion* fit well with the picture of the war that presented itself to the psychiatrists in North Africa and later in Italy and Normandy. What they witnessed was a war of movement which was chiefly fought by the infantry, i.e. by soldiers on foot. It was a war of marching columns, loaded down with weapons, ammunition and provisions. With the passage of time, every soldier was tired and worn out. The Canadian psychiatrist Hanson , who was assigned to the Army of the United States, has given a description of a group of American soldiers who took part in the campaign in Tunisia:

Their faces were expressionless, their eyes blank and unseeing and they tended to sleep wherever they were. The sick, injured, lightly wounded, and psychiatric cases were usually indistinguishable on the basis of their appearance. Even casual observation made it evident that these men were fatigued to the point of exhaustion. Most important of the factors that produced this marked fatigue was lack of sleep.[24]

Taken in this sense, the term exhaustion offered a good portrayal of the face of the war. This was not the only reason why the concept became so popular. Many psychiatrists believed that it also indicated one of the causes for the breakdown of soldiers: overtiredness as the result of lack of sleep and great physical exertion. This line of reasoning was also endorsed by the servicemen themselves. The acceptance of combat exhaustion meant that there was the possibility of sending out a signal for help without having to portray oneself as a 'psycho'. Thus by 1942 combat neurosis, albeit under a new name, was more or less officially recognized and sanctioned among the Allies.

Nonetheless, the differences between the German armed forces and the armies of the Allies should not be overemphasized. Numerous psychiatrists have pointed out that there was also a certain degree of symptom displacement among the Allies, especially at the beginning of the war. Many psychiatric cases ended up in field hospitals and hospitals on military bases with purely somatic diagnoses. Different reasons can be given for this situation. One important factor was the deficient psychiatric know-how on the part of many military doctors. Sometimes these doctors did not know how to deal with a soldier who had suffered a breakdown and they simply reported that he had a back complaint or that he wet his bed. What counted for the soldiers themselves was that during their basic training they had learnt that exhibiting organic disorders was the best way to have oneself removed from military service. Once they were on active duty in wartime the same standards were applicable. Furthermore, in the American army in particular, servicemen with psychological problems ran the risk of being stigmatized as 'psycho cases'. By displaying symptoms of normal somatic illness one did not run that risk. Finally, it should not be forgotten that it was often in the interest of a commandant that a different designation be employed for servicemen who were removed because of suffering a breakdown. This had to do with the fact that army command frequently tended to use the number of psychological breakdowns as a gauge for the morale of an individual unit. Psychiatric cases were bad for the reputation of the regiment as well as for the career of the general involved. Thus many units definitely were not open about their psychiatric patients which means that one cannot attach too great a value to the officially recorded number of cases.

Naturally, psychiatrists during the Second World War did not limit themselves to describing and analyzing symptoms. Much serious and careful thought was devoted to seeking the causes that produced the disorders. Compared with the period 1914-1918, the debate carried out on this subject was broader in scope and of a more sophisticated nature. In addition to the well-known psychological and bio-medical perspectives, social-psychological and sociological conceptual approaches also played a part in the discussion. Thus careful attention was given to the influence of styles of leadership and the significance of primary group relationships. This broader scope was related, among other things, to the additional task which had been assigned to military psychiatry in this war, namely prevention. As a result, psy-

Combat exhaustion

chiatrists were forced to concern themselves more than previously with the prevention of neurotic behavior (see Chapter IX). Along with a broader scope, research
methods had become more sophisticated. Thus the likelihood of a breakdown occurring was related, for example, to situational factors such as the duration and the
intensity of combat.

An old but by no means outmoded topic of discussion, which this time was raised
especially by the American psychiatrists, had to do with the question whether certain personality traits predisposed a soldier to suffer a breakdown. The greatly increased popularity of the psychoanalytical approach in psychiatry reinforced the
belief that such was the case. Indeed, according to this way of thinking, behavioral
disorders were chiefly related to unresolved conflicts and traumatic experiences in
the childhood years. The actual research results may rightly be considered surprising. On the basis of some studies, it turned out that unstable soldiers had a greater
chance of suffering a breakdown than servicemen who were considered unstable.
Nevertheless, it also was shown that unstable soldiers could hold up under stress.
The 'pre-combat neurotic' was in no way doomed to failure from the start. Furthermore – and in this respect there was a very high degree of agreement among American psychiatrists – with the passage of time even the most stable persons would become susceptible to breakdown. Consequently, if there was a difference between
the two categories, it was a difference of degree. This found expression, moreover,
in the widespread notion that everyone had his breaking point. According to one
view, this was after 200 days of combat, according to another, after 240 days, but
everyone eventually would break down. The concept 'old sergeant syndrome' was
the medical phrase for this process of being worn down.[25]

Combat Stress
Although the terms 'combat exhaustion' and 'battle exhaustion' never completely
disappeared from the literature, it is true to say that they were gradually pushed
into the background. Especially after the American military intervention in Vietnam, it became common usage to speak of combat stress or acute combat stress.
This change of name was not the result of the arrival of new symptoms. It was still a
question of cognitive, emotional and functional organic disorders which appeared
in combination with hysterical manifestations. The new division into mild, interme-
diate and acute combat stress corresponds to the old division into neurasthenia,
functional organic disorders and hysteria.

The concept 'stress' refers to the biochemical reactions which occur in the human body when a person confronts what is experienced as a life-threatening situation. When something like this happens, particular chemical substances are se-
creted within the various endocrinological systems. One of the best known of these
is adrenalin. In studying stress, two principal tasks receive attention. To begin with,
an inventory is drawn up of threatening situations and events, the so-called stress
factors. The second step consists in measuring the physiological reactions which
these stress factors set off in the body. Especially in the United States, researchers

by means of large-scale survey studies have attempted to establish classifications of threatening situations and occurrences. An example of this is the extensive list which was drawn up in 1979 by Dr. Thomas J. Holmes.[26] According to his ranking, the death of a spouse or a close member of one's family, for instance, scores very high, whereas taking out a loan or committing minor traffic offenses is low down on the scale.

Due to the rapid developments that biochemistry underwent from the 1960s onwards, research into physiological reactions of this kind was increasingly able to yield more results. Not only were new chemical substances discovered in the body, but more refined measuring techniques were developed which made it possible to quantify the presence of these substances with precision.

In the meantime, it became clear that there are great differences between persons with regard to their reactions to threatening situations. For example, it was established that social and cultural factors play an important role in an individual's processes of perception. These variables, as well, were incorporated into research on stress. Thus the framework within which this research was carried out was more than a specific, physiological variant of the bio-medical model. Indeed, one can maintain that this approach in fact encourages a combination of various perspectives.

One of the institutions where stress had already been studied with great interest in the 1940s was the famous Walter Reed Hospital of the US army. Obviously, for an institution of this kind a war involving the massive use of American troops would offer unique opportunities for carrying out research. The Korean War appeared to be just such an opportunity. However, few sensational discoveries were made during that conflict. Researchers would have to wait for a new opportunity. The occasion came in the middle of the 1960s. We are referring, of course, to the Vietnam War. Peter Bourne, one of the researchers who was to make a name for himself in this field, has described the new opportunities and the difference from the situation in Korea as follows:

Even at the time of the Korean conflict, logistical problems and the relatively unrefined bio-chemical techniques then available for measuring endocrine excretion limited research in the area. It is also true that the greatest period of interest in the biochemical aspects of behavior came after the Korean war was concluded. Fifteen years later, with improved methods of measuring steroid excretion and, specifically, 17-OHCS levels as well as the greater mobility provided by the helicopter, the naturally occurring stress laboratory of combat was ready to be taken advantage of in Viet Nam.[27]

War as a natural laboratory! But just what phenomena did research focus on and what results did it yield? By way of illustration there follows a description of an experiment which was carried out by the above-mentioned Bourne. In fact, the research consisted of two phases involving the detailed study of two separate units that were engaged in quite different combat situations.[28]

The first unit was made up of seven persons who served in helicopter ambulances. Their work was characterized by a high degree of variation in the occurrence of stress. Sometimes they had to carry out several, highly dangerous missions in quick succession. Then there were days when nothing happened and a situation of complete rest prevailed.

The second phase of the research had to do with a commando unit (Green Berets) who were occupying a small isolated post in the highlands. Their situation was constantly dangerous. Thus here there was a permanent confrontation with stress. At the beginning of the experiment the men involved, i.e. the seven medics and twelve commandos, were given as many psychological and psychiatric tests as possible. During the research period of three weeks they were interviewed on a daily basis and observed by experienced observers. The latter also went along on dangerous missions. Bourne himself was also present in the camp of the commandos. In addition, they had to make out daily reports in which all the events of each day were described. Finally, throughout a whole twenty-four hour period urine samples were collected. The samples were frozen and analyzed in a laboratory of one of the army base hospitals.

What results did the experiment yield? The urine analysis involving the medics showed that there were only very small differences in the secretion of steroids (17-OHCS) from one situation to another. It turned out it mattered very little whether a man flew combat missions or whether he had a day of rest. Furthermore, it appeared that their secretion level was on the whole quite low. Likewise, the commandos, who were in fact confronted with permanent stress, also turned out to have a similarly low level.

Bourne concluded from this that situations *per se* cannot simply be classified as high or low in stress. The soldiers had developed methods to avoid stress or to live with it. The behavioral observations that were carried out and the recorded interviews presented a picture of the defense mechanisms which soldiers made use of. These ranged from an absolute belief in the protective power of God to a no less firm trust on a soldier's part in his own military professionalism. Especially among the Green Berets, this sense of certainty was frequently to be found.

It was noteworthy that, in the case of the commandos, only the two officers had higher levels of steroids. Bourne related this to the specific tasks that the officers had to carry out. They bore full responsibility for the survival or the destruction of the whole group and they had to maintain contact by radio with the higher command. Since their superiors were far-off and were not always well-informed about the local situation, these officers often found themselves in a stressful dilemma. Bourne concluded that it was difficult for them to mobilize defense mechanisms in face of tensions of this kind. He also concluded – and on this point we can wholeheartedly agree with him – that the existence of various defense mechanisms had long been recognized and that work as to the function of these mechanisms in combat situations had already been published during the Second World War by Rado among others:

By far the most efficient technique at the soldier's disposal in resolving this conflict is completely to ignore the dangers surrounding him as though disregarding his own life, and thus stop the entire working of emergency control. Transformed from a sensitive man into an insensitive technician of war, he then interprets combat not as a continued threat of injuries but as a sequence of operational demands to be responded to by precise military performances. He is able to take this remarkable attitude because the situation touches off in the depths of his mind the eternal human illusion of one's invulnerability and immortality. With his self-love thus powerfully protected he can afford to lose his identity in the military unit, can give himself entirely to the job in hand and may even perform deeds of heroism.[29]

What was new was the fact that well-known concepts from the behavioral sciences could be provided with a physiological foundation.

Thinking in terms of stress entails certain consequences. The concept clearly suggests an element of continuity. Induction into the army is accompanied by stress. This increases when a soldier is sent to a foreign country and contact with his home and family becomes more difficult. If the military organization succeeds in reestablishing this social contact by means of adequate post and telephone links, the stress diminishes. Similarly, every day spent in the army has its moments when the tension rises and then falls again. Stressful moments include roll call, inspections and participation in certain dangerous operations. Seen in this light, actual combat is something that causes stress just like a drill or an exam, only more so.

In this connection it may be noted that the approach based on stress also implies a further step in accepting as normal the behavioral disorders displayed by soldiers. With the concept 'combat exhaustion' there was already some progress in that direction. After all, terms like these indicated that exhaustion is a normal reaction to extreme circumstances. Consequently, it is not necessary to attach a psychiatric label to the soldier in question. With the term combat stress this process of establishing normality was continued further. Thus conceived, stress is something everyone, soldier or civilian, constantly has to deal with, not only in wartime but in times of peace as well. For example, the title of Bourne's book that we quoted from above is *The Psychology and Physiology of Stress. With Reference to Special Studies of the Viet Nam War*. What one experiences in war, it is suggested, is part of the many experiences that make up human life – a particularly unpleasant experience but not fundamentally different from the other unpleasant things we have to face.

What is problematic, however, is that these assumptions concerning continuity and normality contradict the experience that soldiers themselves have of their war past. It is evident on the basis of countless documents that taking direct part in war is an extremely traumatic experience. When it is all over, the world seems like a different place. Relations with family and friends also take on a different content afterwards. It seems to me, therefore, more realistic to view the experience of war as something characterized by discontinuity. Haim Dasberg has taken up a similar standpoint in an excellent article dealing with the place occupied by trauma in Israeli society:

However, as to *clinical cases*, the experience of being cut-off or of there being no one to trust in this world appeared to be the most characteristic reaction of battle-breakdown in 1973. Thereafter the world is not the same. This is why I would prefer to use the diagnostic expression 'breakdown' rather than the currently used expression 'stress disorder', because stress is not necessarily a break in the world picture. Stress suggests a physiological continuum, whereas 'trauma' connotes a very drastic discontinuity.[30]

In closing, one further remark seems appropriate with regard to establishing the normality of behavioral disorders displayed by soldiers during wartime. Naturally, it is of great importance that servicemen who suffer breakdowns are not discriminated against and stigmatized with a humiliating psychiatric label. By the same token, however, it is of no benefit to those involved if their complaints become trivialized. That danger is now very much present in the approach which sees these disorders as a manifestation of stress. The tendency exists to emphasize the temporary character of the disorders and to assume that with the passage of time everything will be alright once again. After all, we are not dealing with psychiatric patients but with healthy men who have been confronted by abnormal circumstances. However, this is precisely what one should not take for granted. Healthy people, too, can become so damaged by traumatic events that they experience long-term effects. It is even possible that no problems at all appear in the short term but that only years later the soldiers in question suffer from nightmares and memory disorders (see Chapter X). Since our scientific knowledge about how people cope with traumatic experiences is extremely limited, great caution should be exercised in this area.

Forms of Resistance to Military Psychiatry
One of the most crucial questions that can be posed with regard to military psychiatry has to do with its acceptance by the military authorities. Eric Leed has noted that with the recognition of war neuroses armies during the First World War came to dispose over a kind of safety valve. Shell shock in fact functioned as an alternative to desertion, mutiny and fragging. The accumulated tensions and frustrations of trench warfare could find an outlet in more or less bizarre behavioral disorders which were tolerated as manifestations of illness.[31]

Thus psychiatry, which explains and legitimates certain forms of deviant behavior, can perform a function in military organization. But there is a price to be paid for this functionality. Indeed, war neurosis is not only an alternative to insubordination or desertion, but also to continuing to fight. For some commanders this price has been too high. Consequently, from the outset military psychiatry has known some bitter opponents. Naturally, the situation is not such that every officer has adjusted his attitude to this issue by means of a rational analysis of costs and benefits. Much of the actual resistance and rejection can be explained by the fact that the opponents in question subscribed to a system of values and norms in which there simply was no place for neurotic behavior. This was especially true of traditional military morality. Within this morality bravery, a sense of duty and aggressivity held a central position. Soldiers who for unclear reasons failed to do their duty during combat were seen as cowards. They were weaklings who deserved punishment, not medical treatment. Certainly during the First World War soldiers were expected to follow orders without hesitation, even if to do so put their life in danger. And that was precisely what they did. Without this sense of duty, which appears to be so immense in our eyes, that all-devouring war could never have gone on for such a long time. Captain Dunn also held this moral attitude.

We have had occasion earlier on to refer to this brave and intelligent doctor. In his book about daily life in the infantry he only twice makes mention of shell shock patients. The first time he merely points out that the phenomenon, along with trench-foot, had been first described two thousand years ago.[32] When he mentions it a second time, it is in connection with conscripts who have deceived themselves into thinking they are suffering from shell shock.[33] In brief, for Dunn these are men who are overreacting and do not belong in the army. Immediately after the war, Lieutenant-Colonel G. Scott-Jackson expressed himself in similar terms when addressing the previously mentioned War Office Committee of Inquiry into Shell Shock. He declared that in 1915 not a single case of shell shock had occurred in his battalion. He simply did not allow it. In later years, however, he had to yield on this point. The symptoms had in the meantime become generally acknowledged even among batches of new recruits. Moreover, psychiatric patients could count on sympathy and understanding when they returned home. Now it would appear that the dam had burst.[34]

Lord Gort, who was still a lieutenant-colonel at the time, also testified before the same commission. Gort considered the problem to be purely one of morale. In the elite units shell shock did not occur. Well-drilled troops were immune to it. The lord also had a good tip to give the investigating commission with regard to prevention: 'Officers must be taught much more about man mastership in the same way as horse mastership.' Clearly, the existence of war neurosis was undesirable and unnecessary. It represented an assault on the classic British military virtues. Lord Gort declared literally that '...shell shock must be looked upon as a form of disgrace to the soldier'.[35] During the month of May 1940, Gort was supreme commander of the British expeditionary army. As we know, this fighting force was driven into the sea within a few weeks by the *Wehrmacht*. For Gort this will also have signified a great stain on the honor of the British military profession.

During the Second World War the American general George Patton was renowned as the personification of this morality. He advised his men to deride soldiers with neurotic symptoms and to ridicule them. The latter would then see for themselves that there was no place in the American army for fakers and cowards. While in Italy he went so far as to match his actions to his words and gave a resounding slap to a soldier who had suffered a breakdown. In this connection it should be noted that the reaction to this deed on the part of the army leadership was in no way ambiguous. Patton was relieved of his command and obliged to apologize for his behavior. The American army was forced to take this step because the incident had aroused great public indignation in the United States. That a general should strike a soldier was not to be tolerated, at least not in the American army. This incident makes it clear that on the home front there was definitely sympathy for a psychologically wounded soldier.[36] Patton's views on the benefits of military psychiatry were not all that different from the ideas that the British war leader Winston Churchill held on the subject. Half way through the war Churchill became worried by the great number of psychiatrists that were swarming all over the army. In his view, people like that were simply getting in the way of the troops:

I am sure it would be sensible to restrict as much as possible the work of these gentlemen, who are capable of doing an immense amount of harm with what may very easily degenerate into charlatanry. The tightest hand should be kept over them, and they should not be allowed to quarter themselves in large numbers upon the Fighting Services at the public expense. There are, no doubt, easily recognizable cases which may benefit from treatment of this kind, but it is very wrong to disturb large numbers of healthy, normal men and women by asking the kind of odd questions in which the psychiatrists specialize. There are quite enough hangers-on and campfollowers already.[37]

When in March 1942 the bombing of Malta reached its peak, the British army had notices pinned up stating that 'anxiety neurosis' was a concept by means of which the medical profession was trying to make capital out of people's fear. But, according to the author of the notice, no real man with a sense of self-respect would ever allow himself to show fear.[38]

Here it must be said that the British armed forces were, and to some extent still are, rather unique in this regard. During the Falklands War of 1982 as well, British soldiers could expect little sympathy when it came to psychological problems. This was true not only for ordinary soldiers but for pilots too. Thus one particular Harrier pilot was sent back to England in the very midst of the conflict. The man in question had shot down an Argentinian Mirage and began to feel emotionally troubled by the experience. The image of the exploding aircraft from which the pilot had not been able to bale out would not leave his mind. He found no sympathy for his troubled emotions among his superiors. The simplest solution was chosen. He was grounded and was eventually sent back home.[39]

Traditional military morality, as appears from the examples given above, represents an important barrier that military psychiatry must overcome. Moreover, the wider culture of the surrounding community is naturally also of significance. As a social institution the army is involved with this context. Consequently, the process of acceptation of concepts such as shell shock, combat exhaustion and combat stress has also been determined by broader social ideas about courage, fulfilling one's duty and a sense of self-sacrifice. A good example of this is the development of military psychiatry within the Israeli army. In Israel's armed forces recognition that such a thing as combat stress exists only came about rather late. As a result, it has taken an unusually long time before a system of treatment was established. The war of liberation in 1948, the Sinai Campaign in 1956 and the Six Day War in 1967 each exacted its toll in terms of psychiatric casualties. And yet these cases received no recognition.[40] The prevailing morality, both inside and outside the army, would simply not permit the recognition of breakdown. Soldiers who originated from a people that had produced the Masada fighters were not susceptible to suffering mental collapse. In Israeli culture the myth which has been created around Masada with great dedication and little respect for historical facts still occupies an important place. Nonetheless, changes have occurred. This was first apparent in the army. During the Yom Kippur War of 1973 the chaos and panic which emerged necessitated a temporary recognition of the existence of combat stress. During the conflict with Lebanon in 1982 military psychiatry was fully expanded and perfected. This change in attitude came later in the community. The turning-point was brought about by the Gulf War. Before that time it was not allowed for citizens to show fear of threats from outside. During rocket attacks one went down into the shelters and waited with courage and patience until it was peaceful again. Seeking safety by visiting family members who lived elsewhere, for instance, was considered cowardice. In fact, it could even be seen by some as betrayal. During the conflict in Kuwait when Israel was the target of Iraqi scud-missiles a change occurred in this area. Showing fear was allowed, and so was fleeing from danger – the demands of the culture became looser, more adapted to the weaknesses of a modern human being.

This cultural shift is lucidly analyzed by Zahava Solomon who is attached to the medical service of the Israeli army.[41] This author states that the struggle for survival which Israel was obliged to carry on during the first decades of its existence created a specific system of values. Within this system there was no place for individual needs. Any such needs were completely subordinated to those of the collectivity. Traumatized survivors of the Holocaust and traumatized soldiers were not only seen as a burden but also as a threat to the community. With the establishment of a sense of greater security the attitude to this category of casualties changed. During the Gulf War this new attitude clearly emerged into the open. At that time a psychologist could allow himself to make the following remarks in a newspaper:

Just about the most foolish thing that can be done now is to fear anxiety. Anxiety during wartime is an adaptive response, that is, it is an entirely natural response that arises in a situation where there is a real threat to life. If at all, I'd be worried about someone who wasn't anxious. People who are not anxious make me wonder why they are so blocked. Are they denying, repressing, unable to deal with the situation?[42]

If this statement was representative, it can be said that the Israeli population in 1991 no longer had need of the Masada myth. This is a reassuring idea, not only for the Israelis themselves, but for the other inhabitants of the Holy Land as well.

Conclusion

The psychologically wounded soldier appears in many variations. There are enormous differences between the symptoms exhibited, both in intensity and possible combinations. Pretty much every soldier who goes into battle experiences psychosomatic manifestations such as heart palpitations and increased transpiration. At the same time, many are gripped by more or less intense feelings of anxiety. Still others have problems with their ability to concentrate and with their memory. In extreme cases, deafness and blindness, and even symptoms of paralysis, can occur.

We have seen that the disorders are not the same in every war. During the First World War it was chiefly manifestations of hysteria which drew the attention of military psychiatrists. In the other larger or smaller conflicts of the twentieth century this form of manifestations was of less importance. In the Second World War functional organic disorders figured as an alternative to combat neurosis, at least to a certain degree. This symptom displacement has been related to changes that took place during the inter-war years both in psychiatry itself and in the social position of this discipline. In this connection reference has also been made to the developments that warfare has undergone in the years after 1918.

Generally speaking, working psychiatrists have had few problems as far as recognizing symptoms is concerned. The diagnostic methods employed in war are a good reflection of what is available at any particular period in the way of intellectual models and concepts in civilian psychiatry. Military psychiatrists, just as their civilian colleagues, have made use of concepts such as neurasthenia, hysteria, anxiety syndrome and stress. But in addition to this they have also launched certain terms that were specific to an individual occasion. By means of these concepts a relation could be established between psychological disorders and the specific wartime situations in which these disorders manifested themselves. As a term, shell shock has undoubtedly made the strongest impression on the public imagination, whereas nowadays combat stress is the most frequently applied label one comes across.

The military organization received these labels and, more generally, the overall role of psychiatry with mixed feelings. Naturally, military psychiatry could work like a safety valve by means of which potentially more threatening forms of deviant behavior could be prevented. And, naturally, it was an attractive idea that soldiers who had suffered a breakdown could be made functional again. But there was a certain price to be paid. In fact, military psychiatry has come to question the deeply cherished traditional morality of the military. Heroism, a mentality of determination and self-sacrifice, the foundations on which this morality was built, have been relativized and reduced to human proportions. It is perfectly understandable that this has evoked considerable resistance. Consequently, military psychiatry – and we will be dealing with this subject again in the following chapter – has had to fight to win acceptance in the army. In the British armed forces resistance has always been especially strong.

For some years now there has been a debate among medical historians about the relation between war and medical science. The discussion has revolved around the question whether wars have exercised a positive influence on the theory and practice of medicine. The classic viewpoint maintains that such has been the case. Recently, however, Roger Cooter has convincingly challenged this interpretation.[43]

One of the examples which is frequently cited in the context of this debate concerns shell shock. The great importance of this phenomenon is meant to have been that it drew the attention of psychiatry to the behavioral variations that exist between normal and deeply disturbed conduct. The First World War made it clear that the dichotomy between normal and insane is far too simplistic and requires further qualification. In this connection one could say that shell shock smoothed the way for more psychological explanatory models of human behavior and especially for psychoanalysis.

The points put forward in this line of reasoning are not incorrect but they need to be made more specific. Breaking out of the above-mentioned dichotomy was indeed characteristic of the British situation where one can say that attention to lesser psychiatric disorders had been minimal. Likewise, in contrast to France and Germany, the bio-medical framework in Britain was scarcely contested at all. To the great chagrin of Elliot Smith, dean of the Faculty of Medicine at the University of Manchester, some British psychiatrists were not prepared to learn anything from the experiences of war. He expressed his frustration in an article in *The Lancet*:

As recently as Jan. 15th, 1916, the *British Medical Journal* was responsible for the statement: 'The only hope that our present knowledge of insanity permits us to entertain of appreciably diminishing the number of "first attacks" lies in diminishing habitual and long enduring drunkenness and in diminishing the incidence of syphilis.' This statement would have been sufficiently amazing if it had been made two years ago; but when the hospitals of Europe contain thousands of 'first attacks' of insanity, which are definitely *not* due either to alcohol or syphilis, the only conclusion to be drawn from it is that its author must have been asleep since July, 1914, or have become so obsessed by his fixed idea as not to be able to see the plain lessons of the war.

Syphilis, no doubt, is reponsible for a very considerable proportion of cases of insanity, and drink *perhaps* for some more; but the incipient forms of mental disturbance which the anxieties and worries of warfare are causing ought to impress upon the attention even of the least intelligent members of the community that such causes are operating both in war and peace, and are responsible for a very large proportion of the cases of insanity. But what is still more important, it is precisely these cases which, if diagnosed in the early stages and treated properly, can be cured. The chief hope of reducing the number of patients in asylums for the insane lies in the recognition of this fact, and acting upon it in the way of providing institutions where such incipient cases of mental disturbance can be treated rationally, and so saved from the fate of being sent into an asylum.[44]

In the case of Britain the war had acted as a catalyst. As had happened earlier on the continent, during the inter-war years facilities in the field of mental health care became more geared to the neurotic patients. Maudsley Hospital, which was opened in 1915 and where shell shock patients were treated until 1923, succeeded in acquiring a high reputation for itself in this area.

VII - Therapy in Wartime

Introduction

What happened then to the psychologically wounded soldier after he was provided with an appropriate label? What therapies were used in treating him, and what was the relationship between the military setting and civilian practice? Did war lead to innovations in the therapeutic domain or was innovation left out of the picture? These are the main questions which will be addressed in this chapter.

Some well-known and less well-known psychiatrists, along with the range of therapies they made use of, will come under review. As the headings of the various subsections indicate, a certain degree of development took place with regard to treatment. Together with differences in time, diversity of theoretical frameworks also played a role in determining which therapeutic procedures came to be adopted. The assumptions underlying bio-medical models, for instance, led to therapeutic strategies that were quite divergent from those based on psychodynamic approaches. After this overview of therapeutic practice in wartime, which can naturally be no more than a global sketch, an attempt will be made to give a summary characterization of military psychiatry and to pinpoint its specific features.

A Violent Beginning

In the course of the year 1915, the then still unknown Dr. Fritz Kaufmann began to have serious worries. Not about the outcome of the war. At that point there was not yet any reason for concern on the part of the Germans. No, the somber reflections of this psychiatrist had to do with something completely different. Kaufmann was dismayed at the impotence of German military psychiatry. His hospital, the military psychiatric hospital in Ludwigshafen, where he was a doctor on the permanent staff, had also become inundated with more or less hopeless cases that the doctors could offer no further treatment. For the most part, there was nothing else the army could do but send these patients back to civilian society with a disability pension. This was the predicament that preoccupied Kaufmann's thoughts. But to avoid any misunderstandings, it should be stated that he was not primarily troubled by the lot of the patients themselves. In considering the effects of sending patients back into the community, Kaufmann was chiefly concerned about the consequences this would have for other individuals and agencies:

This leads to unpleasant consequences for the family in question. In addition, it leads to a loss in the living work force at the state's disposal. A by no means unimportant further consequence is the considerable burden put on the military treasury. A simple example will serve to clarify this point: if we take the expressly low figure of 100 dismissed patients of this category per year for each army corps district who receive an individual pension including the war bonus of 500 marks, this means that the annual outlay for the 25 army corps districts of Germany will amount to 1,250,000 marks.[1]

It was Kaufmann's merit to have designed a method which made it possible to break out of the prevailing therapeutic pessimism. Essentially, his method consisted of a procedure in which the use of powerful alternating electric current was of central importance. Limbs affected by disorders that hampered movement were subjected to a powerful form of electrotherapy. The current was left on for several minutes at a time. Afterwards the patient had to do exercises, and then the electricity was applied once again. During the treatment the soldier was advised to get well quickly. In Kaufmann's own words the essence of the therapy consisted of 'the use of powerful alternating current with the aid of ample verbal suggestion'.[2] It was important that the patient be psychologically prepared for what was to come. It must be stated clearly that the treatment to be applied was painful but that progress would be made in a single session. In short, the prospect must be held out of a brief healing procedure. In addition, Kaufmann considered it of great importance that the treatment be administered within the military sphere. The exercises that the patient had to do must be communicated to him in the form of actual military commands. In fact, here recourse was had to classic military drilling. The hospital should be transformed into a real barrack. The final element had to do with the behavior of the doctor treating the case. The doctor, with unrelenting determination, must attempt to complete the treatment in one session. In this connection Kaufmann warned that the symptoms frequently did not disappear after a short time but actually became more intense. The therapist, however, must not allow himself to be defeated because of this. It was precisely here that perseverance and the greatest dedication were required. Only in this way could success be achieved.

Naturally, Kaufmann himself knew that his approach was harsh and merciless. It was not for nothing that he spoke of it as an *Überrumpelungsmethode* (a surprise-attack method). He knowingly subjected his patients to an enormous psychological shock in the hope of being able subsequently to influence them for the better.

It was also characteristic that he did not think his method was suitable for out-patients. He maintained that patients should first spend a few days in a section of his institution. They would then have the opportunity to see that their therapists were indeed benevolent, humane individuals who had their best interests at heart. If this form of mutual rapport were not established, there was the danger that patients would feel they had been treated with brutality during the therapy. Moreover, to forestall any possible sceptics, Kaufmann declared that the patients he had successfully treated in the above-described manner were among his most grateful clients. This psychiatrist was absolutely convinced that his method was preferable to all the other approaches current at that time. One of the advantages of his system, compared with the use of hypnosis for example, was that it required very little specialized knowledge or schooling on the part of the doctor. The most important advantage, however, was that his approach left the patient no room for resistance. It was a matter of being cured, whether one liked it or not:

And I consider this to be the second advantage. An unwilling person can always evade hypnosis. But the surprise-attack method forces the patient who is disinclined to being cured to undergo a complete recovery. The powerful impression of pain suppresses all negative mental desires.[3]

Kaufmann was also well aware of the limitations of his approach. He realized that he was not solving any psychological problems but that he was only involved in combatting symptoms. This, however, did not worry him in the least. To his mind, why should someone who had been liberated from the symptoms of his illness, i.e. who was no longer blind or paralyzed, not be able to go back to exercising his old profession again. In any case, this would mean that the patient and his family would no longer have to live at the state's expense. This would signify a great financial saving for the public purse. Kaufmann did not seriously envisage the patient's eventual return to the front. Even active service in a garrison he considered to be too much for some of his ex-patients. Thus the Kaufmann-method had little to do with the need to maintain a high level of fighting power in the German army. After the method was made public in May 1916, it began a virtual triumphant march through Germany and Austria. One of the few doctors who raised any protest against it was Kurt Mendel. He felt there should be a difference between a hospital and military barracks. Similarly, according to his view, doctors were not non-commissioned officers. Finally, he made the point that it was not proper to treat soldiers who had suffered a breakdown as if they were naughty children. However, Mendel's views were an exception.[4] Moreover, less than a year later, even Mendel was converted to the new system and his statement 'pater peccavi' (father I have sinned) refers to the above-mentioned objections he had raised regarding the Kaufmann-method.

Another convert was Professor Otto Schulze. This psychiatrist was the head of a small hospital that was pleasantly situated in the mountains. His original approach had consisted of providing good food and administering sedatives. In addition, he prescribed bed rest and made use of hypnosis. In short, Schulze's hospital was a cushy place to stay. The therapeutic successes, however, were distinctly minor. Out of a total of fifty-four cases treated this way, there were only three where it could be claimed that a clear advance had been made. Consequently, Schulze too decided to follow a different path, and that path was shown to him by Kaufmann. Thereafter things improved. With regard to thirteen out of fifteen patients the treatment was successful. Thanks to the new approach it was possible to reduce drastically the average period of residence in the hospital.[5]

Moreover, this psychiatrist also was of the opinion that there were dubious aspects to the new system. He admitted that some of his colleagues had characterized

A Cartoon based on the Kaufmann-Kur

the method as inhumane. But then with every success there is a price to pay. Nonetheless, in Schulze's view the degree of pain a soldier had to undergo during treatment was not that much more than what a woman went through in childbirth. So, as
he no doubt thought, anyone with just a bit of military discipline would be able to
cope with it.

In the last year of the war an alarm was sounded with regard to the Kaufmann-
method from an unexpected corner. Warnings were voiced by the medical section
of the War Ministry of Bavaria. In a circular letter of March 1918 doctors were advised to avoid using the method because fatal accidents had occurred. On 14 September 1918, the same ministry once again drew attention to the matter:

Regarding the treatment of war neurotics. The active treatment of war neurotics has repeatedly given rise among the public, government representatives and the press to sharp criticism,
in some circles even to ill feelings and bitterness, and occasionally to justified complaints as
well. The reason for this has chiefly been that many doctors in their statements and in their
suggestive influence on war neurotics appear to have overemphasized a point of view concerned with withdrawing pensions and undeserved pension payments.

Therefore, the physicians involved must absolutely avoid anything which will give the impression that they are acting out of financial interest and not exclusively in the interest of the
patient and public health...[6]

From this letter it is clear that even the functionaries in the War Office felt that the
doctors had a tendency to go too far. We are therefore justified in assuming that the

German military psychiatrists had indulged themselves to their heart's content and, that in so doing, they had easily subordinated the interests of the patients to higher goals.

Towards the end of 1916, the Kaufmann-method was discussed in an issue of *The British Medical Journal*.[7] It was rather ironically noted that this was a treatment which had even been characterized as inhumane by a number of Kaufmann's own countrymen. The implicit idea, of course, was that something like this could never be practiced in the British Isles. But this assumption would prove to be a big mistake. England would also have its Kaufmann in the person of Dr. Lewis Yealland who was attached to the Queen Square Hospital in London. This English psychiatrist treated scores of cases of shell shock. Almost without exception the patients were ordinary soldiers, i.e. not non-commissioned or commissioned officers.

The 'quick cure' developed by Yealland and the Kaufmann-cure were as like as two peas in a pod. In Yealland's approach electrotherapy was also used to its ultimate logical effect. Here as well there was total subordination of the patient to the person of the therapist. Finally, it may be noted that Yealland also claimed never to fail. His patients were always cured. Immediately after the war he published a book in which he surveyed a large number of cases of soldiers he had treated.[8] The following example is taken from his book:

Case A1 – Mutism

Private, 24 years of age. Duration 9 months.

This man took part in the Mons retreat, battle of the Marne, battle of the Aisne, and the first and second battles of Ypres. He also fought at Hill 60, Neuve Chapelle, Loos and Armentière. In April 1916, he was sent to Salonica, and three months later, while attending to his horses, fell down unconscious; he says 'on account of the intense heat'. For five hours he remained unconscious, and on waking 'shook all over' and could not speak. When I saw him nine months later he was mute. Many attempts had been made to cure him. He had been strapped down in a chair for twenty minutes at a time, when strong electricity was applied to his neck and throat; lighted cigarette ends had been applied to the tip of his tongue and 'hot plates' had been placed at the back of his mouth. Hypnotism had been tried. But all these methods proved to be unsuccessful in restoring his voice.

When I asked him if he wished to be cured he smiled indifferently. I said to him: 'You are a young man with a wife and child at home; you owe it to them if not to yourself to make every effort to restore yourself. You appear to me to be very indifferent, but that will not do in such times as these. I have seen many patients suffering from similar conditions, and not a few in whom the disorder has existed for a much longer time. It has been my experience with these cases to find two types of patients; those who want to recover, and those who do not want to recover. Though you appear to be indifferent, I recognise the fact that you belong to the latter group. I understand your condition thoroughly and it makes no difference to me which group you belong to. You must recover your speech at once.' He became somewhat depressed; his eyes fell from looking at me, and I left him.

In the evening he was taken to the electrical room, the blinds drawn, the lights turned out, and the doors leading into the room were locked and the keys removed. The only light perceptible was that from the resistance bulbs of the battery. Placing the pad electrode on the lumbar spines and attaching the long pharyngeal electrode, I said to him, 'You will not leave this room until you are talking as well as you ever did; no, not before.' The mouth was kept open by means of a tongue depressor; a strong faradic current was applied to the posterior wall of the pharynx, and with this stimulus he jumped backwards, detaching the wires from the battery. 'Remember, you must behave as becomes the hero I expect you to be,' I said. 'A man who has gone through so many battles should have better control of himself.' Then I placed him in a position from which he could not release himself, and repeated, 'You must talk before you leave me.' A weaker faradic current was then applied more or less continuously, during which time I kept repeating, 'Nod to me when you are ready to attempt to speak.' This current was persevered with for one hour with a few intervals as were necessary, and at the end of that time he could whisper 'ah.' With this return of speech I said: 'Do you realise that there is already an improvement? Do you appreciate that a result has already been achieved? Small as it may seem to you, if you consider rationally for yourself, you will believe me when I tell you that you will be talking before long.' I continued with the use of electricity for half an hour longer, and during that time I constantly persuaded him to say 'ah, bah, cah,' but 'ah' only was repeated. It was difficult for me to keep his attention, as he was becoming tired; and unless I was constantly commanding him his head would nod and his eyes close. To overcome this I ordered him to walk up and down the room, and as I walked with him urged him to repeat the vowel sounds. At one time when he became sulky and discouraged he made an attempt to leave the room, but his hopes were frustrated by my saying to him, 'Such an idea as leaving me now is most ridiculous; you cannot leave the room, the doors are locked and the keys are in my pocket. You will leave me when you are cured, remember, not before. I have no doubt you are tired and discouraged, but that is not my fault; the reason is you do not understand your condition as I do, and the time you have already spent with me is not long in comparison with the time I am prepared to stay with you. Do you understand me?' This evidently made an impression on him, for he pointed to the electrical apparatus and then to his throat. 'No,' I said, 'the time for more electrical treatment has not come; if it had I should give it to you. Suggestions are not wanted from you; they are not needed. When the time comes for more electricity you will be given it, whether you wish it or not.' I had intended at that time to resort to electricity, but, owing to his attitude, I postponed its use and instead made him walk up and down the room repeating 'ah, ah, ah,' merely to keep him awake and to show him that his suggestion regarding the electricity would not be accepted. I did not talk to him unless he stopped repeating 'ah.' Meanwhile, each explosion of the whispered 'ah' was accompanied by an almost superhuman effort, manifested by spasmodic contraction of the muscles of the neck, the head being raised in jerks. However, he advanced no further than the whispered 'ah,' and indeed that was repeated only with considerable effort, though the degree of effort was diminishing materially. As I placed him back in the chair and once more attached the battery to him I said: 'You are now ready for the next stage of treatment, which consists of the administration of strong shocks to the outside of the neck; these will be transmitted to your "voice box" and you will soon say anything you wish in a whisper.' He was quite ready to accept the treatment. With each application of the faradic shock, applied to the neck in the region of the larynx by means of a key electrode, I said to him quickly, 'Say ah, bah, cah, dah.'

I repeated this as I touched him quickly each time. It was not long before he began to whisper the vowels with hesitation. When that was accomplished I said to him, 'Are you glad you have made such progress?' I expected him to answer me, but he did not; instead he began to cry and whispered in a stammer, 'I want a drink of water,' and I replied, 'Yes, you will have a drink of water in a few seconds, in fact just as soon as you can utter a sound.' He again made an attempt to leave the room, and I said firmly to him, 'You will leave the room when you are speaking – speaking normally. I know you do not want the treatment suspended now you have made such progress. You are a noble fellow, and these ideas which come into your mind and make you want to leave me before you are cured do not represent your true self. I know you are anxious to be cured and are happy you have recovered to such an extent; now you are tired and cannot think properly, but you must make every effort to think in the manner characteristic of your true self – a hero of Mons. You are already doing splendidly, and I am satisfied that you are now determined to talk and I am very pleased with you; more than that, I am proud of you.' His attitude then changed considerably, and from that time he made every attempt to recover. 'You must utter a sound,' I said; 'I do not care what the nature of the sound is – whether you shout or cough or moan. You will understand me when I say I shall be able to train any sound into the production of vowel sounds, then into letter sounds, and, finally, into words and sentences.' Immediately before I applied the electrode again to the posterior wall of the pharynx I said, 'Utter a sound when you take a deep breath and as soon as I touch your throat.' He phonated in inspiration, but was unable to produce an expiratory sound. I firmly held him in the chair and said to him, 'It is getting late; I may have to use a stronger current. I do not want to hurt you, but, if necessary, I must.' I then applied shock after shock to the posterior wall of the pharynx, commanding him each time to say 'ah,' and in a few minutes he repeated 'ah' in expiration. I continued with faradism until he could repeat 'ah' distinctly, and I did not discontinue its use until he was able to repeat any letter or any word I ordered him to say. I then relinquished the use of electricity for a time, the patient being rather exhausted, but I persisted with him, commanding him to repeat word after word, which he did with a considerable stammer. When he was able to repeat the days of the week, months of the year, and numbers, he became very pleased and was again quite ready to leave me. I said, 'Remember, there is no way out, except by the return of the proper voice and the door. You have one key, I have the other; when you talk properly I shall open the door so that you can go back to bed.' With a smile he stammered, 'I believe you have both keys – go ahead and finish me up.' Then I said, 'The current has got through all right, but the impulses are still interrupted, the muscles of your neck are contracting in spasms; this will have to be overcome by the administration of more electricity to the muscles of your neck – the spasms in a short time will be overcome, and when that occurs you will be speaking without difficulty. It is quite simple. I am sure you understand me when I tell you that each time you attempt to talk the muscles of the neck pull down the jaw in short, sharp spasms. Now take notice how easily this is overcome; each time you feel the shock to your neck you are to say a, b, c, d, in succession and go right on repeating the alphabet.' Very strong faradic shocks were applied in momentary applications to the neck over the larynx as he repeated each letter, and this current prevented the spasm each time.

This was continued for about ten minutes, the strength of current being gradually diminished until it was discontinued and he was able to talk without the slightest stammer. He was not, however, completely cured, for the condition of spasm or clonus had passed to the left arm, and, as he spoke, there was a paralysis agitans-like tremor in the left upper limb. I said to him, 'Do you see what has happened? The wind has gone down, but the waves are still lingering – look at you left arm.' 'But,' he said, 'doctor, I am talking, talking as well as I ever did in my life; do let me shake hands with you.' I said, 'No, your shaking arm must be treated.' He smilingly replied, 'You will not take long to do that.' I said, 'The shakiness of your arm must be treated in the same manner in which the neck was treated, as it is the same resistive condition, only manifested in another part. The spasm has left your neck and appeared in your left hand.' I applied a weak faradic current by means of a roller electrode up and down the extended fore-arm, telling him at the same time to repeat the days of the week, months of the year, etc. The tremor was overcome in a very short time, but it appeared in the right arm, and before it disappeared altogether had to be chased from the left arm, right arm, then from the left leg, and finally from the right leg, all these parts being treated similarly. He became quite excited and said, 'Doctor, doctor, I am champion,' to which I replied, 'You are a hero.' He then said, 'Why did they not send me to you nine months ago?' With a view to impressing on him the certainty of the cure being permanent, I answered him by saying, 'Such a condition as yours could not have been cured nine months ago. You have had time to rest, your general condition had localised itself in your voice, which could not have been treated so quickly had you come here earlier.'

This hitherto intractable case received four hours' continuous treatment.[9]

The treatment of this soldier shows that the methods used by Yealland were not very different from those used by Kaufmann. One might simply add that the German realized more clearly than the Englishman that his method was actually only suitable in a wartime situation, i.e. a period when the rights of the patient do not count for much. Yealland's book, on the other hand, appeared after the war and bore a foreword in which the form of psychotherapy being presented was warmly recommended for civilian practice as well. It would have been interesting if a German medical journal had responded to Yealland's proposals.

One of the surprising observations that can be made on the basis of the foregoing is that the First World War presents a kind of rebirth of the early nineteenth-century moral treatment – understood in its most 'heroic' form. Once again the patient is viewed as an unruly child that must be educated with a firm hand. Once again the authoritative status of the therapist looms large in the foreground. Here as well this characteristic is essentially more important than the acquisition of any specific professional knowledge. Only now the process of education takes place under great pressure due to a shortage of time. For this reason use is made of new means of help such as electricity. The basic ingredients are the same but the preparation now takes place in a rapid-acting pressure cooker.

A refined system of exerting influence on the basis of reward and punishment was employed in the Salpêtrière in Paris.[10] There Professor J. Déjerine and Major E. Gauckler applied psychotherapy according to 'la méthode coërcitive'. A basic assumption was that advances in the healing process should be monitored as precisely as possible. For this purpose the psychiatrists in question created 'la méthode

Troubles Nerveux

métrique'. This system included taking daily measurements of the angle of movement of rigid limbs and recording them on a chart. Developments in the range of
the angle provided a clear quantitative representation of a patient's progress or de-

terioration. In paralysis cases the time required to lift an arm or a leg could be measured in seconds. Progress was rewarded and deterioration was punished. The means of coercion employed included isolation, denial of the right to receive visitors, withholding mail, and the threat of restricting furloughs. The above-mentioned doctors were not proponents of electrotherapy. They were afraid that this form of treatment would encourage a patient's belief that there was something wrong with his body. Electrotherapy would lead to additional fixation on the symptoms and it was precisely this that must be prevented by every possible means. Although our two psychiatrists were optimistic about the possibilities of their particular approach and published on the subject in medical journals, they admitted without hesitation that the methods employed in the Salpêtrière were no more than makeshift. As far as the personnel was concerned there was nothing but good to report, but what was lacking was a real military regime and the discipline that goes with it. If the psychiatrists disposed over such a regime, the number of recoveries might not necessarily increase but, in any case, the recovery process would certainly be speeded up. Thus with regard to this viewpoint, i.e. the importance of adopting a military setting, Paris was somewhat in advance of Ludwigshafen.

Despite their individual differences, Kaufmann, Yealland and Déjerine had in common that they were advocates of so-called disciplinary therapies. In these approaches the therapist does not attempt to delve into the causes that led to the disorders. Instead, he concentrates on fighting the symptoms and this he does in a very vigorous manner. The therapies are painful and extremely unpleasant. Indeed, they have the character of a punishment. The patient himself is made responsible for his recovery. If a soldier does not get better, it means he is committing an act of insubordination. He is opposing the authority of the doctor who has ordered him to get better. In such a case punishment is appropriate just as in the case of a healthy soldier. Military barracks and the hospital are identical here.

Psychoanalysis in the Pressure Cooker

In all fairness one must say that other forms of treatment were also in use. In fact, a small group of psychiatrists had recourse to psychoanalysis. In accordance with this approach, discussion techniques were employed, at times in combination with hypnosis. The aim was to give a patient insight into repressed traumatic experiences and psychological conflicts which took place in his subconscious. These insights were then supposed to form the basis of the healing process.

In Britain the well-known neurologist and anthropologist, Dr. W.H.R. Rivers was the most prominent representative of the psychoanalytical approach. Although Rivers felt strongly attracted to the Freudian repertoire of ideas – along with E. Jones he was one of the earliest representatives of psychoanalysis in Britain – he nonetheless entertained a number of serious reservations. In particular, the dynamics of sexuality, which occupied such a central position for Freud and even more so for some of his followers, was subjected to criticism by Rivers:

The point is that while we have over and over again abundant evidence that pathological nervous and mental states are due, it would seem directly, to the shocks and strains of warfare, there is, in my experience, singularly little evidence to show that, even indirectly and as a subsidiary factor, any part has been taken in the process of causation by conflicts arising out of the activity of repressed sexual complexes. Certainly, if results are any guide, the morbid states disappear without any such complexes having been brought to the surface, while in other cases the morbid states persist in spite of the discovery of definite complexes, sexual or otherwise, going back to times long before the war.[11]

Rivers was attached to the Craiglockhart War Hospital which was located just outside Edinburgh. Before the war it had been an expensive private clinic where neurotics and alcoholics from better-off backgrounds were treated. The hospital had attractive gardens and recreational facilities of every type. Among other things, one could play golf, tennis and swim. In short, it was a comfortable, luxurious place. After the military took over, the pleasant comfortable aspects of the institution naturally decreased but life there was certainly in all respects tolerable. Unfortunately, treatment was reserved for a small minority, chiefly made up of officers.

One of the patients treated by Rivers in Craiglockhart was Siegfried Sassoon, one of the most celebrated 'war poets' to emerge from the First World War.[12] Sassoon knew what war was. He had served as an officer in the British expeditionary army and took part in the bloody battles in Belgium and Northern France. In 1917, however, it all became too much for this war volunteer. He believed that the war was being unjustly prolonged by politicians while a diplomatic solution was in fact within reach. Of course, Sassoon was certainly not the only one who thought like this but he was one of the few who wrote down his objections. In the summer of 1917 he published a pacifist pamphlet entitled *A Soldier's Declaration*:

I am making this statement as an act of wilful defiance of military authority, because I believe the war is being deliberately prolonged by those who have the power to end it.

I am a soldier, convinced that I am acting on behalf of soldiers. I believe that this war, upon which I entered as a war of defence and liberation, has now become a war of aggression and conquest. I believe that the purposes for which I and my fellow soldiers entered upon this war should have been so clearly stated as to have made it impossible to change them, and that, had this been done, the objects which actuated us would now be attained by negotiation.

I have seen and endured the suffering of the troops, and I can no longer be a party to prolong these sufferings for ends which I believe to be evil and unjust.

I am not protesting against the conduct of the war, but against the political errors and insincerities for which the fighting men are being sacrificed.

On behalf of those who are suffering now I make this protest against the deception which is being practised on them; also I believe that I may help to destroy the callous complacence with which the majority of those at home regard the continuance of agonies which they do not share, and which they have not sufficient imagination to realize.

S. Sassoon
July 1917

This would actually have been a matter for the military courts. But the army command did not at that moment want a public discussion on the subject of 'the continuation of the war'. Indeed, the losses had been gigantic. Moreover, Sassoon had a number of influential friends, among whom Robert Graves should be mentioned. In the end the matter was settled amicably. Sassoon was convoked before a medical, not a judicial, tribunal. The military doctors involved declared him not responsible for his actions. According to the official explanation, his long stressful stay in the trenches had affected his mental capacities. Sassoon was considered to be a shell shock victim.

Of course, in this case we are justified in doubting that we are dealing with a psychiatric patient. As far as Wilfred Owen is concerned, another famous war poet who like Sassoon was treated by Rivers, we should not have any such doubts. Life at the front slowly undermined Owen's mental stability. His final breakdown occurred after he had spent several days in an isolated forward position with the maimed and dismembered body of a fellow-officer lying alongside him. When he was brought to Rivers, he was a psychological wreck. In Craiglockhart the afflicted patients could find rest. The actual treatment aimed at bringing out in the open again traumatic experiences that had been repressed and teaching the patient to live with these experiences. In this connection Rivers felt it was important that the patients also come to see some positive aspects of the painful events. Here one can think of the comradeship soldiers encountered and deeds of bravery they performed.

If one assumes the primary task of a military psychiatrist is to make soldiers who have suffered a breakdown once again fit for active duty, then one can speak of successful therapeutic treatment in the cases of Sassoon and Owen. Both ultimately returned to the front at their own request and in full possession of their mental faculties. Owen was killed by machine-gun fire on 4 November 1918 during one of the last British operations exactly one week before the armistice. Sassoon was wounded but survived the war. He died in 1967, having lived into his eighties.

In Germany and Austria, quite early on, psychoanalysts were brought in to treat *Kriegsneurotiker*.[13] Sandor Ferenczi, Ernst Simmel and Karl Abraham occupied important positions in the various military medical services. In 1916 Ferenczi surprised the participants in a doctors congress held in Budapest with a patient demonstration involving half a company of psychologically disturbed soldiers. He told the audience honestly that at first he had also thought that physical wounds were the basis for the various disorders in question. Gradually, however, his eyes were opened. Freud and Breuer had drawn his attention to the real cause of these hysterical symptoms.

Ferenczi remained primarily active in the theoretical domain. He chiefly used the war casualties to show the supremacy of Freud's thought. In his opinion the war demonstrated that as far as psychiatry was concerned bio-medical thought was bankrupt. His colleague Ernst Simmel was above all active as a practicing therapist. He was well-informed about the psychological state of the front line soldiers and was particularly good at expressing this in words:

One must have experienced the events of war oneself or their recapitulation... through hypnosis to be able to understand what onslaughts the mental state of a human being is exposed to who is obliged to return to the field after having been wounded on several occasions, who has been cut off from his dear ones during important family events for an interminable period, who sees himself abandoned to a murderous monster of a tank or an approaching enemy wave of gas, who is wounded and buried by a direct hit often lying for hours or days under the bloody dismembered corpses of friends and, not least, who has had his self-esteem damaged by an unjust, cruel superior officer – possibly dominated by a complex himself – and who none the less must remain quiet, must let himself be silently supressed in view of the fact that as an individual he has no value and is only an insignificant element in the great mass.[14]

It is clear that a doctor is speaking here who has some understanding of the miserable situation that an isolated powerless individual can find himself in during a large-scale protracted war. What should be done then according to Simmel with soldiers who can no longer tolerate their lot and who go crazy? Well, it turns out that this doctor too was of the opinion that soldiers like these must be retained for the army and the war. To realize this goal Simmel developed a shortened form of psychoanalysis which would make it possible to achieve *Schnellheilungen* (quick cures). It primarily involved hypnosis and suggestion. This therapy was based on a specific view of the nature of *Kriegsneurotiker*. According to Simmel, the war produced two kinds of healthy personalities, namely 'der Held und der Drückeberger' (the hero and the shirker). The altruistically motivated hero was prepared fully to subordinate his own well-being for the sake of a good cause. On the other hand, the coward for the most part only acted out of egocentric motives. Saving his own life was his highest priority.

The *Kriegsneurotiker* found himself between these two types. He was unable to choose one of the two ways of behaving. Therapy was aimed at converting him to heroic action. Sometimes it succeeded quite easily as in the example given below where a soldier who had a paralyzed right hand was restored to active duty in quite a simple way. The soldier came before the doctor holding a package in his left hand:

I have the patient let the package be taken from his left hand, ask him to recount for me what happened to him in the war that caused his disability and, after informing him about hypnosis, I put him to sleep... I succeed at this quickly the very first time, which is not often the case, and I have him play out his account. In the middle of it I interpose the question: 'It's turning out badly? Now would you prefer to run off and go home?' He answers me promptly: 'No! I'm not a shirker.' I say: 'Then get going! Attack the enemy at close quarters. Fix your bayonet! Here, take your weapon in your right hand! You want to fight, don't you?' And then I add: 'What the devil! You can't fight like that! Your right hand is shaking the whole time. What's the matter?' In a tormented tone of voice he answers me: 'But I want to save my life.' To this I reply: 'Your life is saved now. You're at home, come home!' The quivering tremor and the tic disappear. And 20 minutes later the patient is standing before me, his package in his hand, and he is looking himself over mistrustfully from head to foot. He had been shaking his arm for a whole year.[15]

Simmel as well as the other psychoanalysts were perfectly aware of the limitations of their approach. They knew, for instance, that there were many relapses and they knew that the symptoms could not be effectively combatted in everyone. In the more serious cases, where a patient's personality had been transformed, only genuine, intensive analytical treatment could produce results. During the war, of course, there was no time for that but it was already affirmed that this is what would be done after peace had returned.

The so-called *Schnellheilungen* should, therefore, be seen as a concession. In view of the critical situation in which the country found itself, the psychiatrists were prepared to make a compromise as far as psychoanalysis was concerned. In the eyes of the military authorities it must have been a great advantage that the psychoanalytical *Schnellheilungen* were not accompanied by fatal accidents and provided no cause for critical reactions in the press. The psychoanalytical congress that was held in Budapest in September 1918 must also have been applauded by these same authorities. According to Freud, after the congress was over plans were drawn up both in Germany and in Austria-Hungary to create hospitals which would be especially equipped to apply psychodynamic methods of treatment. However, advent of the armistice hindered the implementation of these plans.[16]

Thus the Freudians were willing to adapt the repertoire of their therapeutic techniques to the demands of war. However, they were not prepared to go further than that. As for the Freudian interpretative framework according to which behavioral disorders were primarily traced back to sexual problems, this was not something to be tampered with. Some psychiatrists appeared to be incensed at the fact that certain doctors selected one element or another from the Freudian corpus of ideas in order to take advantage of it in therapy. Rivers, the psychiatrist who treated Sassoon, was someone who did this. Vehement criticism was directed against figures of this sort. In particular, Karl Abraham went to great lengths to explain that war neuroses had an underlying sexual cause. Abraham and his colleagues variously described soldiers who suffered a breakdown as latent homosexuals, impotent and sexually unstable. They viewed them as persons incapable of giving themselves unconditionally to the opposite sex, and who consequently were incapable of committing themselves to the community.

According to this view, psychologically wounded soldiers were men who, as a result of an imperfect sexual development, were predisposed to fail when it came to fulfilling their duty to the community. Abraham stated quite precisely what this shortcoming consisted of:

Besides enduring dangerous situations in the field, i.e. a purely passive achievement, a second task as well is required of them, one which is too often ignored. It is a question of aggressive achievements which a soldier must be ready to undertake at every moment. Along with the willingness to die, the willingness to kill is demanded of him.[17]

Thus, according to this point of view, actively killing is reserved for fully mature, healthy men; only they can do this without being left with psychiatric disorders.

Sophistication and Humanization

During the inter-war years, psychiatry underwent a development which should not be underestimated. A broad spectrum of new therapies were made available and applied with varying degrees of success in the field of mental health care. Undoubtedly, the world of psychiatry was divided into currents of thought which at times clashed fiercely with one another, but generally it was agreed there was movement in the field and that this movement was in a forward direction.

Consequently, military psychiatry, which was revived once again after hostilities broke out in 1939, could make use of a broader and more sophisticated repertoire of therapies than had been available in the past. In addition, it can be said that, at least in the case of the Allies, there was a greater degree of humanization in the treatments employed. This latter tendency was due to a number of factors.

To begin with, there was the new arsenal of actual therapies. Sleep- and rest-cures occupied an important place among these. Then, a variety of forms of psychotherapy had become popular. These included simple behavior therapy as well as more refined and complicated analytical strategies. This new repertoire of therapies lent itself less easily to a violent application than the notorious electrotherapy employed in the previous war.

The trend toward humanization was also related to the change which occurred with regard to the symptoms exhibited. In May 1940 when the conflict began in the West, hysterical manifestations were far less in evidence than in the First World War. It is precisely these disorders – paralyzed arms or legs for example – which particularly lend themselves to a harsh approach. This is especially true if the prevailing idea is that the disorders can be remedied in a very short time by means of firm, vigorous intervention. When success through the choice of a particular method is more or less guaranteed, ethical and humanitarian considerations have a hard time of it. The soldiers whom the psychiatrists came to treat in 1940 presented a completely different picture. They were tense, frightened to death or completely apathetic. It was easy to see from their appearance that they were exhausted and needed sleep. One may obviously assume that when psychiatrists were confronted with patients of this category, they did not immediately think of the great 'heroic' therapies used in the past. Patients of this kind required a different approach.

In this regard the work of William Sargant and Elliot Slater was of great significance. When war broke out, these two English psychiatrists were attached to a military hospital: the Sutton Emergency Hospital. Sutton was a subdivision of the famous Maudsley Hospital. Sargant and Slater came to treat the psychiatric casualties that resulted from the retreat of the British expeditionary army and its evacuation from Dunkirk. They were of the opinion that above all these individuals needed rest and adequate nourishment. To ensure their rest it was necessary to give some of the patients tranquillizers. In order to build up the physical strength of the patients quickly, use was made of a modified insulin cure. This involved putting the soldiers in a very light coma. Insulin was primarily administered to bring about a physical recovery. During the cure, plentiful food was also provided. Only after a patient's physical condition had improved was there a shift to employing psycho-therapy.[18]

The treatment applied in Sutton acquired a high reputation among Canadian and American psychiatrists, some of whom came to inform themselves on the spot as to how the procedure worked. During the early years of the war, Sargant also gave lectures for the Canadian psychiatrists. Furthermore, anyone who wished could become familiar with their work through their publications in *The Lancet*.

What then were the actual therapies employed during the Second World War? In broad outline their therapeutic repertoire can be summarized as follows:
- Rest, at times in combination with tranquillizers, and when necessary, followed by a sleep-cure of two to three days;
- shock therapies, including both insulin- and electro-shock;
- psychotherapy, in groups as well as on an individual basis;
- narcotherapy;
- and hypnosis, sometimes in combination with narcotherapy.[19]

The last three therapeutic categories need a brief clarification. We will begin with hypnosis. In this period as well the military psychiatrists continued to attribute great value to this technique. However, hypnosis was not only part of the actual process of treatment, but it was also used, and sometimes it was the only method used, to establish a precise diagnosis. In fact, many soldiers were suffering from memory disorders at the moment that they came in contact with their therapists. They could, therefore, not tell their doctors precisely what had happened to them and why and when they had experienced a breakdown. By making use of hypnosis, the psychiatrists sometimes succeeded in getting around the problem of memory loss and were thus able to establish the circumstances which had so disastrously undermined the patient's mental stability. Often, if hypnosis did not work when applied in the usual way, it was combined with narcotherapy.

In this last-mentioned method of treatment the patient was given an intoxicating drug, such as pentothal for instance. Once under the drug's influence, he was ordered to recount what he had experienced. The intention was that the soldier, who was now in a twilight state, should relive his traumatic experiences. After he had become informed in this way, the therapist, on the basis of what he had heard, could attempt to lead his patient back to the trauma he had suffered, this time with the patient being in a state of full consciousness. Thus the use of narcotherapy is based on the foundation of psychoanalysis. In this therapy it is essential that the patient liberates himself from his traumatic experiences by articulating them openly before the therapist. The horrific repressed emotions must be brought to the surface and by establishing this consciousness the healing process begins. For the military setting, however, classic psychoanalysis was too time-consuming and labor-intensive. By means of narcotherapy it was sometimes possible to accomplish in a few weeks what would require years following to the traditional method.

With regard to psychotherapy, it may be noted that in the military context there was a clear preference for the more directive approach. If some psychiatrists might have felt attracted to a non-directive method, the possibilities for applying it were in fact extremely limited. On the other hand, the military environment offered an ideal setting for collective approaches, such as group discussions and group therapy. Maxwell Jones was one of the psychiatrists who experimented with this kind of collective approach.[20]

The patients who were treated by Maxwell Jones had one thing in common. They abhorred military service. Their motivation had dropped to absolute zero. The psychiatrists applied the label 'effort syndrome' to these cases. These soldiers did not wish to go back to their units under any condition. And why should they go back to their units? After all, they were sick. Maxwell Jones affirmed that these servicemen were clinging to symptoms which indicated physical complaints, in particular heart disorders.

The first step in the therapy was aimed at convincing the patients involved that their illness had a different cause. Not their heart but their nerves were affected. To make this clear, every other day for a number of weeks group sessions were organized. During these gatherings, Maxwell Jones gave schematic instruction, i.e. he employed drawings and diagrams illustrating how the brain and the central nervous system functioned. On the basis of these lessons, the patients were meant to realize that a disorder of the nerves was just as concrete and real as a heart defect. In this way attention was shifted from the heart to the nerves. After this first step the therapist went on to make it clear that problems that had to do with the nerves could not be considered separately from a patient's total personality. Indeed, the patient in this case had his own responsibility. In contrast to the situation of a heart-patient, it could not be expected that a person suffering from a nervous disorder could simply lean back passively and let the doctor do all the work. No, the patient was to a great extent responsible himself for the continuance of his illness.

However, the problem was that 'the ill person' did not want to get better and felt absolutely no need to prove his worth behind the front, not to mention on the battlefield.

The majority of patients seen here have a very circumscribed outlook and are largely preoccupied with their own symptoms, emotional difficulties, and domestic situation; few have reflected on the reason for their conscription or have stopped to consider what they are fighting for. They seldom read newspapers and have only the vaguest conception of the extent and complexity of the war. To them there exist their home and a vague, ill-defined, unfriendly outside world. With no better sense of values than these it is not surprising that some men quite openly and shamelessly hope for nothing but their discharge from the Army.[21]

The letters the soldiers received from home further reinforced these attitudes. Indeed, family members went on regularly asking about the physical complaints and at the same time constantly expressed the hope that their relatives would be speedily discharged from the army. To deal with this situation Maxwell Jones developed an instruction program. This explained, for example, the advantages and disadvantages of different political systems. With regard to democracy, it was impressed on the servicemen that this system could only exist if every member of society was committed to defending it. In addition, the patients were advised to read a lot, in particular weekly magazines and other periodicals which contained more information than the daily press.

Drawing the soldiers' attention to magazines was primarily the task of the nurses. The doctor himself was only concerned with the formal lessons. These nurses were also required to try to engage the soldiers in conversation with the purpose of arousing their interest again in the army. Maxwell Jones admitted quite honestly that these were simple, obvious matters. He had to limit himself, however, to simple techniques of this kind because their application was in the hands of the nursing staff. In the area of day-to-day contacts he did not envisage any role for the doctor himself:

It would appear undesirable that the physician should himself be too closely identified with this problem, for by so doing he might endanger his privileged position as a doctor.[22]

As far as the final results were concerned Maxwell Jones declared that he was satisfied. In the course of time fixation on the original symptoms disappeared in the majority of cases. In addition, more soldiers returned to the army than in the period before group therapy was put into practice. Unfortunately, no follow-up studies were carried out so that little could be said about long-term effects.

It should be clear that the form of group psychotherapy from 1942 which we have described here was far removed from what came to be practiced in civilian psychiatry under that name after the war. In fact, during the war, scarcely any use was made of the group as a therapeutic instrument. The choice on Maxwell Jones' part to work with groups was primarily the result of efficiency considerations. There were too few psychiatrists and too many patients. By working with groups of fifty, the available medical potential could be better exploited. This approach was also quite far removed from the notion of a therapeutic community, an ideal which Maxwell Jones had had a large part in founding and propagating. In a community of this kind the classic hierarchy disappears and is replaced by democratic relationships. The patients have a high degree of freedom and are treated as adults. Finally, the therapists are not only, or in some cases not primarily, accountable to the directors of the institution but to the community. This ideal was able to flourish for a while in the 1960s. In the context of war, of course, a completely different form of psychiatry prevails.

Humanization in Germany

Many German psychiatrists must have felt redundant during the first years of the war. The anticipated flood of *Kriegszittern* (war-induced trembling) simply did not materialize. Only the internists had a lot of work treating functional organic disorders. It should be mentioned, however, that some psychiatrists suspected from the beginning that behind these new manifestations the classic neuroses were concealed. But it was no easy matter to furnish proof for these suspicions. All in all military psychiatry was confronted with a very perplexing situation.

Only after the commencement of Operation Barbarossa in the summer of 1941 could the army psychiatrists roll up their sleeves and go to work, although the real pressure only started in the summer of 1943. At first the repertoire of therapies employed was not very different from what their Allied opponents disposed over. Thus in Germany as well ready use was made of the shock-therapies that had been developed in the inter-war years for treating psychotic patients. At the same time much use was made of various forms of individual and collective psychotherapies.

There were not only differences in content between the bio-medical approach and the more psychologically oriented views.[23] These two currents within psychiatry also launched their operations from separate organizational bases. The bio-medical psychiatrists had found accommodation with the land forces, i.e. in the army. In 1936 the first course for future military psychiatrists was begun in the *Militärärztliche Akademie* which had been reopened in 1934. By 1937 the first psychiatrists and neurologists began to take up their positions in the medical service of the army. The psychotherapists, on the other hand, came to find shelter elsewhere, namely in the *Luftwaffe*. They were received with open arms in this modern, technologically oriented section of the armed forces. In the air force there was the conviction that aircraft crews had to be dealt with differently from front line soldiers in the First World War. It was considered meaningless to ply frightened, dead tired aircrews with electricity. The members of the *Deutsches Institut für psychologische Forschung und Psychotherapie* had managed to convince the authorities that psychology had more to offer with regard to prevention as well as remedies. The intervention of the Condor Legion during the Spanish Civil War gave the psychotherapists the opportunity to demonstrate the actual value of their contribution to aerial warfare.

The influence of the repertoire of psychological ideas was not limited to the domain of the air force. In the army psychotherapeutic views were also put into practice. This was especially true of the tank units where technical specialists were employed and where high demands were made regarding the level of cooperation of crew members. Airplanes and tanks as manned weapon systems actually have much in common. But psychological views came to have no less important a place in the non-mechanized units. In fact, it can be said that the German army owed a certain amount of its formidable fighting power to the rational use of psychological insights. In this connection one can mention various matters such as the training of commissioned and non-commissioned officers, the system employed to replace casualties in fighting units and the way in which rest and recreation were organized.

Thus German military psychiatry consisted of numerous gradations and was not only active in the curative area but from the beginning made important contributions in the area of prevention. In contrast to the state of affairs among the Allies, the psychiatrists and psychologists did not have to fight their way into the armed forces. The military authorities were convinced of the usefulness of their activities. The discussions that took place had to do with the pros and cons of particular currents of thought within the discipline and with the suitability of particular therapies for specific categories of servicemen.

The really great challenge came in the last phase of the war. After Stalingrad and Kursk it was pretty much impossible to believe in a final victory. On the eastern front the situation became steadily more hopeless, as the Red Army saw to it that the battles took on an increasing intensity. One thing and another added to the growing psychological pressure experienced by the troops on the eastern front. Because of the high number of casualties, the *Wehrmacht* was also forced to put all available manpower into the field. Selection on the basis of mental and physical fitness became virtually impossible. As a result, the quality of the troops decreased. Finally, it should be noted that the new situation presented a serious threat to the social structure of the army, due to which the carefully constituted, preventive system was at risk of collapsing. Because of the rapid change of personnel at the end of the war, the primary groups which formed the kernel of the *Wehrmacht*, began to disintegrate, at least on the eastern front.[24] Similarly, it became continually more difficult to provide rest periods for the fighting units. In the first phase of the war pauses of this kind were used to replace casualties. Newcomers had sufficient time to integrate themselves in the platoons and companies they were assigned to. Only once the members of these units had come to know one another and had become a team were they exposed to battle. Ultimately, this system could not be maintained any longer. Finally, it can be noted that the quality of the commissioned and non-commissioned officers deteriorated. The primary causes of this were faulty selection and inadequate training time.

The developments we have just sketched had great significance for military psychiatry. Put briefly, what it boiled down to was that the chances for the occurrence of psychiatric casualties rose, while the possibilites for taking effective preventive action decreased. The latter was particularly true of the therapists with a psychological and social-psychological orientation. In the new context their repertoire of ideas, especially any provisions regarding the prevention of psychological breakdown, came to be more or less abandoned.

How then did German military psychiatry react to this challenge? At the risk of oversimplification, one can say there were basically two modes of response. On the one hand, an attempt was made to compensate for the social disintegration by strengthening the morale of the individual soldiers. Here Nazi propaganda functioned as an instrument. It was continuously impressed upon the soldiers that they were undertaking a historic task by protecting European culture from the barbarism of the East. This central theme was further elaborated upon in every possible way. *NS-Führungsoffizieren* were put in charge of carrying out this propaganda campaign. These functionaries were comparable to the political commissaries who served in the Red Army. In 1943 the military psychiatrists in the *Luftwaffe* were rechristened *NS-Führungs-Sanitätsoffizieren*. With this change of title the Nazis expressed their appreciation of the know-how that the psychotherapists in the air force disposed over.

The mentality that could be evoked by means of this kind of propaganda is illustrated in the memoirs of a former Stuka pilot. His memoirs were published a few years after the war, first in Germany and later in translation in England. The pilot in question, H.V. Rudel, describes the state of his conscience during the very last days before Nazi Germany capitulated:

...the Red hordes are devastating our country... we must fight on. We shall only lay down our arms when our leaders give the order. This is our plain duty according to our military oath, it is our plain duty in view of the terrible fate which threatens us if we surrender unconditionally as the enemy insists. It is our plain duty also to destiny which has placed us geographically in the heart of Europe and which we have obeyed for centuries: to be the bulwark of Europe against the East. Whether or not Europe understands or likes the role which fate has thrust upon us, or whether her attitude is one of fatal indifference or even of hostility, does not alter by one iota our European duty. We are determined to hold our heads up high when the history of our continent, and particularly of the dangerous times ahead, is written.[25]

Omer Bartov, on the basis of analysis of numerous first-person documents relevant to the eastern front such as soldiers' letters, has shown that Nazi propaganda had a far-reaching influence in the army. In any case, it is clear that the fighting power of the German army remained formidable right up to the final battle for Berlin.

But military psychiatry had still more to offer than giving support to propaganda. This was revealed in its second mode of response which began in the summer of 1943. This path, which was followed by the army psychiatrists who had a bio-medical orientation, consisted of reverting to the experiences of the First World War. What was essential here was the use of old and new forms of electrotherapy. In the new forms as well there was only a very thin line between treatment and torture. In this connection the so-called 'Pansen-treatment' became especially famous.

The Pansen-treatment was developed in a reserve hospital located in Ensen. Here a group of psychiatrists, some of whom had already had experience with the Kaufmann-cure, engaged in specialized experimentation on patients. Professor Dr. Friedrich Pansen, who was the head doctor in charge of the university clinic of Bonn, was involved, along with several other colleagues from Ensen, as an advisor in the K4-Program which had as its purpose the extermination of the mentally and physically handicapped who resided in institutions. These advisors were helpful in drawing up the list of those to be killed. Clearly, the doctors from Ensen knew how to make themselves useful to the authorities in the Third Reich in a variety of ways.[26]

What did the actual therapy consist of? Basically, this was a modified version of the notorious Kaufmann-cure. Friedrich Pansen made two important modifications in the treatment developed by his celebrated predecessor. The first change had to do with the kind of electric current involved. To avoid the dreaded cardiac arrest that had occurred in the First World War, the alternating current was replaced by direct current. The second adaptation concerned the atmosphere in which the treatment took place. Pansen realized that the Kaufmann-cure had been perceived by many soldiers as a form of punishment. They had blamed the psychiatrists for administering the cure. Many sessions of treatment had proceeded in a highly charged, emotional atmosphere in which the therapists and the patients had given free expression to their feelings of mutual hatred. In the Pansen-treatment every effort was made to ensure that the procedure took place in an objective medical setting that was emotionally neutral. To achieve this an attempt was made to enter into the perceptions of the patient. If, for example, the patient related that something was wrong with his stomach or his bladder, he was deliberately allowed to maintain the illusion. The doctor did not try to make it clear to the patient that something psychological was wrong with him and that he only had to have enough willpower to make a recovery. On the contrary, the doctor appeared to go along with the somatic diagnosis and then declared that fortunately there was a remedy for the patient's disorder. Subsequently, the relevant areas of the skin were subjected to powerful electric stimulus.

The doctor could feel satisfied with the final results. Almost all the patients could be cured of their complaints in a short period of time. The experiment carried out in Ensen soon gained a high reputation among military specialists in the field. The internationally renowned neuropathologist Karl Kleist described the Pansen-treatment as quite painful but also quite effective. When he tried it on himself it turned out he was unable to bear more than 30 milliamperes, whereas an intensity of current up to 300 milliamperes was usual. Thus Kleist's positive assessment was solely based on his conviction that the Pansen-treatment was the most successful of all known methods.[27]

To begin with, the pain inflicted by the new cure constituted an important obstacle to its application on a large scale. But what was the problem? In fact, in the *Wehrmacht* a soldier had the right to refuse a painful treatment. Consequently, early on the Pansen-treatment was only carried out on 'volunteers'. The top authorities in the military medical service tolerated the experiment in Ensen, but otherwise made no further effort to promote the spread of the new method. Only on 12 December 1942, was the requirement of the patient's consent abolished, at least within the land forces. After that, the treatment began a veritable triumphal procession through the military hospitals. Ensen became a much-visited location where countless numbers of doctors came to acquaint themselves with the new developments in the field of therapy. None the less, the illustrious proponents of the Pansen-treatment felt that they were not adequately appreciated. They would have liked to see the Führer himself or his chancellery speak out unambiguously in favor of this hard approach and thus distance themselves from soft psychotherapy.

This never actually happened. According to rumors, in the previous war Corporal Hitler himself had been a psychiatric patient and harbored little sympathy for the hard approach. Whether this rumor is based on truth or not is difficult to say. What is more likely, however, is that those in the chancellery remembered quite well how much public indignation the Kaufmann-cure had stirred up. This was something which they now wanted to avoid. It is also probable that Hitler's staff was more aware of the demands that modern warfare made on soldiers than many of the military psychiatrists who were obsessed with the First World War.

To convert the Führer a film was even made on the Pansen-treatment in 1944. It was hoped that by making use of Hitler's favorite medium the final goal could still be attained: recognition that the Pansen-treatment was the most successful method of therapy. For unknown reasons this film was never shown.

Thus right up until the final surrender psychotherapeutic alternatives to medical intervention continued to exist within the German army. On the other hand, the psychotherapists were unable or even unwilling to avoid the demands of the situation that began in 1943. A tougher approach likewise appeared in applying the verbal techniques. By the end of the war, the overt and implicit threats of concentration camps and execution squads formed a normal part of the discussion with some psychiatrists.[28] Psychotherapy and humaneness do not always have to go hand in hand.

Some Recent Developments

With the surrender of Germany and Japan peace returned to some regions. However, the Cold War had already broken out before the above-mentioned countries capitulated. In 1950 the situation turned into a real war. This time the conflict was fought out in Korea. On this Asiatic peninsula, from 1950 to 1953, the first large-scale confrontation between the Western countries, which were led by the United States, and the Communist world took place.

In the domain of therapy the Korean War brought with it little that was new. Both in diagnostics, where one continued to speak of combat exhaustion, as well as in the area of therapeutic methods, the experience of the Second World War still provided the basic framework. In the spring of 1952 Colonel Donald B. Peterson and Brigadier-General Rawley E. Chambers read a paper at the yearly gathering of The American Psychiatric Association. In their paper they presented a survey of the American approach. This consisted essentially of recommending rest, with or without prescribing sedatives. In this connection the authors noted that in fact sedatives were always administered but that the dosage given varied in reverse proportion to the combat experience of the psychiatrist in question. Narcotherapy was also used but in most cases short periods of psychotherapy proved to be adequate. In the brief description that Peterson and Chambers then went on to give of this form of therapy, it appears that once again recourse was had to the good old 'moral treatment'.

The physician must be firm, decisive, fair, moderate, and brief in his statements. He must not leave decisions conditional on improvement or other action of the patient, because the action then forthcoming will almost invariably be such that further duty appears to be impossible.[29]

With a sense of understatement that bordered on cynicism, the two psychiatrists characterized their approach as 'not entirely non-directive'. At the end of their study the authors went on to distinguish categories of patients. The first category consisted of reasonably motivated soldiers who reacted well to the treatment. The second group was made up of immature servicemen who were not endowed with much sense of responsibility and with whom the treatment had less success. Whether the latter were returned to active duty depended primarily on the policy of evacuation pursued. It had to be made clear that an honorable retreat, i.e. discharge from the army on medical grounds, was impossible. Thus the choice these soldiers had to be confronted with was to recover or to be dishonorably discharged. In fact, Peterson and Chambers transport us back to 1917, to the year when the American psychiatrists, with a mixture of amazement and envy, became acquainted with the French system of evacuation. In this system, as we will show in the following chapter, there was no room allowed for 'troubles nerveux psychiques'.

The fighting in Korea had already come to a standstill by the time civilian psychiatry came to dispose over new psychiatric drugs such as tranquillizers, psychotonics, anti-depressants and neuroleptics. But in the Vietnam War these achievements of the pharmaceutical industry were available for use. From the relevant literature it appears that this was in fact the case but that at the same time psychotherapy was also applied. Tranquillizers were not only administered to soldiers who had suffered a breakdown but were also used to allow servicemen to go into battle with a certain calm and composure. This use of drugs followed different norms than those current in civilian society. Robert Colbach, who served as a division psychiatrist in Vietnam, stated that he had let soldiers go into battle who had so many tranquillizers in their body that they would have been barred from driving a car.[30]

The military psychiatrists who served in Vietnam found themselves in a highly privileged position compared with their colleagues in previous wars. The overall number of patients was relatively small. In addition, they had the disposal of drugs which quickly made it possible to apply psychotherapy. And finally, they had at their disposal an enormous range of recreational facilities. For example, in the division Robert Pettera was attached to the patients had use of a swimming pool, a miniature golf course, several tennis courts, a softball and a football field, volleyball courts and a library.[31] The army's facilities were in no way inferior to the most luxurious private clinic. But this luxury carried with it a certain danger. The more comfortable the stay is with the psychiatrist, the more difficult it will be to convince a soldier of the necessity of returning to his unit. Consequently, the American therapists felt themselves obliged continually to emphasize by means of directive forms of psychotherapy the final goal of treatment, i.e. a soldier's return to his old post.

It was just noted above that military psychiatry in Vietnam found itself in an enviable position. Furthermore, it can be observed that as the war proceeded actual combat psychiatry increasingly lost its significance. In fact, after 1968 the American army of intervention, leaving aside its technological superiority, came more to resemble seventeenth- and eighteenth-century mercenary armies than the military formations that were put in the field during the two world wars.

Few soldiers could see a purpose to the war. For many of them it was meaningless and even condemnable. Within the fighting units there was a strong over-representation of everything that could be associated with the underprivileged classes. It was a question of young men who lacked the right connections and had no way of avoiding military service. During the last years of the war the land forces were characterized by a low morale and poor discipline. The frequent occurrence of 'fragging', eliminating your own officers when the latter acted contrary to the will of the group, was one of the indications of this. In an atmosphere of discontent like this, where the general willingness to fight had reached rock-bottom, patching up a limited number of psychiatric cases did not have all too great an importance.

Furthermore, the frequent use of hard drugs presented a greater threat to the army's fighting power than combat stress. Combatting this evil became far more important for military psychiatry and for the whole military medical service. However, describing the US military's anti-drug offensive falls outside the limits of this book.

In a sketch of more recent military psychiatry one cannot omit what Israel has managed to achieve in this area. Since winning its independence in 1948, Israel has found itself in a permanent state of war with the neighboring Arab countries. Hot and cold phases of war have alternated with one another resulting in a sizeable group of psychiatric casualties.

From the start, Israeli military psychiatry has been oriented towards American psychiatry which is revealed, among other things, by the series of articles and conference papers on this subject that have appeared over the last twenty years. Thus one cannot speak of a new approach. The Israelis have made use of psychiatric drugs, as well as individual and collective psychotherapy. Here too there was, and continues to be, a preference for strongly directive forms of verbal therapy. Once again there has been little concern for in-depth, time-consuming strategies.[32]

Simplicity and Harshness: The Two Faces of Military Psychiatry

The reader will be struck by the fact that military psychiatry did not produce any important innovations in the area of therapy. In fact, in all wars an effort was made to adopt whatever intellectual framework or instruments civilian psychiatry had to offer. On the other hand, the specific context in which these achievements had to be applied, i.e. in war and the army, made selection and adaptation obligatory. Some therapies were more suitable for the military setting than others. Especially suitable were forms of collective psychotherapy. By means of such methods large numbers of patients could be treated quickly and economically. The popularity of hypnosis was due to the fact that with this technique quick results could be attained both in making a diagnosis and in treatment. The necessity to achieve above all rapid successes also explains the general preference for goal-oriented directive therapies.

In certain cases it was deemed necessary to adapt existing methods to the needs of the military setting. A good example of this is narcotherapy which as a modification of time-consuming and labor-intensive psychoanalysis proved to be very popular during the Second World War. The *Schnellheilungen* which Ernst Simmel experimented with a few decades earlier are in the same category.

This selective and specific use of the civilian therapeutic arsenal has given military psychiatry its own countenance. It is the countenance of simplicity. Military therapies are simple, of short duration and cheap. Yet having said this, the portrait is still not complete. Not only does military psychiatry have a preference for certain treatments, but it also encourages a particular way of applying them: harshly, systematically and sometimes even mercilessly. This last characteristic requires some explanation. Why did harshness become the complement of simplicity?

Naturally, no simple, comprehensive answer to this question can be given. On the other hand, this harsh intervention, which in some cases was a matter of outright abuse, becomes more or less comprehensible if one takes account of a number of pertinent circumstances. In this regard, the outbreak of war is accompanied by a disturbance of the existing relationships between the individual and the community. Internal disputes within a group are temporarily set aside. Important oppositions are glossed over or forgotten. Only one overriding interest is recognized: the survival of the nation. In 1914 the Dutch socialist leader Troelstra expressed the point well when the Netherlands was on the brink of being dragged into the European conflict:

Everyone must accept as reasonable, indeed, must welcome enthusiastically, that at this moment the present government has not hesitated to mobilize the necessary armed forces. Nor is any criticism appropriate now, because in these serious circumstances the national idea transcends internal national disagreements.[33]

Generally, the people involved experienced these intense feelings of solidarity as something of high value. One felt oneself to be part of a greater whole; existence seemed to have acquired a new meaning. In this sense patriotism has its positive sides. However, there is another side to the coin. The individual, the single human being, comes to forfeit a great deal within the larger whole. His or her lot is no longer of primary significance, but now only the good of the community counts. The center of gravity in mutual human relations shifts to a supra-individual level.

This social change is accompanied by an adaptation of norms and values to the new situation. Existing ethical codes are revised and where necessary are stretched or set aside. This process is not exclusively reserved for totalitarian or authoritarian communities. In December 1993 it was made known that in the United States during the 1940s and 50s, and probably in the period thereafter as well, experiments with radio-active radiation were carried out on a large scale. These experiments were conducted by researchers from renowned institutes and top-ranking universities. The federal government had given permission for these research studies. The victims included, among others, the mentally handicapped, prisoners and pregnant women. In many cases their consent was not requested. In the cases where their consent was sought, the persons involved had no real idea of what exactly had happened to them. They were exposed to radiation, injected with radio-active substances and provided with specially prepared meals. The biologist Joseph G. Hamilton was one of the few individuals who expressed his indignation at what was going on. He noted his objections in a memorandum but was no more than a solitary voice crying in the wilderness.

What is remarkable is that these experiments were initiated immediately after the Neurenberg war-trials of 1947 where medical abuses had been highly criticized and condemned. It is also remarkable that at that moment there was no question of a real war situation. The United States, in the context of the Cold War, simply wished to maintain its nuclear advantage over the Soviet Union. It should therefore be reasonable to assume that in a real all-out war the ethical boundaries would be stretched still further and the ends would even more easily justify the means.

Military psychiatry is no exception in this respect. In the past innumerable military psychiatrists have shown themselves willing to be good patriots. The August issue of *La Presse Médicale*, the first issue to appear after the outbreak of the First World War, is wholly permeated with this spirit. The psychiatrist is simply to dedicate himself to the good cause, according to the journal. Consequently, in the article in question, one will search in vain for any somber reflections concerning eventual casualties or patients. One encounters nothing but the call to serve and to make sacrifices. There is no room for other considerations when the fatherland is in danger.

A few years later in Germany, the psychiatrist Kehrer gave pithy expression to what was now required:

In view of the gravity of the historical moment, the choice of methods cannot depend on aesthetic squeamishness or pseudo-moral reservations. We must devote ourselves with increasing energy to one objective: how, without concern for personal inclination and the consent of doctor and patients we can tranform, in the shortest amount of time, a maximum number of war hysterics into useful workers behind the front – having finally abandoned the hope of rehabilitating any significant percentage of these soldiers for active service in the field... [34]

Even regarding so humane and learned a person as Rivers who was known to be very particular in his choice of methods, it must be said that in the end, despite all his objections and doubts about the war, he went on doing his work as was required. Moreover, in the end, Sassoon as well went back to the front.

A completely different justification which was and still is put forward for harsh, unrestrained intervention has to do with the so-called interests of science. In civilian society there were always troublesome family members or medical inspectors who at least in principle were meant to supervise therapeutic treatment. This implied that the use of painful or potentially dangerous procedures was to some extent subject to restraints. Thus it was not possible to carry matters to the furthest extreme, which also meant that the ultimate effect of applying therapy in such a manner could never be ascertained. In military psychiatry these limitations did not exist. This is true with regard to the whole of military medicine. Military organization is in fact extremely well suited to carrying out experiments in the medical domain. One has at one's disposal a large group of soldiers who for the most part are without rights. Moreover, the few rights servicemen do have are not always easy to exercise within the highly hierarchical structure of the armed forces. In addition, the soldiers are available 24 hours a day. Finally, the physical isolation of the barracks and the front, along with the closed nature of military culture, provided – certainly in the past – the necessary protection against any critical busybodies from outside. In brief, the army represented an almost perfect laboratory where medicinal drugs could be tested and therapies could be tried out. Thus we find that a prominent English physician felt obliged to remind the surgeons in Cromwell's army to abide by the rules of their art and not to experiment recklessly with poor soldiers.[35] Two centuries later, the British troops who were serving in Spain during the Napoleonic wars were regularly subjected to arbitrary bloodletting by army physicians. During the Second World War the Allied soldiers had to be forced to take mecaprine against malaria. A final example can be taken from the Gulf War in 1991. At that time the American army made use of medications which were not yet officially approved. And these medications could be administered to servicemen without getting their consent. A documentary film devoted to this problem has shown that harsh medical intervention is in some cases a more or less natural consequence of the highly bureaucratic character of the armed forces. At a given moment an inventory is made of all the potentially dangerous illnesses. On the basis of this, it is decided to vaccinate everyone. Subsequently, vaccination is carried out without concern for the individual. This may mean only one injection or it may mean ten, in accordance with the views of the higher authorities. The fact that someone feels tired or ill is, generally speaking, no reason for him to be able to avoid conforming to the strictly established scheme. Thus one can scarcely conceive of a better situation for experimenting with medications.

The harsh intervention of military psychiatrists can also partly be ascribed to the fact that they had a special secondary task to fulfill, namely to unmask all kinds of simulators. Identifying simulation is a difficult task for psychiatry. One is rarely dealing with clear diagnostic categories with corresponding symptoms. Moreover, it is often a question of behavior which is very easy to imitate. In the military context it can be taken for granted that a complete company or a whole battalion quickly comes to know what is officially recognized as sick behavior. Thus anyone who is really interested knows exactly what he has to do. Unmasking simulators requires thorough, time-consuming examination, at least if it is to be done in a responsible way. Generally speaking, during an actual war there is neither the time, nor the means, to do this. Choosing unattractive therapies which are painful and unpleasant for the patient can produce results in these circumstances. Naturally, the underlying idea is that the healthy soldier will have great reservations about reporting himself as a psychiatric case.

Of course, weeding out simulators is not a task exclusively reserved for military psychiatry. All the personnel of the military medical service are expected to deal with this problem as a part of their normal activities. Ever since armies have existed soldiers have tried to feign illness or to prolong real disorders as long as possible. Intentionally inflicting wounds upon oneself is also a practice with a very long history. It was expected of doctors that they were the ultimate experts at unmasking cases of this kind.

Thus Freud's characterization of military psychiatry – he referred to psychiatrists as the machine-guns behind the front – has a broad application and includes the whole of the military medical service.[36] Finally, in explaining the harshness of the therapies employed, it must also be mentioned that not every military psychiatrist has had sympathy for the soldiers suffering from a breakdown who were sent to him.

With regard to this point, military psychiatrists differed little from professional army officers. Evacuation from the battle zone on grounds of psychological disorders was, according to some, the equivalent of placing a premium on mental deficiency. The brave, tough young men ran the risk of being killed or maimed, while their more weak-hearted comrades were selected out for a risk-free existence. Due to war there was the danger that the Darwinian social principle of 'the survival of the fittest' would, as it were, be reversed. That was something which must be avoided at all costs.[37]

Conclusion

The psychiatrists who worked in the various military medical services during the great wars of the twentieth century had a difficult task to perform. They were required to help large numbers of soldiers who had suffered a breakdown and where possible to make them fit to return to active duty again. In carrying out their work these doctors made use of what civilian psychiatry had to offer in the way of scientific theory and practical therapies.

However, the given situation, i.e. an army during wartime, imposed a procedure of selection and adaptation with regard to available therapies. Above all, simple, easy-to-apply therapies of short duration were chosen. Being in a state of war also made it possible to bend the ethical rules according to which treatment was to be provided. It appears that for various reasons many therapists were perfectly willing to take advantage of the new opportunities. Thanks to all these factors military psychiatry came to have its own specific countenance: one characterized by simplicity and harshness. On the other hand, the degree of harshness varied in accordance with the range of therapies in use at any given moment. In particular, electrotherapy in the hands of doctors such as Yealland, Kaufmann and Pansen could develop into a method which was dangerous as well as violent.

On the whole it can be said that the wars did not lead to important discoveries in the area of therapy. With regard to methods of treatment, military psychiatry was not very innovative. When military psychiatry first came into existence during the

First World War, it was even considered by some to be a step backwards in history –
indeed, to the period around 1800. That had been the period of moral treatment,
the period when the founders of modern psychiatry were active. Military psychiatry
did in a certain sense revive the ideas of Tuke, Pinel and Reil. These early pioneers
had viewed their patients as children, at times as rather naughty children, who had
to be directed to adulthood with a firm hand. Only the latter-day military psychiatrists had less time at their disposal. Therefore the process of 'parental' upbringing
had to be accelerated and intensified. But this was not simply a question of making
the soldiers once again fit for active duty. Even patients who were only expected to
have a future in civilian life were dealt with in the same way. Military psychiatry was
not solely interested in maintaining the level of fighting power of the armed forces.
Keeping the number of potential pensioners to a minimum was also high on the
agenda. One of the most notorious therapies, the Kaufmann-method, was in fact
originally developed with this rather ignoble goal in mind.

VIII - The Basic Principles of Military Psychiatry

Introduction

Many readers who for whatever reason have delved into writings concerned with mental health care will find that their first encounter with military psychiatry has something refreshing about it. In place of woolly prose and dense philosophical reflections one finds a lucid, concrete form of language. In a well-known American handbook on psychiatry, the chapter dealing with military psychiatry begins as follows:

The methods developed for the treatment of combat reactions are fairly simple. The patient must be treated as near as possible to the place where he had his emotional breakdown. The patient must expect and be expected to return to his former duty after a short period of self-organization.[1]

In this quotation two of the so-called basic principles of military psychiatry are presented, namely 'proximity' and 'positive expectancy'. A third commonly referred to principle is that of 'immediacy'.

These three basic principles recur in every treatise the military has published that deals with this subject. The message is impressed on the reader in a style that has direct associations with a soldier's basic handbook. These three principles represent the essential features, the rest is of secondary importance. Many such treatises are also furnished with a historical introduction, the main purpose of which is to show that the basic principles referred to have already proven their worth in the past beyond any doubt. If one follows these prescribed principles, success is surely within reach. With regard to this point there is a great degree of consensus between the psychiatrists who were active in the First World War and those who are presently employed in the military. By applying this approach, the overwhelming majority of psychologically wounded soldiers can be returned to active duty within a period of a few weeks.

These basic principles correspond to a system of care with a specific form of organization. In that system the existing facilities for treatment are divided into three echelons. Although in practice variations occur, in theory three different levels of help can be distinguished. The first echelon is located within the fighting units. Most of the time these are the divisions, but sometimes also the brigades. Here one finds the out-patient and semi-out-patient facilities. The period of stay in these facilities is short, usually not more than a week. Soldiers who cannot be helped within this time span are moved on to the second echelon. Ideally the facilities of this level of treatment are still located in close proximity to the front. The arrangements allow for a longer period of residence. Here one is thinking in terms of weeks rather than days. Military-base hospitals and specialized clinics situated far from the fighting represent the final echelon. These institutions make up the ultimate stage of combat psychiatry.

In this chapter we will first attempt to trace how these basic principles and their corresponding system of care came into being. Then we will describe the main developments which have taken place within this system in the course of time.

An Unnoticed Beginning

The Russo-Japanese War was a conflict during which in many areas aspects of the First World War were foreshadowed. There were elaborate trench systems furnished with barbed-wire barriers and the large-scale slaughter that occurred in the big offensives would certainly not have been out of place in The Great War.

It was during this war that military psychiatry took shape as an institutionalized subdivision of the armed forces.[2] This pioneering role fell to the lot of the Russian army. Here for the first time experiments were undertaken with what was later, after the First World War, to be described as 'forward psychiatry'. Thus the Russians created separate lines of evacuation for psychiatric casualties. At the front there were aid stations that were staffed by psychiatrists, neurologists and paramedical personnel. Additionally, in Harbin, which was located directly behind the lines, a central psychiatric hospital was set up. The institution's rate of admissions varied from 43 to 90 cases per day. Thus real use was made of these facilities. Only when forward treatment failed to produce results was a patient evacuated to a hospital in Moscow. This trip, which was naturally effected by train, took about forty days. It is therefore clear that the hospital we mentioned in Harbin was born out of necessity. The Russians were simply fighting too far from their social center and could not fall back on their normal services. Thus it was necessary to find another solution and the Russian psychiatrists did this in an inventive manner, in a manner which was certainly no less inventive than that of their colleagues in later wars. The Russian system was in practice confronted with a circumstance which is characteristic of mental health care in general and of military psychiatry in wartime in particular. The phenomenon I am referring to is that once certain facilities are made available, a demand for them is more or less automatically created. Military psychiatrists can help their soldiers to obtain a legitimate withdrawal from the field of battle. In this way the well-known evacuation-syndrome can come into existence. Virtually overnight thousands of soldiers become mentally disturbed and declare themselves no longer capable of performing their normal duties. This is precisely what happened in the Russian army. It has at times been said that on the eve of the revolution of 1917 the Russian soldiers voted with their feet. This refers to the fact that at this time these soldiers deserted on a large scale, which made it impossible to carry on the war. In this earlier case then, it can be said that they voted massively with their 'head'. As a result, the psychiatric facilities were inundated and the whole system more or less broke down. Thus there came to be greater emphasis on evacuation to behind the lines where the Red Cross took over the job from the military medical service. Furthermore, it must be said that this first attempt at institutionalized assistance did not achieve a very high level of effectiveness. The hospital in Harbin only succeeded in returning 54 out of 265 admitted officers to active duty. As for the ordinary soldiers, the rate of success was even far lower. Out of 1072 servicemen who were treated, no more than 51 recovered. The rest had to be evacuated to the hinterland.[3]

Thus Russian military psychiatry associated with the Russo-Japanese War cannot be described as a success story. On the other hand, it is remarkable that these first attempts virtually fell into total oblivion. Their lack of success cannot explain this completely. The experiments carried out by military psychiatry in the First World War were also not all that successful in the beginning. And yet, in every historical survey they are always referred to. Possibly the innovations in the area of psychiatry did not receive the attention they deserved because, generally speaking, Russian military medicine during this war remained on such a low level. In the flood of misery which resulted from this situation the small positive aspects of military psychiatry were perhaps more or less submerged. Moreover, the achievements of the Japanese in the area of military medicine undoubtedly also played a role here. The latter succeeded in creating a model military medical service on the basis of what the Germans had learned in 1870. The Japanese medical service achieved big successes both in the preventive and the curative sphere. The classic infectious diseases, until that moment the greatest enemies of every army, were brought under control by means of vaccination programs and strictly applied hygienic rules of conduct. In addition, the wounded could benefit from a well-equipped system of provisions and a transport capacity that had been adequately calculated in advance. In other words, the Japanese army was the great discovery to emerge from this war.[4]

There was still another reason why the Japanese armed forces were so highly eulogized in the West after 1905. In the years around 1900 a debate took place in military professional journals about the relative importance which the factors of fire-power and morale had in waging war.[5] When the Boer War ended in 1901, the tacticians in Britain saw themselves obliged, much against their will, to recognize the superiority of the factor of fire-power. There was no way they could avoid this conclusion since there had been times when the Boers simply blasted the British soldiers out of the field like rabbits. In 1906, however, the Japanese demonstrated that highly motivated soldiers who were prepared to suffer casualties were actually capable of overcoming well-entrenched opponents. This was a conclusion which onlookers in Britain, and elsewhere as well, had been anxiously awaiting. If this war had established one thing, according to the Western observers, it was the importance of a high morale. Their high morale had made it possible for the Japanese to win the war. It seems reasonable to assume that this fascination left no room for considering the phenomenon of the psychologically wounded soldier. During the following war the existence of such soldiers would have to be discovered once again.

From Experiment to System

The reaction of the medical service in the British army to the first wave of shell shock patients was predictable. All the clear cases were sent back to the mother-land and admitted to military hospitals. When these became full in 1915, a number of private and public institutions were taken over by the army. Many psychiatrists were given a commission in the Royal Army Medical Corps overnight. In total the army administered roughly twenty such institutions in this way. Of the soldiers ad-mitted only very few went back to the front. For the most part the journey across the Channel was a one-way trip. Far from the front the patient could wait for the war to end. Only in 1917 did the British begin to change their policy. This modification in policy was partly imposed by the new state of unlimited submarine warfare. As a re-sult, the overseas transport of sick and wounded became seriously hampered. Con-sequently, many wounded, including psychiatric cases had to be kept in France, out of necessity. At the same time, another factor was that the French had shown that shell shock patients, if they were not evacuated to behind the front, really could be returned to active duty. At the beginning of the war the French medical services had followed the same procedure as their British counterpart. The French army was not only larger than the small British expeditionary army but took upon itself the greater part of the offensives and counter-offensives. Thus the number of casu-alties it had suffered was correspondingly higher. The French were thereby forced to open more and more hospitals at an increasingly closer distance to the front. The therapeutic significance of this had not been anticipated but only emerged in prac-tice. The principle of 'proximity' was confirmed on the basis of experiment. Since it was no longer possible to be sent to the safe hinterland, it would not be rewarding to display the symptoms of hysteria – according to the reasoning of the psychia-trists. The Germans also quickly discovered that it would be better not to evacuate the psychiatric cases. The psychiatrist Nonne recommended setting up hospitals just behind the front, not only for soldiers who suffered a breakdown during battle but for neurotics who caused problems in the interior of the country as well.[6] Ac-cording to Nonne, there must be absolute clarity regarding the principle that the only discharge from the hospital would be in the direction of the front. Both the French and the Germans at times carried the principle of proximity to extremes. In Eric Leed's study, the treatment of one particular *poilu* who suffered from hysteri-cal deafness is described. This patient was brought to an underground shelter in a trench which was frequently under fire. There he was given hypodermic injections of painful drugs. In this case the remedy only appeared to help for brief periods. The soldier had to be given the same treatment the following day. His therapists re-mained convinced of the usefulness of this front line treatment.[7] The above-men-tioned Nonne noted that in some German army units it was 'therapeutische Gep-flogenheit' (therapeutic practice) to send neurotic soldiers to spots where there were constant artillery barrages going on. He stated, moreover, that the military doctors in question were convinced of the great preventive effect of this practice.[8]

From the above it appears that proximity was and actually still is the most important basic principle of military psychiatry. Not only because of the preventive function which undeniably resulted from it, but also because the other principles could scarcely be realized without proximity. Before the advent of the helicopter, evacuation from the battlefield in fact took so much time that 'immediacy' could only be realized solely and exclusively right behind the front. Similarly, 'positive expectancy' could only come into force if the patient was not transported to safer places. However, giving up the policy of evacuation was not enough on its own. What had to be done was discovered by French psychiatrists and once again involved following the path of trial and error.

In making it less attractive to have hysterical symptoms, the French made a distinction between the 'simulateur de création' and the 'simulateur de fixation'. In the first case, it was a question of soldiers who made use of neurotic symptoms to escape from punishment or to be able to stay in a safe place. In what was described above we saw how the army psychiatrists dealt with that. As for 'le simulateur de fixation', here one was confronted with soldiers who displayed real symptoms but who then continued to cling to them, as it were, to be able to improve their situation. The principle of positive expectancy was developed in the first place to fight against this prolongation of the symptoms. It quickly emerged that the best results could be obtained if the soldier himself was made responsible for his cure. The acting psychiatrists made sure there was no misunderstanding in the matter. The procedure began in an atmosphere of caution. First the soldier in question was requested in a friendly but firm manner to cooperate in the healing process. If in the judgement of the doctor involved this did not proceed quickly enough, then disciplinary measures were applied. Solitary confinement and the threat of revoking furloughs were frequently used aids. In general it can be said that the French saw to it that the longer the stay went on, the more uncomfortable it became for the patient. Emphasizing the patient's military identity was also part of the effort directed against his accepting the role of patient.[9] This meant, among other things, setting up rehabilitation programs which were supervised by officers and not by doctors. It should be remembered here that there was always a large contingent of lightly wounded or self-rehabilitating officers on hand who could conveniently be employed for these purposes. Maintaining the military setting in this way would quickly develop into one of the chief ingredients of positive expectancy. One thing and another led to the therapists conducting themselves primarily like officers and not like doctors. In many recent publications on military psychiatry sustaining the military context during treatment has even been upgraded to a separate basic principle.

A logical step in attempting to limit the prolongation of symptoms was the abolition of diagnostic categories which stirred the imagination of the soldiers. Accordingly, in July 1917 the British army command forbade the use of the term 'shell shock' (see the illustration on p. 142). When medical information regarding psycho-

General Routine Order No. 2384

CLASSIFICATION AND DISPOSAL OF OFFICERS AND OTHER RANKS
WHO WITHOUT ANY VISIBLE WOUND BECOME NON-EFFECTIVE FROM
PHYSICAL CONDITIONS CLAIMED OR PRESUMED TO HAVE ORIGI-
NATED FROM THE EFFECTS OF BRITISH OR ENEMY WEAPONS IN
ACTION.

(1) All officers and other ranks who become non-effective in the
    above category, and whose transfer from their unit or division is
    unavoidable, will be sent to the Special Hospital set apart for
    their reception under the order of the Army Commander.

(2) The Regimental Medical Officer, or officer commanding a med-
    ical unit, who in the first instance deals with a case which it is
    necessary to transfer to the Special Hospital, will not record any
    diagnosis. He will enter on the Field Medical Card or other
    transfer paper the letters 'NYDN' (Not Yet Diagnosed, Nerv-
    ous) only, and note any definitely known facts as to the true
    origin or the previous history of the case. . .

(5) . . . In no circumstances whatever will the expression 'shell-
    shock' be used verbally or be recorded in any regimental or other
    casualty report, or in any hospital or other medical document,
    except in cases classified by the order of the officer commanding
    the Special Hospital. The DAG, GHQ, 3rd Echelon, will notify
    the commanding officer of the unit of any case so classified.

(6) These orders do not apply to cases of gas poisoning, which will
    be dealt with as heretofore.

(7) All previous orders and instructions on this subject are cancel-
    led.

A British Army Order of June 7 1917

logically wounded soldiers was reported, no more would be done than noting down
the letters NYDN (NOT YET DIAGNOSED NERVOUS). In the German armed
forces a similar regulation had already been in effect for a year. The French army
did not have to abolish any labels that had become disreputable because they had
never been in use.

   In a completely different respect as well the French doctors were in an enviable
position. The American psychiatrist Bailey remarked with a certain degree of jealousy that the French, in their fight against neurosis, disposed over a powerful
weapon which psychiatrists in most other countries could not make use of. In
France shell shock victims did not in fact have a right to a disability pension. Nor

was the presence of this disorder grounds for being discharged from military service.[10] Bailey was one of the psychiatrists who were sent by the American army to the battlefields of Europe to study how the Allies dealt with their psychologically wounded soldiers. The findings of these psychiatrists were meant to form the basis of the medical strategy adopted by the United States. Thus the Americans were in a comfortable position; they could make use of the experiences of others and that is precisely what they did.

On 2 April 1917, the United States officially declared war on Germany. From a military point of view this action was of little significance for the time being. The Americans only had a small professional army at their disposal. It was sufficient to intimidate neighboring Mexico, with whom the United States was on bad terms, but for the European war zone it was a totally unimportant force. Several hundred thousand men had to be mobilized, trained and armed before one could speak of a full-fledged American contribution to the war. And this was a time-consuming process. On 1 January 1918, there were still no more than five American divisions in France, of which only one was combat ready. The Americans were almost entirely dependent on their allies for training, which mostly took place in France, and for their weapons. In particular, the heavy weapons such as tanks, artillery and airplanes, were provided by the British and the French. During the spring and summer of 1918, the American contingent was slowly brought up to full strength. Nonetheless, this military force was still too small to undertake an offensive on its own. American divisions were quartered with the Allied armies and army corps. Only in the summer of 1918 did General Pershing, the commander of the American expeditionary army, have his own sector assigned to him. This was located to the southeast of Verdun. In September the Americans were able to begin their first big offensive. Thus from the time of declaring war to the first real, large-scale battles a period of almost a year and a half had elapsed. This time had been used, among other things, for building up a psychiatric branch of the military medical service. In 1917 Thomas W. Salmon had been appointed head of this section of the expeditionary army. When the Americans moved out of their positions and entered the trenches located in no man's land, their military psychiatric service was prepared.

In the system designed by Salmon, all the basic elements of modern military psychiatric care were present.[11] The division psychiatrist performed a pivotal function in this complex. He was entrusted with a great number of advisory tasks and had responsibility for the out-patient and semi-out-patient care. Psychiatric victims were separated as quickly as possible from the other wounded, preferably in the battalion or regimental first-aid stations. Treatment was administered in small mobile hospitals that were set up directly behind the front. If this treatment was not successful, then the patient was evacuated to the psychiatric section of a military hospital further away. These hospitals were located, among other places, in Paris and in Tours. At the end of the chain there were the facilities that were available in the United States itself. Just as in Britain there were various institutions and hospitals in the United States that were more or less assigned to the army by the government.

In distributing the patients an effort was made to place the serious cases in institutions located in their home state.

Salmon and those in his camp understood quite clearly that this system could only work if a specific therapeutic atmosphere was created. Therefore the Americans didn't have any objection against cultivating positive expectancy either. It was impressed on the soldier by every possible means that the war was still not over for him. At the same time, the existence of plans for evacuating the serious cases back to the United States indicates that the psychiatrists involved were aware of the limits of their capacity to exert influence. But who will be surprised at this realism on the part of the pragmatically minded Americans?

The work undertaken by Salmon has become classic. In almost every study to do with military psychiatry reference is made to his system. Always in a positive sense. At the same time, however, it is always pointed out that the Americans had been able to benefit from the experiences of the Allies. What was positive then about Salmon was that, after having compared the French and the British approaches, he had chosen for the French, and in so doing he had adopted the most effective system. He had thus exercised sound judgment, nothing more and nothing less. This line of reasoning does not seem to me to be wholly inaccurate, but it does not present the full picture. It is true that the Americans were able to benefit from the experiences of their allies. They had in fact sent observers to see how their future partners solved problems pertaining to the psychologically wounded soldier. Similarly, they were able to acquire a multitude of information from medical journals which regularly devoted attention to the phenomenon of militry psychiatry. Nonetheless, this still does not explain fully the American approach. Indeed, with regard to other aspects of the war the same situation prevailed, and yet in reality it can be shown that the Americans did not always make the best choice. A brief digression on the practice of American warfare would appear to be appropriate at this point.

It is striking that, as far as tactics were concerned, the Americans learned very little from their instructors.[12] The American doctrine was based on a combat handbook compiled in 1917. This text was in fact no more than a somewhat adapted version of a similar work published in 1911. The Americans liked to speak frequently of 'open warfare'. In wars of that kind they would excel, given their 'tradition of Indian and partisan warfare'. As to what exactly this entailed in concrete terms, there was unfortunately no literature. All things considered, what it came down to in practice was the following: a preference for offensive campaigns and an absolute trust in the effectiveness of rifle-fire. The machine-gun, which had in the meantime emerged as one of the most feared weapons in the war, was not held in high esteem by the Americans. They viewed it more as 'a weapon of emergency'. In order to achieve superiority in fire-power during an attack they gave preference to well-aimed rifle-fire.

Pershing and his staff also placed great faith in the morale of their soldiers. This characteristic made these troops particularly suitable for launching an attack. What had not escaped the Americans was that going on the attack in this kind of trench war would require sustaining quite a few casualties. In view of this, the strength of the infantry divisions was somewhat increased. These extra reinforcements would make the Americans capable of effortlessly pushing their way through where the French and British divisions had become bogged down. That, along with the absolute size of the infantry divisions other factors had also played a role in the many offensives that had completely or partially failed, had not yet penetrated the tactical thinking of the American camp.

Both the Germans and the Allies watched the American military intervention with amazement. The Americans perished in the same way that all the parties involved had perished during the first years of the war: side by side and wave after wave. Even the British officers, who served in the most conservative army in the whole war, found the American mode of action astonishing. At the risk of exaggerating, it can thus be said that the army of the United States set off to battle in 1918 as if the Great War had just begun, and had to discover the hard reality of trench warfare all over again.

And yet, this army had been trained by British and especially French instructors. Likewise, the individual divisions could have acquired experience during the time that they had formed part of the Allied units. When it came right down to it, this knowledge and experience was not used; preference was given wholly to their own doctrine and organization. We must be cautious, therefore, in drawing conclusions about how use is made of the experience of others. Even when modes of action according to a specific model or organization are demonstrably more effective than other available alternatives, this is still no guarantee that they will actually be imitated.

If one's own mental framework is too far removed, there is the possibility that certain insights will not appear reasonable or will simply be denied. That the medical service of the American army deliberately chose what rightly qualified as the most efficient system cannot be attributed to pure logic alone but also had to do with specific historical circumstances.

On the eve of the declaration of war the American military medical service was absolutely unequipped to treat psychologically wounded servicemen.[13] The authorities were well aware of this and it was decided at an early stage to call in expert help to deal with the problem. An appeal was made to the National Committee for Mental Hygiene and, at the risk of exaggerating, one may say that this body single-handedly provided a psychiatric service. In sharp contrast to the state of affairs during the Civil War, now in the field of civilian psychiatry there was actually a big interest in war. The National Committee, with financial support from the Rockefeller Foundation, organized 'study trips' to the battlefields of Europe and also sent psychiatrists to Canada and to the American troops stationed at the Mexican border. In this way knowledge was gathered about the kind of psychiatric problems military organizations had to struggle with, while an inventory could be drawn up of the various existing methods of treatment. In March 1917 the head of the military medical service organized a conference where the various reports could be presented and analyzed. The National Committee did more than just make information available. It provided a figure like Thomas Salmon. In 1915 he stepped into the position of director of the Committee. He had in fact become known through his studies on the psychological problems of immigrants. In 1917 he became the head of the psychiatric service of the expeditionary army. Pearce Bailey, also associated with the mental hygiene movement, was appointed head of the psychiatric section of the military medical service of the American army.

Providing these top functionaries was only the first step. The bureaus of the National Committee were also helpful in the recruitment and placement of expert personnel. The same bureaus saw to it that the tasks of the various designated military-base hospitals in the United States were coordinated with one another. Thus a very close link existed between American military psychiatry and the mental hygiene movement, a movement which at the outbreak of the First World War had been experiencing a vigorous expansion.

The fact that the very representatives of this current of thought gave form and content to the psychiatric service explains why that service was receptive to the French system. The latter system corresponded closely to their own conceptions about what psychiatric care should look like. Indeed, in the mental hygiene movement strong criticism was leveled against the psychiatric establishment. The movement particularly pleaded for prevention and for out-patient care, and adherents cast a sharp eye on the negative effects of long-term confinement in psychiatric institutions. In their view mental health care was ready for a fundamental renewal. For psychiatrists who came to Europe with this sort of attitude, it will not have been difficult to make up their minds. The British system symbolized classical psychiatry, whereas the French approach was an expression of the wish for renewal. So the choice will not have been a particularly difficult one. In fact, one can go a step further and conclude that it was precisely the war which offered the mental hygiene movement an enormous scope to develop its abilities. The ambitions were great, but the reader will be aware how difficult it is to implement changes, not to speak of changes of a fundamental nature, in the structure of a health care system. This is not only true of the Netherlands, but of the United States as well.

The medical service of the American army, which as we mentioned was actually completely unequipped for providing psychiatric care, offered the possibility of beginning with a clean slate. Behind the front there were no inflexible institutions which had to be reshaped, but one was free to experiment from scratch. What action group or social movement would not wish for a situation like this.

Further Development of the Basic Principles
Speaking in systematic terms about basic principles is somewhat misleading. The impression is given of unambiguity and continuity. On closer examination, however, it becomes clear that as far as immediacy, proximity and positive expectancy are concerned, we are by no means dealing with accurately defined constants. In reality these concepts, both as to content and structure, vary greatly.

In the Second World War the concept of immediacy acquired a different meaning than it had had previously. The accent came to be on giving the soldier in question pain-killers or knocking him out with sedatives. Only after this period of forced rest did actual treatment begin. In later wars this remained common practice.

With respect to the basic assumption of proximity, there was also further experimentation during the Second World War. Not only was attention given to the geographical aspect, i.e. that treatment should take place as close as possible to the front, but there came to be greater interest in the social component of proximity. Thus psychiatrists began to allow more visits from and talks with comrades from the same unit, and later this was even encouraged. Generally speaking, the therapists involved were satisfied with the results. The inclination to return to one's own unit was, in most cases, clearly increased by visits of this kind. In this connection, however, it should be noted that the system the Allies used to replace personnel losses largely cancelled out these positive effects. According to this system, soldiers who recovered were not directly sent back to their old units but ended up in depots. From these assembly points they were then assigned, along with new recruits, to those units where the need for personnel was greatest. Thus after his recovery a serviceman was faced with problems of readjustment that were always present in the military organization.[14] This example illustrates how various services in the military organization could work at cross purposes.

The principle of proximity underwent a particularly unusual adaptation during the Israeli invasion of Lebanon in 1982. At that time Israeli psychiatrists were successful in involving family members and spouses in the therapy. This decision was based on considerations of a practical nature. In fact, the treatment centers were inundated with Jewish mothers who were knocking at the doors every hour to see their sons. When the psychiatrists realized they could not stop this, they decided to make a virtue out of necessity and began to include the mothers in the treatment plan. Thus in this case the hinterland was brought to the front.[15]

It is not actually surprising that this adaptation of the principle has not occurred in other armies. Military psychiatrists have perhaps not unrightly assumed that, even when enthusiasm for war is great among the population, women are not willing to sacrifice their own husbands or sons. Even at the best of times they will do everything possible to bring home their own Tom, Dick and Harry and certainly not make great efforts to restore him to combat fitness.

The same Israeli treatment is also a good illustration of the form that the principle of positive expectancy can take. In this case it was a question of a location which belonged to the second echelon. Soldiers were admitted who could not be returned to active duty after a brief treatment behind the front, i.e. during a period of 12 to 48 hours. In this somewhat more distant center the period of residence was fixed at twenty-one days.

The staff consisted of psychiatrists, psychologists, social workers and sport instructors. They were all reservists who had already worked together before the outbreak of the conflict and who were committed to the ideology of the center. The following goals were given top priority:
1. To return the soldier suffering from combat reaction to optimal physical and mental functioning, as early as possible, whether as a soldier or as a civilian.

2. If possible, to keep him within the framework of the army and prevent his expulsion as not fit for military service, with a psychiatric stigma.
3. If possible, to enable him to return to his original military unit.[16]

In order to achieve these goals it was thought necessary to develop a wide range of activities. The therapeutic work concentrated on three areas. The first and the most important of these was the military setting. The patients, who even retained their uniforms, were part of a larger military whole. They also made use of the normal facilities that were available on the base. The psychiatrists were of the opinion that the flights of airplanes and helicopters that regularly passed overhead contributed to the real military atmosphere. Secondly, there were the activities. These included talks which were conducted on an individual basis as well as in groups. And then of course sports. Here also the military aspect was not lacking. The patients had to participate in parade drills and they were obliged to keep their marksman skills up to standard on the shooting range. Finally, the last area consisted of group activities. Here the purpose was to ensure that all the actions undertaken were achieved as much as possible through group participation. Those involved were divided, upon arrival, into groups of ten. This unit had the status of a platoon with the psychiatrist as the platoon commander. The staff were not unsatisfied with the final results, although no exact figures are cited in the relevant article of Neumann and Levy. Mention is only made of one soldier who had to be sent to a civilian institution, whereas the rest (49) were discharged after having greatly improved their condition. Even in this almost optimal therapeutic climate, the treatment results therefore could still only be presented with certain reservations. Thus the reader is given some cause for reflection.

Moreover, the creation of a therapeutic climate that aimed at returning patients to active duty did not meet with the same level of success everywhere. Even in Vietnam, where the problems were less serious compared with those of the world wars, success was not always achievable. Robert L. Pettera, who served as a division psychiatrist in Vietnam in 1968, reported that the principle of expectancy regularly came to be pushed into the background and constantly had to be rediscovered. Real successes could only be achieved once it had been impressed on every serviceman that regardless of the seriousness of his symptoms, he would have to return to his old function.[17]

During the Second World War as well, the ideal therapeutic climate often remained far out of reach. The English musician, actor, writer Spike Milligan dwells at length on his vicissitudes with military psychiatry in his memoirs about the war.[18] At the end of January 1944, during the Italian campaign, Milligan suffered a physical as well as mental breakdown. To begin with everything went according to the book. In the first-aid station he was rendered unconscious by means of medication. The following day he had to see the psychiatrist who was referred to by the men as 'the trick cyclist'. After a short talk the psychiatrist explained the goal of the treatment: 'You are going to get better. Understand?' After a few days' rest, during which the required knock-out pills were administered, Milligan attempted to go back to active duty once more. Almost immediately thereafter he broke down again. After that he ended up in a rehabilitation camp behind the front. The situation in this therapeutic center is described by Milligan as follows:

The camp is to be run by a loony officer; he's been blown up on the Volturno and blown down again at Cassino. Captain Peters of the Queens. Tall and thin, large horse-like face, pale blue eyes with a rapid blink and a twitch of the head; all done with a strange noise at the back of the nose that goes 'phnut'. He·is balding and has a fine head of hair. Speaks very rapidly due to an overdraft at Lloyds.

To date one had the feeling that the Rehabilitation Camp was totally unknown and unrecorded in the Army lists. With the coming of Captain Peters all that changed. The camp went on being unknown and unrecorded, but now we had an officer in charge. The camp had a turnover of about a thousand men, all in a state of coming and going, unlike me who couldn't tell if I was coming or going. Under Peters the food improved. He intended for twice the amount, and sent scrounging parties to buy eggs, chicken and fish, all of which the cooks dutifully boiled to shreds. 'I think they put it in with the laundry,' said Peters. He also allowed men out for an evening, but the effect of alcohol on some of the loonies who were on tranquillizers was alarming. It was something to see the guard commander and his men holding down a half naked, shit-covered, wine-stained loony alternately being sick, screaming and singing. Some loonies tried to climb Vesuvius. God knows how many fell in. A resident psychiatrist arrived. He immediately dished out drugs that zombified most of the inmates, who walked around the camp starry-eyed, grinning and saying 'Hello' to trees.[19]

It cannot be denied that an important facet of positive expectancy is quite emphatically present here. The patients remain soldiers in uniform and the leadership consists of officers. In short, a clear military setting is maintained. On the other hand, it is perfectly obvious that one cannot speak of an optimal psychological climate in which everything is aimed at returning patients to active duty. Consequently, one should not expect that Spike Milligan's camp will be presented in a handbook on military psychiatry in order to illustrate the latter principle of forward psychiatry.

Undoubtedly, there will be people who do not trust the memoirs of Milligan 100 percent. But those with a sceptical outlook can be referred to a source which is above suspicion, namely the British psychiatrist Robert Ahrenfeldt. Indeed, the description he has given of Northfield Military Hospital in Birmingham is to be warmly recommended.[20] This hospital was taken over by the army in April 1942 to treat military patients. The institution was then divided into two sections, a hosptial wing with 200 beds and a training wing with 600 beds. In the hospital section the soldiers wore blue hospital-clothing, while in the other section they wore army khakis. The two wings were strictly separated from one another. Thus there was a treatment section with a hospital atmosphere and a training department where a military atmosphere prevailed. According to Ahrenfeldt, there was no trace of any therapeutic optimism. Morale was low both among the staff and among the patients. The latter did everything they could to be able to stay in the hospital section. The military staff in the other section looked on with amazement and repulsion at how soldiers without any compunction behaved in the most childish fashion in an attempt to deceive their psychiatrists. For their part, the doctors did not have a very high opinion of the way in which the professional military personnel dealt with the servicemen entrusted to their care. It took until November 1944 before a good therapeutic climate was established in Northfield and any successful work could be achieved in returning to active duty soldiers who had suffered a breakdown. Extensive reorganization and the replacemnt of a large part of the permanent staff preceeded this change in atmosphere. After the capitulation of Germany the system once again completely collapsed. Once more the patients refused to be cured since if such were the case fighting in the Far East against Japan was in store for them. As for the staff, it can be said that their attention was primarily focused on their future in civilian society. Thus Northfield at the end of the war degenerated into a sort of human storehouse which would not have been out of place in the nineteenth century. In short, positive expectancy is not a constant, but a factor which has displayed great variations according to time and place.

Problems of Applying Principles

Immediacy, proximity and positive expectancy appear to be straightforward matters but in reality their implementation has not always been so simple. Therefore, it may well be useful at this point to remember that the principles in question were developed in the context of a particular type of war, i.e. trench warfare. In a more mobile form of warfare where the front lines are more flexible and can suddenly change, it becomes much more difficult, for example, to follow a policy of treatment based on proximity. In this regard guerilla warfare will certainly pose serious problems.

In general, there was no real front line to speak of in Vietnam. Servicemen who suffered a breakdown there were admitted to special psychiatric sections of hospitals on the big army bases. In any case, transport by helicopter guaranteed treatment could be begun quickly, but proximity in this situation came to have a completely different geographical interpretation than in the previous wars the American army had taken part in.

Moreover, the possibilities for setting up a system of forward psychiatry were also seriously limited by the intensity of battles waged. In this connection one should bear in mind the following consideration. One of the essential situational factors with which military psychiatry is confronted in every war has to do with the strength of the armed forces involved. If an army's numbers are below standard and this begins to exert a negative influence on its fighting capacity, then psychiatric care as well as medical care will be put under great pressure to return as many wounded as possible to active duty. The willingness to release soldiers temporarily from performing combat tasks generally decreases greatly when the number of available personnel in the army declines. In theory a situation like this can provide good breeding ground for a powerful optimism to flourish in. However, in reality this is not usually the case. The amount of patients is in fact not constant but rises and falls unevenly. Fierce battles can cause an unexpected flood of wounded. As a result, medical and psychiatric services have not infrequently been inundated with a stream of casualties, which they were utterly unequipped to cope with. In the case of the psychiatric services this has had a twofold consequence. To begin with, patients who could have recovered after a few days rest were sent back to the front too quickly, where of course they continued to carry out their tasks in a rather unconvincing manner. At the same time, soldiers who required a little longer treatment were immediately sent on to the hinterland and were thus abandoned by forward psychiatry. Even the most highly motivated psychiatrist will simply have to knuckle under in circumstances like these, because in fact it is no longer possible to effect any cures. This kind of situation came about in the summer of 1944 on the western front. When the Allied armies had entrenched themselves in Normandy after an invasion that turned out favorably, they were confronted with an unexpectedly fierce resistance by the German forces. The initial euphoria gave way to deep disappointment. A veritable epidemic of 'combat exhaustion' plagued the Allied armies. Forward psychiatry was not prepared to deal with such high numbers. However, the narrow bridgehead generally offered no possibilities for setting up extensive medical facilities.

In this regard, certain passages from the diary of the Canadian psychiatrist Dr. B. McNeel are enlightening. He was present in Normandy and was a witness to the crisis that manifested itself there:

13 July 1944: The first twelve patients arrived at 1200 hrs. The majority of these were from the RRC (Royal Regiment of Canada) which had been in action two days... Histories were taken, each man was given three grains of Sodium Amytal and put to bed.

14 July 1944: Forty-one patients were admitted today. About 15 of these are cases which have been out of the line for about a week... cases seen yesterday and today have shown chiefly anxiety symptoms... The precipitation factor in most cases is said to be blast – mortar more frequently than shell.

15 July 1944: Twenty-six patients were admitted today and with a top accommodation of 110 beds, it is apparent that our plan of two days sedation and three days rehabilitation will not be practicable... As we are now discharging patients, psycho-therapeutic talks to groups about to be discharged have now been instituted. These consist of simple explanations of psychogenic symptoms 'exhaustion versus shell shock', etc.... Many of the men understand the mechanism of their trouble alright, and most are ready to admit that the origin is emotional rather than physical but many are without any incentive to carry on further.

16 July 1944: Twenty-three patients have been admitted today and our bed strength is now eighty-four.

17 July 1944: Hope of adequate treatment and rehabilitation will have to be abandoned... The treatment cases are without pyjamas and the convalescents have to wear their dirty and tattered clothes.

18 July 1944: We were awakened this morning by a terrific roar of gunfire... rumour is that 'This is it' and that the show should soon be over. So far, our admissions have not exceeded the usual level: about twenty-two today... We face a serious shortage of sedative.[21]

In these circumstances the British, who were less prepared for the situation than
the Americans, decided to give up attempting to treat psychiatric cases behind the
front and to evacuate them directly to military hospitals in Britain. Consequently,
to begin with events in Normandy brought about a recurrence on the British side of
the system that had existed during the First World War.[22]

Not only anonymous, impersonal forces can block the development of a positive
therapeutic climate. In the military setting as well, such a climate is naturally very
dependent on what the therapists bring with them in the way of professional and
non-professional conceptions and patterns of thought. In civilian society psychiatrists are expected to make the patient their central concern. They treat individual
human beings who are seeking help for a certain behavioral problem or difficulty in
their life. The psychiatrist who enters the military sphere is expected to give up this
orientation. It is no longer the interest of the individual but that of the group which
must be made the central concern. The British psychiatrist Lieutenant-Colonel T.F.
Main expressed this in the following words:

The mental health of a fighting force is not the same thing as the mental health of a nation at
war. With the differing functions, different standards are needed. If a sergeant can recover his
poise for one month, it can be regarded as a satisfactory therapeutic result in an Army fighting for its very life. Then the stresses which such a man must be capable of withstanding are
very different from those which would operate upon him in civilian life – and they must be
fully understood by the psychiatrist. Lastly, the positive factors which will support the mental
health of such a man are different in the forward area from those in the rear areas. The job of
the psychiatrist, in fact, demands a grasp of the social as well as the medical variants which influence treatment and disposal.[23]

Albert Glass has stated that, both during the Second World War and at the time of
the conflict in Korea, many American psychiatrists had difficulty with this obligatory reorientation. Glass has indicated a sort of soft-heartedness among many of
his colleagues. The latter found it unacceptable to be able only to hold out the prospect of returning to the front to soldiers who had suffered breakdowns. Moreover,
this 'weakness' was particularly observable among psychiatrists who served behind
the front, for example in military-base hospitals.[24] Glass was not alone in making
this observation. Robert Pettera discovered the same tendency in Vietnam. In that
war as well, psychiatrists often felt such strong compassion for the servicemen entrusted to their care that they found it very unpleasant not to be able to offer them
the perspective of returning home to the United States.[25]

Moreover, it is striking that in this case sympathy for the soldier and for his problems increased the more the psychiatrist was removed from the front. This is exactly
the reverse compared with many other matters connected with military organization. Within army and army corps headquarters there often prevailed an atmosphere of mistrust towards the echelons directly involved in the fighting. When an
attack or an offensive failed, frequently the first reaction was to assign blame to
one's own combattants. In the course of this century, a great deal of lack of

willpower has been attributed to front line soldiers from the safety of the hinterland. The losers have never received much sympathy or compassion within their own armed forces. By contrast, the history of military psychiatry presents a very different picture in this area.

But now to come back to the principle of positive expectancy. Thinking fundamentally in terms of the interests of the group and suppressing one's feelings of sympathy for individual casualties may well be features of military psychiatry which are officially held in honor, but in themselves they are no guarantee of the existence of a correct outlook among the therapists. 'Expectancy' is in fact a belief and on the basis of psychiatry it is possible consciously or unconsciously to muster doctrines and dogmas against a belief. Two English psychiatrists, William Sargant and Elliot Slater, were engaged in offering relief and treatment to British servicemen in June 1940. These patients along with their healthy comrades had been literally driven from the Continent. Both before and during the evacuation from Dunkirk, they had been put through everything imaginable. They were completely exhausted, disheartened and filled with mortal fear. The above-mentioned psychiatrists had mixed feelings about this groups's chances of recovery.

The experience so far gained with these patients is still too recent for any firm statement to be made about the prognosis. As a rule we have not thought it advisable in the early stages to say anything at all to the patient about his returning to an active army life; we have thought it better to shelve that subject completely in the apparent confident expectation that he is going to make a complete recovery and be as well as ever. But many of those with whom the matter has been broached have expressed a conviction that they could never go through such an experience again without breaking down at once. Such a conviction, if it persists, is tantamount to a fact; if a man firmly believes that he will break down in a particular way in paticular circumstances, and has already done so once, then he will again. The conviction has to be shaken and destroyed. It is here that the fragment of truth is based in the quoted opinion of a high military authority that shell shock is nothing but insufficient training. Even if this morbid belief is abolished it still may be true that a recurrence of the circumstances will bring about a recurrence of the breakdown. On the other hand, it seems probable that the number of soldiers subjected to such an intensity of trial on a foreign shore will not be nearly so large in the future as it has been in the recent past. A man who has broken down under a severe strain will not necessarily break down under strains less severe or prolonged.[26]

Thus Sargant and Slater were obviously convinced that certain forms of traumatic experiences could make soldiers unfit for dealing with severe stress. An assumption like this is naturally difficult to reconcile with the idea of positive expectancy. The same can be said of the conception shared by many of the Allied psychiatrists that after a period of 200 to 240 days of combat a soldier was virtually burned out. In this connection one often spoke of the so-called 'old sergeant syndrome'.

The ideas of the Canadian psychiatrist Doyle present a good example of another kind of barrier which repeatedly confronted the principle of positive expectancy. Doyle was attached to the First Canadian Infantry Division as division psychiatrist.

In the winter of 1943/44 this unit was engaged in the heavy battles in the vicinity of the Adriatic port of Artona in Italy. At a given moment the whole division was on the point of suffering a breakdown. The morale had sunk to below zero and the commanding officers were beginning to lose their control over the men. Consequently, General C.W. Alfrey, the British commander of the army corps to which the division belonged, was clearly very worried. However, the psychiatrist Doyle was able to give him reassurance; there was nothing unusual going on. 'The division had simply had a good and overdue house cleaning of its weakest and most susceptible soldiers.'[27] Actually, the particular soldiers in question should never have been accepted into the division. They should have been selected out during the recruitment process or during training. Thus, as far as Doyle was concerned, these were soldiers predisposed to suffer breakdowns and in cases like these the power of the psychiatrist was restricted. One cannot expect that someone who has been unstable for years can be helped back onto his feet after a short period of treatment, however intense it might be. This is a bit like a lawyer who snaps at his client: 'Sir, you can't expect me to make good in one lawsuit the mess you've made during your whole lifetime.' The belief in predisposition created an impediment, not only in Doyle's case but among many of his colleagues, to unconditional acceptance of the principle of positive expectancy. In reality, this reserve had been present in military psychiatry from the very beginning – even in the era when Salmon held sway among the Americans. Thus it is no coincidence that already in 1917 the Americans had begun to give psychological tests to recruits. In this way it was hoped that those who were unfit would be kept from entering through the garrison's portals (see Chapter IX).

The Discontinuity of Combat Psychiatry
Military psychiatry, as has already been observed, presented the basic principles as a more or less guaranteed formula for success. On the other hand, anyone who imagines that the armies that went off to war after the First World War were equipped with a system of care based on these principles will be disappointed. The history of combat psychiatry is not uniform in character. The value of such a service continually had to be demonstrated anew in the practice of waging war.

Within the Armed Forces of the United States Salmon's ideas were quickly forgotten so that the army entered the Second World War wholly unprepared in the area of psychiatric care. During the campaign in Tunisia the first steps were taken in setting up a system of treatment. Further experimentation in this connection was carried out during the campaign in Italy. But it was only in Normandy that recourse could be had to a well-structured forward psychiatry. After the Second World War this system fell out of use so that in 1951 when fighting broke out in Korea it had to be started up all over again. For the most part the same can be said concerning Vietnam.

In 1939 the British army, at the initative of the Ministry of Pensions, reflected on the consequences of a possible new wave of shell shock patients. This process of reflection did not give rise to many concrete activities. Therefore, in May 1940 there were only very limited possibilities for looking after psychiatric cases. The scope of these facilities slowly increased in the course of the war. However, when peace came in 1945, combat psychiatry ceased to exist in Britain as well.

In Germany there was a great degree of continuity between the two world wars. Reflection on these matters, in contrast to the state of affairs in Britain, was indeed followed by relevant policy measures. Discontinuity only occurred in Germany when the *Bundeswehr*, for reasons which remain obscure, decided to break with this tradition.

Thus, in general, it can be said that in the period after the Second World War interest in combat psychiatry has been limited in most Western countries. By the end of the 1980s, the armed forces of West Germany, France, Belgium and Canada did not have the disposal of an organization which could provide relief to victims of what had in the meantime come to be known as combat stress.[28] At that time in the Netherlands and in Britain there was some experimentation with setting up an organization of this kind. The dominant frame of reference for this activity was provided by the United States and Israel. Indeed, after Vietnam the United States, to some extent in contradiction to its own tradition, decided not only to make use of forward psychiatry but to expand it further and to perfect it. The Israeli army was won over to combat psychiatry during the Yom Kippur War in 1973 and has since then forged ahead with making further improvements to the system.

How then is one to explain this discontinuity that we have noted? Besides specific factors, which will be examined presently, a more general circumstance also plays a role here. I am referring to the great difference that has always existed, and still exists today, between armies in peace-time and armies that find themselves at war. The latter situation represents an exception. Indeed, most armies, past or present, have not had to fight very frequently. Consequently, there is always the danger that among the servicemen the central purpose of military organization, namely the production of violence, may recede into the background. By the same token, military medical services, which must offer help to the victims of violence, become imperceptibly shifted to the margins of military activity. In a recent study on the British army Hugh McManners has shown what crippling effects can result to military organization from long-term peace.[29] Significantly, one of the key chapters of his book, which presents an analysis of how the British armed forces functioned in the Falklands and in Kuwait, is entitled 'Fighting the Peace'. From this viewpoint, combat psychiatry is one of the areas which very easily becomes neglected in peace-time. However, there are also more specific factors that can be mentioned. This brings us to the counter-currents which military psychiatrists were confronted with when they were incorporated in the armed forces.

Up to this point we have only spoken of the forms of resistance to military psychiatry which existed in the officers corps. It would appear that the phenomenon of the psychologically wounded soldier did not always fit with the ways of thinking that were moulded by traditional military morality. Ahrenfeldt and Rees, on the basis of their own experience as well as that of their British and American colleagues, point to the cool reception which was accorded to military psychiatry on the part of the other military doctors. They give no clear explanation for this themselves. The lack of enthusiasm, which at times can turn into open opposition, is recorded with a certain surprise.[30]

To an outsider this negative attitude is less surprising. Looked at from the medical point of view, these military psychiatrists in fact did something rather unusual. They denied the role of patient to the soldiers who were placed in their care. This was certainly, at the time of both world wars, extremely unusual. Sick and wounded servicemen more than anyone else had the right to attention, care and protection. While they underwent treatment, their military duties were temporarily suspended. Only after their recovery were they to take up their place in military life once again.

It will be clear that the therapeutic principles adopted by military psychiatry were diametrically opposed to this way of thinking. It should also be obvious that not every military doctor would understand these principles, let alone find them acceptable. Thus the position of the military psychiatrist was paradoxical in the extreme. His presence in the army was legitimized by the acknowledgement that soldiers could become wounded psychologically as well as physically. But when it came to treating the psychologically wounded, their being wounded was actually denied on the basis of certain therapeutic strategies.

Those medical colleagues who did not find this strange had another valid reason to be critical of the arrival of military psychiatry. Indeed, the result of the arrival of the psychiatrists was that the ordinary military doctor's monopoly in the area of diagnostics was now contested. The American sociologist Freidson has described diagnosis as the most crucial activity of medical intervention.[31] The right to make a diagnosis distinguishes doctors from other professional practitioners in health care. It forms the basis of the medical profession and the autonomy that goes with it. Within the military medical service there now appeared to be two captains in charge of the ship. In the course of time, this inevitably resulted – to retain the same image – in a dividing of the large ship into two smaller ones. Two systems of care emerged, one for the physically wounded, and another for the psychiatric patients.

It would be very unrealistic to expect that a process of differentiation like this within the medical service would take place without friction. Thus the military psychiatrists could certainly count on a certain degree of resistance. The same can be said regarding the activities they developed in the area of prevention. Here the military psychiatrists portrayed themselves as superexperts in connection with the overall functioning of the military organization. They gave advice on recruiting, officer training, combat instruction and on counselling disabled veterans. All this was done, moreover, by the members of a professional group who only occupied a very modest position in the hierarchy of the total medical profession. Taken all together, this provoked surprise and resistance. But the military psychiatrists, for their part, found it difficult to understand this reaction.

One of the big opponents was Major-General E. Philips, director of the medical services of the British army and, as such, one of the top advisors to Montgomery. In Philips' eyes psychiatry was not much more than: 'a new form of witchcraft'.[32]

Therefore, he hesitated to assign facilities to this dangerous innovation. Only in February 1944 did the combined British and Canadian invasion force come to dispose over a psychiatric advisor, and that despite the fact that planning for the invasion had already started in the spring of 1943. So the British, in contrast to the Americans, were absolutely unequipped to deal with the large stream of psychologically wounded soldiers that appeared during the high point of the fighting in Normandy. It was for this reason that they reverted to the above-mentioned procedure which had been followed during the early years of the First World War, i.e. evacuation to Britain.

Another famous fault-finder in the British camp was Captain Dr. H.J.C.J. L'Etang who was employed in the medical service of the British army from 1943 to 1946.[33] Basically, his chief objection was that the psychiatrists had unnecessarily withheld a great amount of manpower from the army. In his view the psychiatrists operated as members of a kind of fifth column who undermined the army's fighting power from within. According to L'Etang, they did this by declaring unfit for service those soldiers they thought would suffer a breakdown in combat. In this connection he accused these psychiatrists of being both soft and ignorant. They were soft because, in his view, even the servicemen who could barely stand it during battle could nonetheless make a useful contribution to the campaingn as a whole. It was better to do a little than to do nothing, according to his way of reasoning. Furthermore, he accused his psychiatric colleagues of not being aware that there were countless possibilities for also employing less warlike persons in the army. If the latter approach were applied systematically, many additional stronger individuals would be made available for actual combat functions.

There were also times when the military psychiatrists were confronted with unexpected actions on the part of combat units. For example, it is well-known that some Canadian units which took part in the campaign in Italy in the Second World War found a solution on their own for helping their weaker comrades. The latter were soldiers who had already suffered a breakdown or who were on the point of doing so. The servicemen in question were temporarily employed in the kitchen or the mess. After a few days of rest and relative safety, they returned to their normal functions. In this way, with the best of intentions, military psychiatry was simply left out of the picture.[34]

Conclusion

The basic principles formed the core of combat psychiatry. At the risk of exaggeration, one could say that immediacy, proximity and positive expectancy are the gospel of military psychiatry. In some surveys maintaining the military setting which we have discussed as a subdivision of positive expectancy is introduced as a fourth principle. Similarly, simplicity with regard to the therapies employed is sometimes presented as a separate basic assumption.

In practice the basic principles were discovered through the method of trial and error. During the Russo-Japanese War, for the first time there was experimentation to set up a system of care which corresponded to these principles. The Germans and the French, who were moreover unaware of the earlier Russian attempts, introduced forward psychiatry during the First World War. It was the American psychiatrist Thomas Salmon who formulated the basic principles in words. When the army of the United States launched its own first offensive, from the very beginning it disposed over a system of psychiatric care based on these principles.

Psychiatrists have frequently presented combat psychiatry as a blueprint for absolute success. Recovery rates of between 80 and 90 percent were predicted. In reality, however, setting up an adequate system of psychiatric care entailed quite a number of problems. Moreover, there is not really all that much that can be claimed for the actual results of combat psychiatry. What is striking is the intermittent pattern of development of military psychiatry. This discontinuity is particularly evident in the Anglo-Saxon countries where in every war the psychiatric services almost had to be started up once again from scratch. The fact that in these countries military psychiatry met with great resistance, indeed even on the part of the regular army doctors, is a partial explanation for this state of affairs.

In bringing this chapter to a close, it seems to me appropriate to give some attention to how the basic principles discussed above relate to the theory and practice of civilian psychiatry.

The idea of immediacy is as old as modern psychiatry itself. Around 1800 when this profession began to take shape, there was widespread unanimity concerning the view that treatment of the mentally ill should begin as quickly as possible. But in the course of the nineteenth century this idea, for practical as well as theoretical reasons, receded into the background. Many asylums had waiting lists and, therefore, speedy admission was by no means always possible. Moreover, speedy intervention according to the new up-and-coming bio-medical school of thought counted less than it had according to the traditional psychological model. Whereas bio-medical thought did offer a theoretical explanation for the occurrence of mental illness, to begin with it had little to say in the way of providing a starting point for setting up a concrete plan of treatment. The principle of positive expectancy is not clearly present in psychiatry as a constant factor. The introduction of other methods of treatment or new medicinal drugs has been, and to a great extent still is, accompanied by great therapeutic optimism. Most often this euphoria decreases with the lapse of time. Pessimism and optimism regularly alternate with one another in psychiatry. In the field of military psychiatry a positivist stance is always adopted, at least on paper. The principle of proximity is in direct opposition to classical psychiatry where until deep into the twentieth century primacy was accorded to asylum care. In the latter case patients were deliberately removed from their original social surroundings and banished to institutions where they were given treatment in total isolation. Only in the last decades, at least in some Western countries, have adequate out-patient and semi-out-patient facilities been provided, with the result that this process of banishment has more or less ended. The importance of proximity has been widely acknowledged in modern mental health care. Thus, in this respect, the military sector had been in advance of the rest of society. That does not mean that the military had fostered a completely new vision concerning the structure of mental health care. In any case, in the mental hygiene movement as well similar conceptions had been developed. What can be said is that the military setting made it possible actually to implement these ideas in practice. The military psychiatrists made use of these possibilities and saw to it that quite early on a whole new path was pursued in the army.

In some respects the characteristic ideas of military psychiatry show similarities with the world of ideas of antipsychiatry. They have in common their aversion to psychiatric asylums. They also have in common the distance they adopt *vis-à-vis* the medical model and their rejection of the role of patient. The most visible parallel has been their abandonment of the doctor's white coat. As early as the First World War, military practitioners exchanged their specialized medical clothing for an army uniform. At the end of the 1960s the antipsychiatrists traded in their professional dress for a sports jacket.

This does not cancel out the crucial differences which exist between the two groups. The movement of democratization has had virtually no effect on military psychiatry. The therapeutic relationship in the army has always been based on an authoritarian and hierarchical structure and remains so today. Non-directive therapies have never been able to thrive in the military environment. Of essential significance is the difference in their fundamental starting point. Antipsychiatry has been first and foremost concerned with 'the patient'. The latter must be given help and, if necessary, protected from an environment that may be malevolent or responsible for making an individual sick. In the military context, from the outset it was not a question of the requirements of 'the patient', but rather a question of the needs of the army or of society. The interests of the individual who is seeking help have been entirely subordinated to this higher priority.

IX - Prevention Is Better Than Cure

Introduction

Psychiatry, both in the civilian as well as in the military sector, began by offering concrete help to people with problems. As time went by curative intervention in both sectors was supplemented with action that was more directed towards prevention. Albert Glass, an eminent figure in American military psychiatry, distinguished three different areas within his professional field. The domain of primary prevention, i.e. prevention of the occurrence of psychiatric disorders. The area of secondary prevention, the aim of which is to treat disorders in such a way that they cannot be prolonged, and finally tertiary prevention, which is concerned with the institutional treatment of serious forms of mental illness with recovery as the ultimate goal here as well. During the First World War experience was acquired with secondary and tertiary prevention. Primary prevention came to be a new field of work in the Second World War.

The shift to primary prevention was prompted by two factors in particular. On the one hand, there were the experiences of combat psychiatry. We have already seen that many doctors during the First World War subscribed to the conviction that shell shock patients were more or less predisposed to this disorder. According to one school of thought in psychiatry, this was the result of hereditary disposition, whereas the other school held that it was the result of a disturbance in the normal psychodynamic process of development. Even when it turned out that completely normal soldiers had a breaking point, the idea persisted that great differences between individuals and groups could occur with regard to mental vulnerability. So what could be more obvious than to proceed to eliminate these mentally weaker individuals from combat functions, indeed to eliminate them from the army altogether. Thus the need for selection, an important subdivision of primary prevention, emerged as a logical extension of combat psychiatry.

The second factor which prompted the step in this direction had to do with the problems of adaptation which in particular many American and British soldiers experienced in the Second World War. In a short period of time several million men were removed from their civilian existence and incorporated in the military organization at a forced pace. For some of them this transition was simply too abrupt. For others the thought of being transported to overseas territories, far from hearth and home, was unbearable. Here the military psychiatrists took on a task alongside those who had administered spiritual care from time immemorial. They now functioned like a form of industrial welfare worker. The industry, in this case the military organization, was advised regarding 'human relations' techniques. At the same time, the recruits themselves were given a greater understanding of the demands of the military way of life.

This enormous expansion of their work terrain meant that, in their struggle for the psyche of the soldier, the psychiatrists were confronted with competitors. The psychologists came up with a battery of tests, and in order to cope with the problems of adaptation an appeal was made to the social scientists.

Selection: The Right Man in the Right Place

Earlier we saw how The National Committee for Mental Hygiene in 1917 offered its services to the American army. Grateful use was made of this offer. The American Association was another source of help which put itself at the disposal of the military authorities with just as much enthusiasm. Together with the National Research Council, the association delivered a group of top psychologists who could be put to work on building up the armed forces and planning ways of waging war. Work groups were formed which busied themselves with such diverse tasks as psychological warfare, the use of gas masks and the selection of pilots.

One of the most crucial subjects concerned the selection of hundreds of thousands of recruits who had to be inducted in a short period of time.[1] The contribution of the psychologists consisted in developing simple testing methods by means of which educated and uneducated prospective soldiers could be quickly selected. English-speaking literate candidates took the army-alpha test, whereas for the non-English-speakers and illiterates there was the army-beta test. Both tests were intended to establish a person's level of intelligence.

The United States occupied a unique position in this respect. During the First World War no other country made use of formal psychological testing methods. Generally speaking, a superficial physical examination was deemed sufficient. This was true of Britain as well. When war broke out in 1914, the latter country had found itself in a situation comparable to that of the United States in 1917. In Britain as well within a short period millions of recruits, at first volunteers and then from 1916 on conscripts, had to be medically examined for military service. The problem was solved by the fact that the army only set minimal physical demands. Likewise, the military organization simply accepted the existing social order without much discussion. This meant that servicemen who came from the higher social strata were thought to be suited for officer functions, while the lower classes were seen as the reservoir from which the ranks of the ordinary soldiers could be filled.

France and Germany were in a somewhat more comfortable position because at the outbreak of hostilities they could make use of large numbers of previously tested and trained reservists. Moreover, in these countries too the conscripts in question had, for the most part, only been examined with regard to their physical qualities. In France on the eve of the war only the feeble-minded were rejected and men who weighed less than 50 kilos. There was no time for a thorough examination, a fact which is clear from the instructions to the medical examiners not to process more than thirty men an hour. In the German army as well attention was primarily given to the physical suitability of the candidates. The necessary mental qualities would have to be instilled during training.

This extremely limited concern for everything that had to do with selection is a striking fact. Indeed, the First World War provided one of the most spectacular examples of the industrial way of waging war. In the decades that preceded this conflict there had been extensive debate in military circles concerning logistical achievements, new weapon systems and new military doctrines. In this connection the soldiers themselves were only viewed in quantitative terms. How many divisions can a country with a particular system of conscription raise? That was the issue. Thus in 1914 one had not in fact come much further than Napoleon and his assertion that it's the big battalions that win wars. In this respect the First World War was more of a conclusion of the nineteenth than the beginning of the twentieth century. The world war that was to follow presented a different picture.

The selection procedure adopted by the American army during the Second World War was more inclusive and thorough than that of 1917. Three criteria played a role in this procedure, namely physical suitability, professional qualifications and capacity to learn. In establishing physical suitability use was made of the so-called conveyor-belt system. This meant simply that the recruit was not examined by one doctor alone, but that he was conveyed past a whole battery of medical specialists. One doctor looked at his eyes, another at his ears, and another still at his lungs, and in this way the main organs and limbs were checked. In the end there ensued a classification in one of the four following categories:

Category A: suitability for tasks in combat zones and suitable for undertaking strenuous activities.
Category B: suitable for auxiliary combat tasks.
Category C: suitable for communication tasks and tasks on home territory, as well as for tasks on overseas bases.
Category D: unsuitable.

The last specialist one had to appear before was the psychiatrist. It was his task to decide whether an individual was mentally suitable for military service. In practice this was done on the basis of posing simple questions such as: 'Do you ever hear voices?', or 'Do you think people are watching you?', or 'Do you like girls?'

After this physical and mental examination there followed a classification on the basis of professional competence. For this purpose the army had the disposal of a list of 800 military functions. In the case of functions where there was an equivalent in civilian society such as cook, driver or telegraphist, this was stated. An effort was made to coordinate the professional qualifications of the recruit with the available military equivalents. By means of this strategy the army would be able to make optimal use of the knowledge and skills of the recruit. And for his part, the recruit would be spared excessive problems of adaptation.

After this professional classification there then followed at the end a measurement of one's capacity to learn. For this purpose the Army General Classification tests were employed. The more points one scored on this test, the higher one's ability was assessed to follow specialist secondary education. It is striking that in the American army great significance was given to the initial selection. Indeed, on the basis of the examination results the recruit was immediately assigned a function in a particular subdivision of the army. Following this system implies an unusually high degree of confidence in the capacity for prediction of medical and psychological tests.

With the British this certainty existed to a far lesser extent. After the reintroduction of conscription in 1939, the British armed forces as well were again faced with the task of sifting through a great stream of potential soldiers on the basis of their suitability for the military. With this in mind a system was devised that made it possible to sketch a sort of profile of every recruit. The profile had the form of a formula: *Pulhems*, each letter of which was accompanied by a number from 1 to 5. *Pulhems* stood for Physical, Upper extremities, Lower extremities, Hearing, Eyes, Mental, and Psyche. For our concern the *M* and the *S* are of particular interest, as these stood for intelligence and emotional stability respectively. At the same time the following possibilities were distinguished:

M1 indicates: no defects including dumb.
M2 indicates: very dumb to slightly feeble-minded.
M5 indicates: imbecile, etc., unsuitable on the basis of mental capacity.
S1 means: apparently suitable for combat functions at the front.
S2 means: apparently suitable for non-combat functions at the front.
S3 means: limited suitability, for non-combat functions behind the front.
S5 means: unsuitable.

In order to measure intelligence objective psychological tests were used. Emotional stability was established in an interview with a psychiatrist. The selection which finally took place in the British army can be characterized as extremely crude. Only very dumb and wholly unstable persons were identified through this form of inspection. There was no question of a thorough examination. In fact, it was assumed that a further selection would be carried out during basic training by the officers involved. The test results achieved during the initial examination could play a role to a greater or lesser extent at this later stage. Finally, it can also be noted that also during the Second World War the British military authorities still attached great importance to a recruit's social background and the status of the school he had attended.

In the *Wehrmacht* a procedure was followed that deviated even more clearly from the American model. Of course, here as well the recruits were tested medically and psychologically, and here as well an attempt was made to establish the psychological stability of the recruit in an interview. However, that is where the similarities ended. In the German army, selection primarily took place on a practical basis. The medical examiners only determined whether someone was not capable of performing military service. If their judgment was positive a summons followed to report for induction. Where a recruit might finally end up was still completely unclear. Only after induction and basic training was it decided what weapon or area of service the soldier would be assigned to. The officers of the unit in question subsequently determined which specific function the new arrival was most suitable for. In brief, what this system came down to was that the commanders in the field were allotted the key role in the selection process. In the American army this role was reserved for the bureau experts of the examination board.

It seems logical to link this powerful position of the officers with the unique place the German armed forces had held in society from far back in time. During the eighteenth century the state in Prussia was an institution whose primary task was to maintain the army. In later times in Germany the army continued to occupy an exceptionally important position. Citizens only counted if they were reserve officers. Doctors, psychologists and psychiatrists felt it was an honor to be able to be of service to the armed forces. The latter, in turn, made use of whatever civilian society had to offer in the way of knowledge and skills. However, with regard to the balance of power between them there was no lack of clarity. The military were in charge and they determined what could and could not be considered useful knowledge. The idea of relinquishing the procedure of selection to a group of semi-military personnel, civilians in uniform, did not accord with this balance of power.

Risk Groups

A chief goal of the selection process is to see to it that unsuitable individuals are kept out of the army. From the Second World War on the authorities primarily had in mind two sorts of persons, the very dumb and psychopaths.

But someone who is all brawn and no brain would make a good soldier. According to General J.R. Rees, one of the best known and highest placed psychiatrists who served in the British army during the Second World War, this popular conception had often proved to be true in the past. In his view, however, modern warfare presented a fundamentally different situation. Armored units, for example, required men who possessed an above-average intelligence. Similarly, the knowledge and skills that ordinary infantrymen had to have at their disposal made certain demands on the mental capacities of those in question. Thus there was actually no place in the army for really dumb and subnormal soldiers. If they managed to get in, they would only cause trouble. They failed to understand instructions, caused accidents and continually violated rules they had not understood. One way or another this meant they needed extra time from instructors, took up more space in the hospitals and, last but not least, provided the military courts with a lot of work. According to Rees, in terms of manpower effiency they cost more than they produced. The situation in civilian society was no different. Again, according to Rees:

In civil life we at least know that the bulk of chronic sickness and of recidivism comes from a very small section of the population. This is the constitutionally inferior group, the psychopathic tenth of the community, and again its cost to the country is something which needs to be demonstrated.[2]

But the problem here was that Britain could not afford to keep the subnormal out of the army and out of the war. In the army, just as in industry and in agriculture, there was an acute shortage of manpower. Thus everyone wherever possible had to be called up to serve. The solution, as it turned out, was the Pioneer Corps. In this corps the subnormal, of whom several different grades were distinguished, were made useful for the war. They undertook heavy forms of physical labor that involved digging and carrying, behind the front. Roads were built, campsites set up and other similar work was carried out that required muscle power but little intelligence. The least intelligent were not issued any weapons at all, whereas the others were armed with simple weapons for self-defense. There were also 'dullards' who for one reason or another remained outside the actual army. They were formed into agricultural companies which were employed for farming during the war. After work these civilians resided in special lodgings where they were expected to spend the evening and the night together.

By organizing these intellectually inferior individuals into special military and civilian units it was possible to kill several birds with one stone. It meant not only could a work force be exploited that would otherwise have been lost, but it also gave the less intelligent an opportunity to make themselves useful to the community. Rees also pointed to an additional significant advantage to this approach. Within these companies the men could enter into ties of friendship since everyone there was on the same intellectual level. In normal life these individuals always ran a great risk of becoming isolated. This in turn led to their looking around for a wife and their eventually ending up with an equally subnormal partner. The result, according to Rees, was easy to foresee: a huge family made up of backward children. It goes without saying that there were many besides this military psychiatrist who were repulsed by such a prospect. The army's strategy, by means of which these sorts of things could be avoided, filled him with pride and he felt that social medicine could learn a lesson from this:

There are few aspects of social medicine more important than this. Aldous Huxley in his book *Brave New World* was planning to produce a section of subnormal men who would do the dull jobs of the community: we don't really need to produce them for there are too many already. If we can employ them, and if we care for their morale, i.e. their mental health, there will be fewer of them and as a group they will be contributors to the life of the community and not consumers or problem makers.[3]

In Germany the military psychiatrists thought along similar lines. They pleaded for assigning functions to the subnormal behind the front and in the war industry as well.

Psychopaths constituted a second problem group. Among the military psychiatrists there was also a great degree of agreement concerning this category. Psychopaths did not belong in the army. The Allies simply attempted to exclude these soldiers from military service. The German army, as we shall see, dealt with the matter in a more thorough manner. Already several years before the war military psychiatrists had reflected at length on this problem. Two types of psychopaths were distinguished, namely *der Versager* (the failure) and *der Störer* (the trouble-maker).[4] The 'failures' were seen as cowardly and untrustworthy, and were simply judged to be unworthy to serve in the army. As for the 'trouble-makers', the authorities went one step further. The more active attitude of these persons was perceived to be very dangerous. Not only were these psychopaths useless in the military sense but they were also politically untrustworthy, which was in fact much more serious. During the inter-war period in Germany there even emerged a psychiatric variant of a conspiracy theory. According to this theory, certain psychopaths were supposed to have gotten themselves exempted from fighting in the trenches and then, after the armistice, become active as agitators in the revolutionary movement. Clearly, military psychiatry did not wish to be made a fool of a second time. In cases such as these merely removing an individual from service would not be sufficient. After all, that would only mean that the army's problems had simply been shunted onto civilian society. For this reason the psychiatrists in authority recommended that such persons be sent to prison and concentration camps.

The repulsion that this category aroused in the psychiatrists, which at times turned into outright hatred, had a rather special background. We have already referred to the sharp criticism that the Kaufmann-cure had evoked even while the First World War was in progress. After the armistice was declared, the German psychiatrists still had to deal with two unpleasant matters. The first had to do with the numerous spontaneous recoveries which occurred in November 1918. Countless *Kriegsneurotiker* lost their symptoms from one day to the next. What military psychiatry had not been able to effect was realized at one stroke by the advent of peace. But that was not all. Many who had been patients brought a lawsuit against their former therapists. Alone or in combination with one another they instituted legal proceedings on account of bodily and mental maltreatment. In Vienna the celebrated Wagner von Jauregg who had developed the malaria-cure became the object of a formal investigation for maltreatment. Freud was one of the expert witnesses called in to testify in this trial. These lawsuits were seen by the doctors involved as an antipsychiatric witch-hunt. When German military psychiatry was set up again in the 1930s, those involved had not forgotten this humiliating episode. In the previous chapters we have seen that the therapists in the next war had every opportunity to settle this unresolved account.

The Limitations of Selection
Great significance is rightly attributed to selection in our day and age. Precisely for this reason it seems appropriate to say something on the basis of past experience about the limitations which the selection of recruits is subject to. The character of this book dictates that we will primarily deal with the contributions of the psychia-

trists to the selection process. In fact these experts were meant to establish whether the recruits were mentally suitable for military service, which boiled down to determining that the persons in question were emotionally stable.

It is not difficult to have considerable reservations concerning these contributions of military psychiatry. Is it really possible in a brief talk of fifteen minutes to establish whether someone is mentally suitable for military life? Certainly, this cannot have been the case with every candidate. The human psyche does not reveal itself to scrutiny so easily. In addition, there is the fact that, generally speaking, psychiatrists adhere to particular schools or lines of reasoning. This implies that they will be inclined to pose a particular set of questions which fit in with their line of reasoning. Due to lack of time – the interview cannot go on too long -, this narrow focus is still further accentuated. The result may be that an interview consists of no more than a short series of simple questions which evoke equally simple answers. These must then be interpreted by the psychiatrist. The final results can at times appear bewildering. Richard F. Feynman, one of the most eminent physicists in recent history, has described his experiences with a selection committee of the American army.

During the war Feynman worked in Los Alamos on the development of the atom bomb. Immediately after the war he was called up for an examination for military service. Indeed, the army had need of servicemen for the occupation forces in Japan. After he had worked his way past the tables of the medical specialists for the eyes, the ears, the legs, etc., Feynman arrived at the psychiatrist's office. He handed over his papers and the conversation began:

I sit down at the desk, and the psychiatrist starts looking through my papers. 'Hello, Dick!', he says in a cheerful voice. 'Where do you work?' I'm thinking, 'Who does he think he is, calling me by my first name?', and I say coldly 'Schenectady.' 'Who do you work for, Dick?', says the psychiatrist, smiling again. 'General Electric.' 'Do you like your work, Dick?', he says, with that same big smile on his face. 'So-so.' I just wasn't going to have anything to do with him.

Three nice questions, and then the fourth one is completely different. 'Do you think people talk about you?', he asks, in a low, serious tone. I light up and say, 'Sure! When I go home, my mother often tells me she was telling her friends about me.' He isn't listening to the explanation: instead, he's writing something down on my paper. Then again, in a low, serious tone, he says, 'Do you think people *stare* at you?' I'm all ready to say no, when he says, 'For instance do you think any of the boys waiting on the benches are staring at you now?' While I had been waiting to talk to the psychiatrist, I had noticed there were about twelve guys on the benches waiting for the three psychiatrists, and they've got nothing else to look at, so I divide twelve by three – that makes four each – but I'm conservative, so I say, 'Yeah, maybe two of them are looking at us.' He says, 'Well just turn around and look' – and *he's* not even bothering to look himself! So I turn around, and sure enough, two guys are looking. So I point to them and I say, 'Yeah – there's *that* guy over *there* looking at us.' Of course, when I'm turned around and pointing like that, other guys start to look at us, so I say, 'Now him, and those two over there – and now the whole bunch.' He still doesn't look up to check. He's busy writing more things on my paper. Then he says, 'Do you ever hear voices in your head?' 'Very rarely', and I'm about to describe the two occasions on which it happened when he says, 'Do you talk to yourself?' 'Yeah, sometimes when I'm shaving, or thinking: once in a while.' He's writing down some more stuff. 'I see you have a deceased wife – do you talk to *her*?' This question really annoyed me, but I contained myself and said, 'Sometimes, when I go up on a mountain and I'm think-ing about her.' More writing. Then he asks, 'Is anyone in your family in a mental institution?' 'Yeah, I have an aunt in an insane asylum.'[5]

When the interview was over, it turned out that the psychiatrist had made the fol-lowing notes:

Thinks people talk about him.
Thinks people stare at him.
Auditory hypnogogic hallucinations.
Talks to himself.
Talks to deceased wife.
Maternal aunt in mental institution.
Very peculiar stare.[6]

The result, which comes as no surprise, was that Feynman was rejected on grounds of psychological instability. Even those who find the above example somewhat ex-aggerated will none the less have to admit that the lack of time and the preoccupied state of mind of many psychiatrists can present an important barrier to adequate selection.

A completely different problem, which concerns not only the psychiatrists in-volved, has to do with the defective knowledge that has always existed regarding the mental qualities demanded for combat functions. Clear profiles of drivers, me-chanics and telegraph operators had already been formulated during the Second World War. For actual combat functions no such profile existed and consequently a precise selection based on objective tests could not be carried out. Fundamentally, this situation has still not changed. What is difficult, of course, is that it is precisely the persons fulfilling these functions who are exposed to the greatest risks and who confront the most extreme forms of stress. Thus for the riskiest sector of the army, this preventive safety net did not exist, and still does not exist.

The fact that selection is subject to limitations, even when objective, scientifically responsible tests are employed, was made abundantly clear during the Second World War. The armed forces of the United States, which in this respect however adopted a rather unique position, found itself obliged to exclude temporarily 2,354,000 men for various reasons from military service.[7]

New Tasks
Thus the first activities which were deployed by the military psychiatrists in the area of prevention were connected with the selection of recruits. But this was not to be their only task because, even in the British army where the resistance to psychiatry

was great, the military psychiatrists succeeded in extending their field of work. In the context of this book two of these new areas in particular deserve some attention, namely training and watching over morale.

One of the problems which basic training had to struggle with was the decreasing motivation of many recruits.[8] Although the greater part of these soldiers entered through the garrison gates with great enthusiasm, boredom was quick to set in. The psychiatrists who were called in for help maintained that this had to do with the traditionally structured way instruction was given. The recruits had to know everything about their weapons. They dismantled their rifles and reassembled them an endless number of times. On the other hand, they never got around to firing them. The advice of the psychiatrists was to begin the shooting lessons earlier in the training and only later to practice taking the weapons apart and putting them back together again.

Another piece of psychiatric advice had to do with preparation for battle, 'battle inoculation'. At the beginning of the war the idea had emerged in the army that the soldiers should be made ready for the battlefield by means of realistic exercises. This meant that the servicemen in traversing the assault course were confronted with blinding flashes and overwhelming noises. Unfortunately, the procedure did not result in making the men accustomed to battle but clearly the very contrary took place. Indeed, from the beginning the men involved were overcome with fear for their life. On the basis of psychiatric advice the program was then organized differently. Habituation was now built up on the principle of gradual exposure. At the beginning of the training only a relatively low level of noise was used and the terrifying thunder claps were kept for the final phase. The psychiatrists also taught the instructors that artificially stimulated feelings of hatred toward the enemy could not be brought about in a short period of time. Well-meaning officers had attempted to achieve this, among other things, by scattering offal from a slaughterhouse over the assault course. In practice this as well only provoked terror and did not lead to feelings of hatred toward the Germans.

In addition, the assignment the psychiatrists received to watch over morale was important. Thus they set about making realistic radio programs and documentary films intended for the troops overseas. Indeed, as it appeared, propaganda programs which presented all too rosy a picture of the situation at home had a contrary effect. It only resulted in uncertainty and distrust of one's own authorities.

A completely new challenge was posed by the women who flooded into the armed forces *en masse* during the Second World War. A special problem emerged concerning the women who were employed for other than housekeeping and administrative duties. For example, many female military personnel operated the radio equipment which played so crucial a role in tracking and destroying the German bombers. After a certain amount of time, those involved in this work were troubled by an intensely heightened interest in 'feminine matters of dress and appearance'. Likewise, the rumor began to circulate that the radio equipment emitted rays which caused sterility. The military psychiatrists were familiar with this phenomenon. Similar rumors had circulated among the male soldiers for centuries.

Anxiety about becoming impotent can be considered one of the basic military fears. New medicines and vaccines all too often released a stream of rumors in which the chief element of threat from these new acquisitions concerned male sexuality. This was also the reason why many Allied soldiers refused to take their anti-malaria pills. In the first instance this form of 'sabotage' met with very little understanding on the part of the medical service. When the causes behind this behavior became known, the doctors involved launched an information campaign by means of which the problem was eventually brought under control.

After psychiatry and psychology demonstrated that the sciences dealing with the human mind could be of value to the military, it was the turn of the social sciences to prove their worth. The Second World War gave them their chance. This development was to be chiefly an American phenomenon. This was by no means a coincidence. It was particularly in the United States that the army leadership had considerable experience with absorbing the 'know-how' that the social sector had to offer. This tradition, which went back to the Civil War, made possible an amazingly rapid development of the armed forces. An additional factor was that on the eve of the Second World War the social sciences can be characterized as being extremely oriented toward practical application. American sociologists were more accustomed to function as social engineers than their European colleagues.[9]

In order to make optimal use of the services of the social scientists, the military leadership decided to concentrate the expertise they had incorporated into the armed forces. This was achieved in the Research Branch of the Information and Education Division, US Army. Two main currents of American sociology were in fact represented here: public opinion researchers and industrial sociologists. In the egalitarian American society public opinion from way back had played a different role than in the more hierarchically structured societies of Europe. The Americans attached great importance to it and saw it as one of the pillars of democratic government. When the mass production of goods began to increase, many firms quickly came to appreciate the value of market research as well. During the interwar years political parties and business companies came to make intensive use of public opinion researchers. The establishment of The American Institute of Public Opinion by George Gallup in 1935 can be considered a milestone in this development.

The first military activities that were undertaken by these researchers consisted of applying what they had previously done in civilian society. They investigated what the soldiers thought about certain things, for example what they thought about their winter clothing, and why they disliked certain things such as taking anti-malaria pills. Gradually, however, they went further and as the war proceeded, deeper research was carried out into the psyche of the servicemen. For example, at a certain point the fears that soldiers experienced were studied. This included carefully establishing which particular weapons of the enemy actually caused fear. In measuring this capacity to inspire fear, the distinction was made between soldiers who had real experience of the weapon systems in question and those who had not. And the manifestations of fear were studied. What percentage of soldiers had trouble with heart palpitations and what percentage experienced excessive sweating, etc.? The questions that were posed were not only about the enemy's weapons but about the enemy himself. How did one picture the enemy? Everything was measured, from the estimated competence to the supposed cruelty of the Japanese and the German opponents.

Naturally, in this mass of statistics views about one's own military organization were not left out of consideration. The front line soldiers could say what they thought about the echelons working behind the lines. In addition, they could give their judgment about the quality of their own officers. There was no doubt that research on combat motivation was extremely important. Why were soldiers prepared to put their life in jeopardy? Did ideals play a role in this or was it a question of feelings of hatred that had developed toward the enemy?

The researchers in the Research Branch did not limit themselves to the American army. In 1944 they were employed to investigate the effects that Allied propaganda had had on German soldiers. For this purpose Edward Shils and Morris Janowitz organized an inquiry among German deserters and prisoners of war. What they discovereed, among other things, was that the Allied psychological warfare that aimed at encouraging German soldiers to surrender and desert was only effective with servicemen who no longer belonged to close-knit primary groups. It appeared that the feeling of solidarity present in small groups was the cement which allowed the *Wehrmacht* to maintain its strength to the bitter end.[10]

This last contribution brings us to the second group of social scientists who were incorporated into the army, the industrial sociologists. In the United States industrial sociology came into being during the inter-war years, in 1927 to be precise. That year, in the factory of General Electric in Hawthorne, experiments were carried out which were intended to increase productivity. All sorts of variables to do with the work surroundings were investigated to determine their influence on work behavior. Since the results posed a puzzle for the researchers, the help of the sociologist Elton Mayo was sollicited. The latter came to a surprising conclusion after he had intensively studied the workers in question. Mayo 'discovered' what has since then been referred to as the informal group. The significance that this group had for the level of performance of individual members was great. After the Hawthorne study, American sociologists acquired an enormous interest in personal, face-to-face contacts in the work place. Work groups and the functionaries in charge of these units became the object of study *par excellence* of the industrial sociologists.

That these scientists also pointed to the fundamental importance of primary groups within the military organization was therefore not particularly surprising. Rather, it would have been extraordinarily bizarre if the researchers had ignored this phenomenon in a context in which men are completely dependent on one another for their very survival. If there is any one place where primary groups can flourish and show their worth, certainly it is in an army during wartime.

The various findings that were collected by the social scientists were published and also applied in policies, at least in part. During the war a whole series of brochures was published in which it was reported how the American soldier thought about a wide range of subjects. Thus it could be made attractive for the servicemen in question to give their point of view. In any case it was clear that the collected statistics were not simply destined to sit in a desk drawer. The army leadership also found this course of events useful since one quickly acquired insight into all sorts of matters which could have a positive or negative influence on morale. Along with the brochures just mentioned, a work in four stout volumes was published in which Samuel Stouffer and others systematically presented the chief research results. These volumes, which appeared under the title *The American Soldier*, constitute a classic of military sociology.

Thus during the Second World War various experts, in particular psychiatrists, psychologists and social scientists, were active in the area of prevention. The prevention of combat exhaustion was only one subdivision of a much broader policy which aimed at influencing behavior on the battlefield in general. This situation continued after the war and is still current at present. The underlying idea is that the factors which exercise a positive influence on this behavior can, in the reverse sense, lead to ineffective behavior as in the case of combat exhaustion.

Colonel Gregory Belenky, who is attached to the Walter Reed Army Institute for Research in Washington, D.C., offers a good illustration of this line of reasoning. Belenky maintains that behavior on the battlefield can be represented on a scale. The two extremes consist of battle shock and heroism, whereas effective action is located between these poles. The form of behavior that will be displayed will depend on the individual qualities of the soldier, the characteristics of the unit in question, and the nature and intensity of the battles waged. Figure 2 provides a representation of Belenky's line of reasoning in the form of a graph.

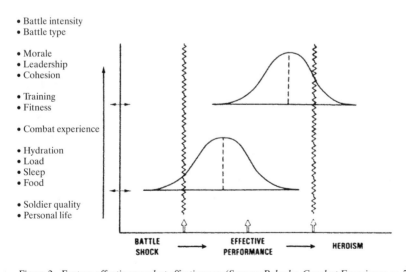

Figure 2. Factors affecting combat effectiveness (Source: Belenky, Combat Experience, p. 71)

The curve in the graph shows the distribution of behavioral variation which occurs in a given unit. Improvement of one of the variables on the vertical axis, for example higher morale or better leadership, leads to a shift of the distribution to the right. In the ideal situation the cases of battle shock will have disappeared, while heroic actions will have become typical. Lieutenant-Colonel Scott-Jackson, who testified before the War Office Committee of Inquiry into Shell Shock in 1922, would have been in full agreement with these conclusions reached in 1986.

However, in the American army one was perfectly aware that ideal situations rarely if ever occurred and that combat stress, in all its gradations, would continue to exist.[11] With this in mind the American army started up a program in 1985 which aimed at an integrated approach to combat stress. The following year this program was implemented through the inclusion in the US Army Field Manual of the training package 'Management of Stress in Army Operations'. The American approach is integrated because every individual and all subunits are involved in the assessment of the problem. Moreover, on the basis of historical experience it is assumed that stress management should be put in practice not only during, but before and after, combat operations. Servicemen learn to recognize and control the signs of stress both in themselves and in others in all kinds of circumstances. In this connection simple techniques of self-control are practiced which the soldier can have recourse to in case of emergency. This would include techniques for inducing relaxation, auto-suggestion and meditation. In stress counseling one learns how to help a buddy to control his stress reactions. This system of stress management has been a source of inspiration for other NATO countries including the Netherlands.

The Army as a Mirror
Of all this preventive work, which was taken very seriously expecially during the Second World War, what has filtered through to civilian society? After that war military psychiatry was not put on trial. Quite the opposite was the case. In books and learned journals, at congresses and symposia, society was informed of the successes that had been achieved in the army. The pretensions were not small. Just as the psychiatrists had previously claimed the whole military organization as their work terrain, now with equal ease they claimed the whole of society as their field of activity. In this respect the army became a mirror which was held up to the rest of society. What had been achieved there in the way of primary, secondary and tertiary prevention, could serve as an example for society at large.

The British psychiatrist J.R. Rees, whom we mentioned earlier, expressed some rather explicit ideas in this regard. In his book *The Shaping of Psychiatry by War*, published in 1945, he indicated how society could profit from the experiences gathered during the war. Thus he was in favor of appointing regional and district psychiatrists. They should be added to the already existing in-patient and out-patient facilities. They would be charged with maintaining contacts with schools and industries, and should also have a task to fulfill in ambulatory patient care. More ambitious still was Rees' proposal for creating at the national level a system to draw up an inventory of all industrial jobs and to asses them. Subsequently, by means of selection procedures the population could be assigned to the different functions, just as had happened in the American armed forces. With regard to the dumb men, Rees hoped they would remain in the agricultural companies after the war. Then society would be delivered from an important social problem group and in this way a further step would be taken in solving the problem of hereditarily determined mental disabilities. For subnormal women employment could undoubtedly be found in the housekeeping sector if sufficient effort was made to do so.

Finally, we would like to mention Rees' proposal to revise the recruitment procedures for the respectable professions. Rees wished to assign a role to the psychiatrist in admitting candidates to professional and executive work positions. The political sector was not to be excluded either:

It is a legitimate phantasy that a truly democratic country may in the future choose its legislators on grounds of personality and character instead of selecting them for those reasons that now obtain. Our present methods of selection for this important work of government can hardly be said to be altogether satisfactory.[12]

Given the strong class differences which characterized British society, this proposal was not only bold but was quite unrealistic.

Some psychiatrists went still one step further than Rees. These psychiatrists felt that the prevention and cure of mental illness should no longer be the only task of mental health care. After 1945 this branch of care should also aim at the prevention of a new war. The goal was to produce citizens of the world who were capable of living together in peace.

Not every psychiatrist was gripped by this urge for innovation. There were serious doubts within the professional discipline about the feasibility of attaining these horizons sketched by Rees and others. In the Netherlands the Utrecht professor Rümke took up a clear position against the innovators. Rümke wanted psychiatry to limit itself to the study and treatment of sick people. According to this professor, his professional colleagues did not dispose over specific expertise regarding healthy people. His fear that the psychiatrists would substitute psychiatry for communal life has turned out to be ungrounded.

With hindsight it may be affirmed that these lofty ideas did not get much further than the particular publications and congresses we have mentioned. All this had scarcely any significance for the practice of post-war mental health care in Europe and the United States. After the war the psychiatric institutions continued as before. At the same time the out-patient sector expanded, following in fact the lines that had already been traced in the inter-war period. The only effect which can be attributed to all these high-flown plans consists of a possible increase of respectability on the part of mental health care. Truly fundamental changes did not take place in the field until the 1960s, i.e. in the period when antipsychiatry first made its views heard.

In that turbulent period, during which psychiatry was put on trial (see Chapter V), various authors once again brought the achievements of military psychiatry to the attention of their co-workers in the field of mental health care. In 1967 W. Hausman and P. Rioch published an article with the revealing title *Military Psychiatry: A Prototype of Social and Preventive Psychiatry in the United States*. John Talbott published a study in 1969 with a no less revealing title *Community Psychiatry in the Army. History, Practice and Application to Civilian Psychiatry*. In both articles the historical merits of military psychiatry, from the First World War up to and including Vietnam, are enlarged upon. As much as these authors were well aware of the special aspects of the military situation, they none the less were convinced that quite a number of recommendations could be applied to civilian society. Talbott was of the opinion that as many as ten lessons could be learned from the military experiences:

1. To understand or treat an individual best, you cannot separate him from his family, his culture, or his community.
2. The caretakers of the community are of extreme importance. Civilian community leaders, police, teachers, visiting nurses, recreation workers, etc., are as important as military commanding officers, chaplains, legal officers, Red Cross workers, and dispensary physicians.
3. Loss of time and effectiveness can be markedly reduced by prompt, proximate treatment of emotional illness.
4. Environmental manipulation can keep a large number of neurotics and psychotics at work and living within their communities.
5. Social and situational factors are frequently of equal or greater importance in precipitating malfunctioning than personality or psychodynamic factors.
6. High levels of expectation, along with a healer's desire to help, can be very effective treatment tools.
7. We should not become fixated on the 'motivation' for help while ignoring the unconscious or preconscious 'cry for help' – be it on an individual or group basis.
8. Social contact with the consultee can be most important. Consultation is not treatment nor supervision, and a cordial off-the-job relationship is an under-utilized and over-depreciated tool.
9. The recommendations of psychiatrists, psychologists and other social workers carry tremendous weight, often in excess of their importance. It is important not to use this influence to ax-grind or remake the world.
10. Social workers, psychologists, and psychiatrists can cooperate and learn from each other.[13]

This message was in fact no different from what Talbott's colleagues had already presented to society in the 1940s. Only lesson number nine betrays any hint of modesty, which was not yet present in the early post-war years. It would soon enough become clear that this modesty was appropriate in another respect. At the time of the publication of Talbott's article, the first Vietnam veterans presented themselves to the mental health care therapists. The range of problems associated with this group made it clear that the possibilities of psychiatric care in the army had been greatly overestimated. This subject will be dealt with further in Chapter X.

Conclusion

After the psychiatrists in the First World War had shown that they could be of service to the army in treating soldiers who had suffered a breakdown, in the following war the next step was taken to implement prevention. Only in the American armed forces had the introduction of preventive and curative activity occurred more or less simultaneously and that had been during the final phase of the First World War.

An important part of prevention had to do with selection. In this case selection took place not only in order to keep potential psychiatric patients out of the army. It was also a method for distributing the soldiers in an optimal way throughout a military organization that had become extremely complex. The Anglo-Saxon countries had great trust in objective psychological tests. On the basis of these tests it was determined where someone should be assigned in the army. In the case of the Germans, however, the officers in the army units played a crucial role in deciding where personnel would be employed.

During the Second World War, the social scientists also got the chance to demonstrate their usefulness for running an army. In particular the American army made grateful use of the information that had been gathered by the sociologists and psychologists.

After 1945 American industrial sociology, also having been influenced by the research carried out during the war, entered upon a phase of accelerated development. Between 1945 and 1960 countless studies on industry and subdivisions of industry appeared in which careful attention was given to styles of management and the functioning of small groups. Thus the experience within the army acted as a catalyst in this field of research. Meanwhile, the systematic study of military organization itself came to an abrupt end with demobilization. The researchers returned to their institutes and left the army to fend for itself. *The American Soldier* was finally published in 1949 by Princeton University Press and not by the American army. After 1945 military psychiatry could claim, with a certain degree of justification, that experience had been acquired in the army regarding the functioning of organized social-psychiatric care. This system the military psychiatrists held up as an example for civilian society. The actual influence emanating from the military model was, however, quite limited. Fundamental changes only began in mental health care in the 1960s, and military psychiatry had little or nothing to do with these developments.

X - When the War is Over (PTSD)

Introduction

The First World War had a considerable number of surprises in store for the conservatively oriented British psychiatric establishment. Chief among these was the fact that even perfectly normal, stable young men, it had to be admitted, could become shell shock patients. Hereditary predisposition, as it turned out, was not a necessary precondition.

American psychiatry was caught by surprise in no less disconcerting a way by the war in Vietnam. In complete contradiction to expectations tens of thousands of soldiers who had trouble with all sorts of behavioral disorders presented themselves after demobilization. The phenomenon was by no means a new one. It had occurred in all the great wars of the twentieth century. Once again it turned out that the doctors involved had tended to misjudge the length of duration of the disorders that had arisen in the course of combat. It was far from true that every soldier came to experience a spontaneous recovery once peace had been concluded. Moreover, there were servicemen who only began to have problems for the first time long after they had been discharged.

And yet, the state of affairs in the Vietnam War may rightly be considered exceptional. What was unique in this war was precisely that there were so few soldiers who fell victim to combat stress during the conflict. At the time some leading military psychiatrists held the view that the problem of the psychologically wounded soldier had been brought under control. The structure of organized social psychiatry appeared to be based on a solid foundation in the American armed forces. The surprise which was to follow proved to be not only great but extremely disturbing as well.

The situation around the Vietnam veterans was also special because the problems involved manifested themselves within a complicated socio-political context. American society had become intensely divided by the war. At the beginning of the 1970s the popularity of the military intervention had fallen to absolute zero. As a result of this and other developments, the veterans came to find themselves in a precarious social situation. They had taken part in a mistaken war. They could forget about knocking at the door of the agencies that were normally in charge of offering help to veterans. The old war veterans, from the Korean and the Second World War, looked with contempt on these young kids returning from Vietnam.

From this position as underdogs the Vietnam veterans set about taking action: against the continuation of military intervention and on behalf of improving the image of the Vietnam veterans. An effort was also made to obtain help for the psychological and social problems that a certain number of them were struggling with. This last objective required formal medical recognition of their disorders. The recognition they were seeking came in 1980 when American psychiatry accepted the diagnosis of 'post-traumatic stress disorder' (PTSD). In this chapter the contents of this diagnostic category and how it came to be established will be sketched. But in order to understand this development better, it is first necessary to consider briefly certain aspects of the Vietnam War and the nature of American military psychiatry at that time.

Vietnam

Between 1964 and 1973, 2.9 million American soldiers served in Vietnam. On the American side approximately 300,000 servicemen were wounded, and 58,000 died – 47,000 as a result of enemy fire, the rest through accidents, illness and friendly fire.[1] The psychologically wounded soldier only played a limited role in all this. In a lecture given before the American Psychiatric Association (APA) in May 1966 two army psychatrists were able to present their audience with some reassuring information. Only 5 percent of all evacuations had taken place for psychiatric or neurological reasons. During the Second World War the figure had been 23 percent. For the first two years of the war the official statistic was three psychiatric cases out of a thousand men per annum. Later this figure would rise but in the end the average only came to twelve men out of a thousand per annum. In fact this meant that Vietnam provided no more psychiatric cases than occurred in the segment of the army that remained in the United States.[2]

Various psychiatrists, including Peter Bourne whom we have already mentioned, attempted to explain this phenomenon.[3] Two main elements regularly recur in the explanations that were offered: the character of the war and the package of preventive measures that were implemented by the army. In connection with the first factor the American superiority in heavy weapons must be borne in mind. The GIs were only rarely exposed to heavy artillery shelling or bombardments where they were forced into the role of helpless victims. This was the lot of their opponents. Moreover, the fighting in Vietnam, just as in every guerilla war, had an intermittent character. Combat could be intense but the duration was pretty much always limited. After strenuous effort there followed a period of rest.

The preventive measures were comprehensive and diverse. A lot of attention went to creating recreational facilities. One had the choice of going to a bar, a brothel or a sports field. And naturally any combination of the three was possible. In addition, every soldier had the right to a week's leave which could be spent in Thailand, Hongkong or Hawaii. And thought was also given to contacts with the home front. The military organization disposed over excellent post and telecommunications, by means of which soldiers could remain informed of what went on among their family and friends. Moreover, the military psychiatrists set great store by the fixed practice of the one-year tour of duty. This practice meant that the individual soldier only had to serve in Vietnam for a limited period of time, namely one year. After that amount of time had elapsed his safety was guaranteed. Adherence to this time-limit was observed with the uttermost bureaucratic efficiency. Servicemen were on occasion virtually discharged in the middle of a battle because their last day of duty was up. By means of this system it was hoped that the notorious 'old sergeant syndrome', which had been so characteristic of the Second World War, would not have a chance this time. Finally, on top of all this one should mention that the military organization did its best to publicize knowledge about combat stress and everything connected with it. This approach had begun after the Korean War. In this connection ordinary military doctors, chaplains and commanding officers were given refresher courses or updated information. Thus the military psychiatrists in Vietnam had transferred a part of their task to others, which fit in with the ideas that General William C. Westmoreland, the American supreme commander in Vietnam, held about community psychiatry.

The psychiatrists themselves were only scantily represented in Vietnam. In 1968 only eleven of the sixty-eight psychiatrists stationed in overseas territories were on duty in Vietnam. And yet, at that moment there were upwards of 200,000 American servicemen in the latter country. In fact, the largest number of these psychiatrists (29) were sitting safely in Germany where the Cold War was in progress.[4] Thus individually each one of the psychiatrists who was on duty in Vietnam had an enormous number of troops to attend to. In 1968 Edward M. Colbach, along with a colleague on loan from the air force, were responsible for providing psychiatric help to 45,000 men. Consequently, on the whole the American army was not equipped to deal with any rather large groups of psychologically wounded soldiers. In the first instance such groups did not appear and it seemed that the policies of prevention had worked. Nonetheless, not everyone was so sure about the future. Even the psychiatrists who gave the previously mentioned lecture to the American Psychiatric Association – a lecture which overflowed with faith in the possibilities of this professional discipline – were not wholly reassured:

The absence of combat exhaustion may have to do with seasoned and motivated troops; if this is true, we might expect a change if 'greener' or less motivated troops replace those who have completed their tours.[5]

One did not have to wait very long for the arrival of units of this sort. After 1966 'green', poorly motivated units began to be more and more prevalent in the battlefield. Yet even then the psychologically wounded soldier continued to play a limited role, at least in Vietnam itself. In the United States increasingly more veterans came forward who claimed that they had been psycholgically damaged by the war. How was this possible? Were the veterans impostors, or did the preventive measures not really work as they were supposed to in theory?

Let's begin by considering 'the one-year tour'. This well-intentioned system had a number of unintended consequences, both for morale and for fighting power. In many soldiers this fixed policy evoked a survival mentality which was purely oriented toward the individual. The soldiers, particularly during the last months of their tour, adjusted their whole behavior with the purpose of reaching that final day. Meanwhile, winning the war and the lot of the unit one belonged to assumed less importance. This mentality, along with the accompanying individual replacement system, also created a significant barrier to the emergence of a clear sense of group cohesion. Vietnam produced 'lonely' soldiers *par excellence* who did not have a good capacity to look after each other and provide one another with psychological support. In this regard the American army was the exact opposite of what the *Wehrmacht* had been.

A second weak point had to do with the recruiting system. The way the rules regarding conscription were applied resulted in fighting units acquiring a very specific composition. In these units the young and the underprivileged were predominantly represented. The average age of 'the combat soldier' was nineteen. In addition, the soldier in question generally possessed a low level of intelligence and had not been through schooling of any significance. His social background was that of the lower strata of American society. The sad thing is that precisely these servicemen were exposed to the greatest ordeal. It was they who went out on patrol and did all the actual fighting. Those who were older and better educated were primarily occupied with providing the support services.

A third and final factor which should be mentioned here was the unpopularity of the war. From the very beginning the war was contested, and after 1968 one could find few Americans who believed in a good outcome and did not have doubts about the legitimacy of the military intervention. The excellent post and telecommunications saw to it that this prevalent attitude on the home front could also reach the troops. This can be seen as a textbook example of an unintended effect of policy. Naturally, the question presents itself as to why, in this context, the American army experienced such small numbers of psychiatric losses. Various explanations of this fact are possible.

It appears to be of great importance that at this time the American army was afflicted by two other plagues, namely a low willingness to fight and an excessive use of alcohol and drugs.[6] In Chapter II it was noted that in the 1970s the Americans had to deal with cases of open refusal to fight and fragging. Clearly, the level of discipline was very poor. In addition, the use of alcohol, and later drugs, presented a very big problem. In 1970 10,000 servicemen were prosecuted for the use of hard drugs. Actual use was probably far higher. The following year it was revealed that as many as 50.9 percent of servicemen had smoked marihuana, whereas 28.5 percent had taken heroin or opium. No less than 30.8 percent had experimented with other psychedelic drugs. Faulty discipline and drug addiction – these were the main problems the American army had to deal with. In this context the manifestation of combat stress was not all that much of an issue. The phenomenon, just as had been the case in pre-industrial armies, was covered up in the face of more urgent matters. One could well imagine that the psychiatrists were not adequately on the look-out for the psychologically wounded soldier and consequently they perceived very few.

It is also perfectly possible that the latter were classified and treated under different names, such as desertion, insubordination and drug addiction. Thus the low figures relating to psychiatric losses may well have been doctored.

A completely different explanation, which has been given by Mardi Horowitz, concerns the character of the conflict and in particular the alternation of intense pressure with periods of rest.[7] According to Horowitz, the servicemen were reasonably able to deal with these short periods of stress. Their repression mechanisms made it possible for them to function normally during the war. After their homecoming and the normalization of their life that ensued, the repression mechanisms began to slacken, as it were, which meant that their war experiences could once again emerge in their consciousness. Thus in this viewpoint delayed stress reactions are characteristic of certain kinds of combat situations. Guerilla wars as well as many UN operations, such as those carried out in Somalia, Lebanon and Bosnia, can be included in this category. If Horowitz is right, the phenomenon of delayed reactions may well prove to be the chief problem confronted by military psychiatry in this day and age.

The Struggle for Recognition and Help

In a rich and prosperous America the servicemen who had brought Japan and Germany to their knees were not forgotten.[8] They could count on receiving not only financial support but the necessary medical and social care as well. The Veterans Administration (VA) was charged with the implementation of the care in question. This agency managed the policlinics and medical insurance schemes that were specially created for the veterans. The VA operated within juridical and financial frameworks defined by the government. The House Committee on Veterans' Affairs played an important role in setting up these frameworks. The veterans themselves exercised considerable influence through their own organizations, one of the best known of which was the American Legion.

The above-mentioned congressional committee, the VA and the veterans organizations together formed what was known as 'the iron triangle'. To begin with there was no place within this system for the Vietnam veterans. This was initially the case because the system of care had not been aimed at them. The provisions of the VA had grown along with the needs of the Second World War veterans who were steadily getting older. With the passage of time the latter were experiencing ailments which were exlusively connected with aging and had nothing to do with their period of military service. Addressing the needs of the young Vietnam veterans would have meant that the system of assistance would have had to set itself other priorities and up until then no one felt the inclination to do that.

Part of the problem was that this group of newcomers was not particularly liked. They were, after all, the representatives of the lost war, and no one had any sympathy for their predicament. Another element was the paradoxical fact that belief in a final American victory was seriously shaken by the Tet-offensive in 1968, despite this having been, from a purely military point of view, one of the biggest American victories. The communist propaganda machine, which operated with extraordinary success, was able to create a very different image, one of the Americans as large-scale losers.

The veterans were also not popular because they had participated in a dirty war. Of course, guerilla wars are always dirty but in the case of Vietnam there were some additional factors. For instance, the Americans, in contrast to many European countries, were not accustomed to this kind of a war. After 1945 France, Britain and the Netherlands had all been involved in conflicts like this associated with the process of decolonization. It was also significant that the dirty aspects of the Vietnam War were shown so openly on the home front. In previous guerilla wars, only those who were directly involved were aware of what went on. Now the whole population, on a daily basis, could see on television what actually takes place in a real war. The extent of the devastation, the executions, everything was shown. Vietnam was the first war that was fought out before the eyes of the camera. The American army has learned that this is not the way to maintain support on the home front.

Similarly, the legitimacy of the military intervention in Vietnam was problematic. The Dutch had gone out to Indonesia to restore law and order among the local population who had invited them to do so. At least that was the official standpoint. Thus the Dutch had also spoken of 'police actions' at that time. The French attempted to suppress an uprising in Algeria which they considered to be a province of France. What the Americans had to do in Vietnam was much harder to legitimize. This was especially true of the 1960s when independence movements and freedom fighters enjoyed an enormous popularity among young people in the West.

Consequently, the Vietnam veterans found themselves in a rather unenviable position. There was no way they could reckon on getting psychiatric help; the gap between them and the mental health care system was simply too great. In all honesty it should be said that the isolation of the veterans was in part the result of their own conscious choice. As a group they had learned to mistrust the government and everything that was affiliated with it. The result of this was that many refused to attend the clinics of the Veterans Administration. Instead, they chose a system of care that was set up under their own control.

In this case the initiative was taken by a small organization, all of whose members had a manifest aversion to the war: the Vietnam Veterans Against the War (VVAW). This organization had set itself the primary task of promoting debate on the American intervention in Vietnam. At the same time the attempt was made to convey greater understanding to the public about the difficult position the repatriated soldiers found themselves in. In order to be able to offer the veterans some concrete help in the short run, in 1971 contact was sought with two psychiatrists who had made a name in the anti-war movement, Robert Lifton and Chaim Shaton.

These psychiatrists began to organize psychiatric sessions that were especially aimed at Vietnam veterans. In New York, and later in other places, informal 'rap groups' were set up which attracted hundreds of interested persons. In these groups the spirit of antipsychiatry prevailed.[9] Which subjects would be discussed and what therapeutic strategies would be adopted was decided collectively. Thus these 'rap groups' represented a completely different form of group therapy from the variant that had created a sensation in military psychiatry since the Second World War. They were informal, democratic and free of obligations. But of course these are all characteristics which would be difficult to reconcile with a military setting.

In the meantime, the VVAW had not forgotten its other, more political objectives. In the Senate Alan Cranston, a staunch opponent of the war, proved to be ready to stand up for the Vietnam veterans. Thanks to his efforts, in 1971 the Senate approved a bill that aimed at providing money for special aid programs on behalf of Vietnam veterans. But the bill was defeated in Congress after the official veterans organizations came out in fierce opposition against it. The same thing happened again in 1973 and in 1975.

With the election of Jimmy Carter as president, a new period began for the Vietnam veterans. In 1977 Carter appointed Max Cleland, himself a Vietnam veteran, as director of the Veterans Administration. In the years that immediately followed there began a complicated process of political horse trading which formally came to an end on 13 July 1979. On that day, namely, the president signed a law which released funds for setting up an adapted aid program. At the same time a particular week was designated during which tribute would be paid to the veterans (Vietnam Veterans Week). But even then there was a certain air of reluctance and the price that Congress exacted for this gesture of rehabilitation was high. The *Washington Post* noted this with poignant clarity:

As their price for approving the special treatment for the... Vietnam vet, members of the House Veterans' Affairs Committee have demanded from the president and the Veterans Administration veto power over all significant future VA hospital and medical facility construction... Next to tipping over a wheelchair, it is hard to imagine a shabbier way for Congress to mark Vietnam Veterans Week.[10]

Nevertheless, in 1979 the establishment of new centers for veterans was begun. In November of that year the first one was opened. Two years later there were already 137 of them operating throughout the whole country. Still, the fact remains that by 1990, for one reason or another, only half of the veterans suffering from PTSD had received any real help.

The Struggle over the Label

In 1952 the American Psychiatric Association (APA) for the first time published a manual by means of which psychiatrists could establish precisely what was wrong with someone. In the *Diagnostic and Statistical Manual* (DSM-I), as it was entitled, the category 'gross stress reaction' was included. This was described as a temporary condition which was caused by exceptionally stressful situations such as war and catastrophes.

Thus in the first version of the DSM it was recognized that soldiers could suffer psychological damage in war. This was also true of servicemen who had never previously been under treatment or had to struggle with psychological difficulties. But these problems would only be of a temporary nature and after the war ended they would automatically disappear. This sort of optimistic viewpoint is more or less inherent in the stress paradigm. Indeed, according to this approach behavioral disorders are conceived as normal reactions to abnormal events. What then could be more obvious than to assume that everything would be alright once the circumstances were normal again? This assumption also has a certain empirical basis to it. At the end of a war everybody wants to go home. Patients no longer have an interest in prolonging their illnesses. Psychiatrists want empty hospitals because they as well wish to return to their jobs in civilian society. Seen in this light, it is understandable that both after the First and the Second World War the number of psychiatric patients, after hostilities had stopped, greatly decreased.

In the DSM-I one encounters the great therapeutic optimism which had flourished among the military psychiatrists of the Second World War. After all, the latter had shown that, with the famous basic principles as their guiding standard, they were able to restore to active service almost every soldier who suffered a breakdown. This reassuring attitude came at just the right moment, since by that time the United States was involved in the Korean War.

Manuals like the DSM are not intended for eternity. They have to be adjusted at regular intervals in order to take account of new insights. The first important adjustment occurred in 1968. For the purpose of our study, it is of relevance that in the edition of that year the category 'gross stress reaction' was scrapped. From that moment on experiences in war no longer counted as causes of psychiatric disturbances, as far as establishment psychiatry in the United States was concerned. Of course, what is paradoxical is that this new edition of the manual appeared in the year of the Tet-offensive, i.e. in the same year that the failure of American military intervention in Vietnam began to become apparent. Thus precisely at that moment it seemed that psychiatry was sweeping the war under the carpet. How is one to explain this situation?

The dominant position which psychoanalysis managed to achieve for itself in post-war America appears to have been an important cause. In traditional psychoanalytical theory only traumas, and then only sexual traumas from one's childhood, are held responsible for serious, long-term psychological disturbances. Traumatic experiences which occur in a later stage of development cannot be easily fitted into this intellectual scheme. Consequently, for most psychoanalysts soldiers who suffered a breakdown had been predisposed to do so by their childhood experiences (see Chapter VII). The dossiers which these psychiatrists put together on traumatized Vietnam veterans were full of details on the childhood of the latter and the situation in their family. One will search in vain to find information about the time they spent in Vietnam, because data of that kind were considered irrelevant. In short, scrapping the category 'gross stress reaction' was perfectly understandable if we take into consideration what was fashionable at that moment in psychiatry – namely, psychoanalysis.

From Vietnam itself no contradiction to this point of view appeared to emerge. As we noted earlier, the number of psychiatric cases due to combat stress remained low during the first years. Moreover, Peter Bourne in his on-the-spot study even explained why this was so. The individual soldiers turned out to possess adequate defense mechanisms for dealing with stress (see Chapter VI). In an article published in 1970 in the *American Journal of Psychiatry* Bourne, full of confidence, speaks not only about the war in Vietnam but about future conflicts:

...that the average soldier is capable of making a highly effective adaptation to the combat environment at both a psychological and physiological level... As a result there is reason to be optimistic that psychiatric casualties need never again become a major cause of attrition in the United States military in a combat zone.[11]

And so this great propagandist for the physiological approach to behavioral disorders and the psychoanalysts were in agreement in one respect: shell shock and combat exhaustion were phenomena that belonged to the past. For modern warfare these and other concepts were no longer necessary.

Actual developments, however, were to prove otherwise. Two years later, in 1972, Bourne had to acknowledge that his earlier conceptions concerning the imperviousness of Vietnam veterans to traumatic stress had been premature:

That the incidence of emotional problems, even the level of hospitalization, is so high among today's veterans, makes depressingly hollow the claim that we have cut combat psychiatric attrition to a minimum. To merely delay the time at which the peak incidence of psychiatric breakdown occurs is not a notable accomplishment.[12]

This new insight was not only the result of the agitation of Vietnam veterans, although the importance of these actions can scarcely be overestimated. New information from other directions was also brought to bear. During the 1960s increasingly more longitudinal studies were published in which veterans of the Second World War and Korea were observed over many years. From this research it emerged that some veterans had to struggle with persistent disorders which continued to occur up to twenty years after the war. European and Israeli psychiatrists discovered the same persistence among survivors of the concentration camps and former resistance fighters. These data indicated that the diagnosis 'gross stress reaction' should not have been scrapped, but actually should have been extended. By extending the diagnosis, proper recognition would be given to the possible duration characteristic of certain symptoms.

Along with these long-term studies, research findings now appeared based on studies of Vietnam veterans that had been carried out at the beginning of the 1970s. Chaim Shatan, in a series of newspaper articles, acquainted the broader public with the psychological problems that these veterans had to struggle with. He pointed out that the disorders which this group suffered only became manifest at a later time, namely from nine to thirty months after coming home. Shatan himself spoke of a 'post-Vietnam syndrome'. In 1973 Lifton published his book *Home from the War*. In it he gave an overview of the specific problems that were characteristic for the Vietnam veterans. At the same time he reported in his book on the experiments that had been carried out with 'rap groups'. One year later Mardi Horowitz and George Solomon predicted in the *Journal of Social Issues* that their colleagues in mental health care would, in the short term, be confronted with veterans who experienced delayed stress reaction.[13]

Thus there was no lack of new insights. Nevertheless, Lifton and others were perfectly aware that there was simply not a sufficient level of available knowledge to guarantee reinstating this category of disorder in the DSM. For this purpose influence would have to be exerted on the American Psychiatric Association. With this goal in mind a group of experts from the field of mental health care joined together and formed the Vietnam Veterans Working Group (VVWG). The editorial committee which in 1976, at the request of the APA, was engaged in preparing the revised edition of DSM-II appeared to be open to the arguments presented by the VVWG. This group had proposed as a new diagnosis 'catastrophic stress disorder'. The disorder would then not only be applicable to Vietnam veterans, but to anyone who had been traumatized by an event that lay outside normal human experiences. This broad definition was necessary because the legacy of Vietnam still divided Americans, and Lifton and Shatan were seen to be strong supporters of the Vietnam veterans. Thus these authors had to make it clear that this was not simply an issue affecting the veterans. Consequently, in the arguments they put to the editiorial committee they made use of case histories of civilians who had been involved in fires, accidents and disasters. Presenting dossiers of Vietnam veterans alone as evidence would not have been sufficient.

Moreover, civilian society offered adequate proof to support the position that stress reactions could occur after long delay. One of the best documented events was the disaster which took place in 1972 in Buffalo Creek Valley, West Virginia.[14] In February of that year, after a prolonged rainfall a dam, which held back a large reservoir filled with water and mineral waste products, gave way. This breaching of a dyke, which destroyed sixteen towns, was responsible for the death of 125 people. Many of the survivors suffered trouble from nightmares for years and would feel the recurrence of strong anxieties whenever it began to rain. A group of victims started legal proceedings against the mine management which had been held responsible for all the damage that resulted from the bursting of the dam. In the trial that followed both the plaintiffs and the defense made use of psychiatrists in support of their divergent claims. The defense maintained, in full accord with prevailing scientific opinion, that the psychological problems of the plaintiffs could not be attributed to the catastrophe, but that these persons had been predisposed in their childhood to suffer the symptoms they now exhibited. On the other hand, the plaintiffs were able to show that virtually none of them had ever had anything to do with a psychiatrist or a social worker, whereas now virtually everyone of them had disorders. Moreover, their complaints varied from fits of rage to excessive consumption of alcohol. The final outcome was that the catastrophe could indeed be held responsible for the problems which had emerged among the victims. The facts concerning this and other disasters, such as a fire in a restaurant and the structural collapse of a discotheque, together with the available information pertaining to the Vietnam veterans, ultimately led to an adjustment being made in the DSM. The editorial committee in charge of revising the manual accepted the standpoint of Lifton and his camp in 1978. The proposed name for the new diagnosis, however, was not accepted, but it was changed to 'post-traumatic stress disorder' (abbreviated as PTSD).

PTSD

It is not surprising that in a manual to do with diagnosis which was prepared in the 1970s considerable attention was given to stress reactions. To avoid any misunderstandings it should be noted that not everyone who is confronted with threatening, stressful situations automatically suffers problems subsequently. However, this is sometimes the case and pathological reactions can occur.

In the manual three kinds of problems to do with adjustment and coping are distinguished. The 'adjustment disorder' includes a range of adjustment difficulties that can be the result of a great number of circumstances. The stress factor may have to do with marriage problems, moving one's home, the transition to a new job or a multiplicity of other matters which cause an individual to be confronted with a number of more or less threatening situations. The symptoms accompanying these adjustment problems are not described in detail. They can take numerous forms of manifestation such as feelings of anxiety, depression and an inability to maintain social contacts. Generally, the symptoms make their appearance quite quickly after the occurrence of the stress factor. The manual states that they should appear within three months.

The second category, the 'brief reactive psychosis', manifests itself much quicker, i.e. immediately after the occurrence of the stressful event. What is characteristic in this case is the presence of psychotic symptoms. It is possible, for example, that the individual in question experiences hallucinations or lives his or her life under certain delusions. Moreover, it is admitted in the DSM-III that knowledge about this syndrome is still limited because the only relevant studies that have been carried out are retrospective in character.

What is of particular interest for the subject of the present book is the third category, the 'post-traumatic stress disorder'. Put in general terms, in the case of PTSD one is dealing with reactions to very special occurrences. It is a question of experiences which do not form a normal part of a person's daily life. In this regard one may mention natural disasters, serious traffic accidents, rape and experiences in war. Specifically, it is a matter of PTSD if the individual who has been through something like this repeatedly relives the traumatic experience. Reliving a traumatic experience can occur in different ways. For example, certain Vietnam vete-

rans are known to be tormented by recurrent nightmares. The faces of women and
children they killed appear in their dreams. Members of the SS who were in charge
of exterminating Jews behind the lines on the eastern front were also well acquainted with this form of relived experience. The example of a completely different form of relived experience is presented by the British officer who is so well described by Pat Barker in one of her books on the First World War: *Regeneration*. The
officer in question had become as thin as a rake because whenever he was confronted with food, it made him throw up. Indeed, every meal invoked a specific image in his imagination. Each time he would re-experience the moment when, seeking cover from enemy fire, he had ended up in the presence of a dead soldier's
half-decomposed corpse and come to know the look and smell of death in this distressing manner.

Along with the relived experience an additional symptom is the compulsive
avoidance of the stimuli which accompanied the traumatic event or in some cases a
kind of general numbing. The victim becomes, as it were, benumbed and is no
longer capable of functioning socially. The tendency to avoid certain stimuli can be
manifested in a complete or partial memory loss, while the numbing can express itself in a feeling of detachment and the inability to give or receive affection.

Heightened irritability is the final characteristic feature of those suffering from
PTSD. This condition can express itself in fits of rage, sleep disorders and physiological reactions such as excessive sweating.

The above-mentioned symptoms can manifest themselves in an increased measure if the individual involved finds himself in a situation which evokes associations
with the original traumatic event. In the case of German veterans of the eastern
front, this could be an extremely cold winter. Many Vietnam veterans can suddenly
be transported in their mind back to the fighting in the jungle by a hot, humid summer's day. Official commemoration ceremonies and the unveiling of war monu-
ments can have a very detrimental effect on some veterans.

As appears in the outline presented on page 191 a patient does not have to display all the symptoms in order to be diagnosed as suffering from PTSD. It's always
a question of one or more forms of manifestation per category. The symptoms do
have to last more than one month. If this is not the case, then according to the manual a different diagnosis is required. Moreover, making the correct diagnosis, even
when all the criteria have been met, is not an easy matter. Indeed, sufferers of
PTSD, in most cases, also have to deal with fits of anxiety and moods of depression.
According to the DSM-III, these complaints can be so intense that diagnoses of
'anxiety disorder' or 'depressive disorder' are appropriate. Thus in the 1980 edition
of the DSM, where PTSD is spoken of for the first time, two subtypes were already
distinguished, namely the 'acute' and the 'chronic or delayed' types. In the first
case, the symptoms begin to manifest themselves within six months after the
trauma. Here the duration of the manifestations is limited to a half year. In the second category the symptoms last longer than a half year, while they also only first reveal themselves after six months. When the DMS-III was revised in 1987, this distinction was dropped. All that was stated was that, for the most part, the symptoms

---

Diagnostic criteria for 309.89 Post-traumatic Stress Disorder

A.   The person has experienced an event that is outside the range of usual human experience and that would be markedly distressing to almost anyone, e.g., serious threat to one's life or physical integrity; serious threat or harm to one's children, spouse, or other close relatives and friends; sudden destruction of one's home or community; or seeing another person who has recently been, or is being, seriously injured or killed as the result of an accident or physical violence.

B.   The traumatic event is persistently reexperienced in at least one of the following ways:

    (1)   recurrent and intrusive distressing recollections of the event (in young children, repetitive play in which themes or aspects of the trauma are expressed)

    (2)   recurrent distressing dreams of the event

    (3)   sudden acting or feeling as if the traumatic event were recurring (includes a sense of reliving the experience, illusions, hallucinations, and dissociative [flashback] episodes, even those that occur upon awakening or when intoxicated)

    (4)   intense psychological distress at exposure to events that symbolize or resemble an aspect of the traumatic event, including anniversaries of the trauma

C.   Persistent avoidance of stimuli associated with the trauma or numbing of general responsiveness (not present before the trauma), as indicated by at least three of the following criteria:

    (1)   efforts to avoid thoughts or feelings associated with the trauma

    (2)   efforts to avoid activities or situations that arouse recollections of the trauma

    (3)   inability to recall an important aspect of the trauma (psychogenic amnesia)

    (4)   markedly diminished interest in significant activities (in young children), loss of recently acquired developmental skills such as toilet training or language skills)

    (5)   feeling of detachment or estrangement from others

    (6)   restricted range of affect, e.g., unable to have loving feelings

    (7)   sense of a foreshortened future, e.g., does not expect to have a career, marriage, or children, or a long life

D.   Persistent symptoms of increased arousal (not present before the trauma), as indicated by at least two of the following:

    (1)   difficulty of falling or staying asleep

    (2)   irritability or outbursts of anger

    (3)   difficulty concentrating

    (4)   hypervigilance

    (5)   exaggerated startle response

    (6)   physiologic reactivity upon exposure to events that symbolize or resemble an aspect of the traumatic event (e.g., a woman who was raped in an elevator breaks out in a sweat when entering any elevator)

PTSD in DSM III

appear immediately or shortly after the trauma, but that it is also possible for there to be a period of latency which can last months or years.

Post-traumatic stress disorder is a rather colorless concept which does not stir the imagination – certainly if we compare it to such vivid terms as shell shock, trench neurosis and combat exhaustion. It is in fact the result of compromises which had to be made between various parties. Thus in America during the 1970s there was no room for recognition of a diagnostic category which was exclusively connected with casualties of the unpopular Vietnam War. This problem group could only be recognized as a subdivision of a far wider category of casualties due to traumatic events.

At the same time a balance had to be found between the complaints of these people and the demands of the welfare bureaucracy. Clearly, not every patient had to deal with the same problems. There were differences among patients both in terms of the relived experiences of trauma and avoidance of the accompanying stimuli. The same can be said concerning increased irritability, fits of anxiety and moods of depression. On the other hand, there were the demands of the agencies that were in charge of awarding compensation and providing benefits. These authorities asked for clarity, they wanted hard criteria by means of which it could be established whether someone was sick or not. The character of compromise regarding post-traumatic stress disorder is manifest in the following. In presenting the various symptoms the DMS-III does justice to the complexity of the illness. At the same time, however, exhibiting a fixed number of symptoms is prescribed in a bureaucratic manner for each category. For one reason or another this means, for example, that the patient may choose how he exhibits his increased irritability. Only this must occur in at least two different ways.

Compromises which are entered into after difficult negotiations often have something contrived or forced about them. The description of PTSD also suffers from this flaw. The compilers of the DSM-III wanted to offer certainty in an area where, given the available level of knowledge, this was simply not possible. Clear pronouncements were made about the moment when these symptoms should appear and about the length of time they should last. On the basis of this, a number of subtypes were then distinguished. The fact that this kind of subdivision was left out of the 1987 edition indicates that, at the very least, some doubts had been raised in this regard. In the latest revision of 1994 this distinction has returned. In this latest version the acute subtype has become an independent entity. PTSD is therefore exclusively reserved for disorders which appear after a delay.

On the other hand, not every psychiatrist found it useful to conceive of PTSD as a separate clinical entity. Colonel Belenky, for example, has pointed out that it is more accurate to speak of 'combat reaction spectrum disorder' (CRSD). Then all known reactions brought about by combat can be located within this spectrum:

This spectrum ranges from immediate (combat reaction, battle shock, shell shock, and explosion blow), through acute (combat fatigue, battle fatigue, and acute posttraumatic stress disorder [PTSD]), through delayed (reactions during combat lulls, while home on pass, and following rapid demobilization), through late (old sergeant syndrome and delayed PTSD), to chronic reactions (war neurosis and chronic PTSD), and includes a variety of not strictly psychiatric reactions, such as nonbattle injuries, evacuation syndromes, exposure to low-dose chemical warfare agent, and exposure to chemical warfare agent antidote. These reactions must be distinguished from the normal reactions to combat – fear, excitement, and the accompanying autonomic arousal – and the normal sequelae of combat exposure – euphoria, fatigue, mild apathy or depression, and grief over lost comrades.[15]

What is attractive about this approach is that a great number of possible reactions are assumed to exist. Moreover, a role is allotted to non-psychological factors as causes of behavioral disturbances. The debate which broke out after the Gulf War among veterans of this conflict seems to confirm the usefulness of this approach.

Nature and Extent of the Veterans Problem
In 1980 it was officially established that servicemen, even years after the event, can display behavioral disorders which go back to wartime traumas. In the wake of this acknowledgement the question naturally arose as to how many traumatized veterans there actually were. With this question in mind a number of different epidemiological studies were carried out in the 1980s. One of the best known which should be mentioned in this connection was The National Vietnam Veterans Readjustment Study (NVVRS). This research project was undertaken by a group of researchers who were assigned the task by the Veterans Administration. The government was generous in providing the financial means for carrying out this study. The results were published in book form in 1990. What then can be said regarding the prevalence of PTSD on the basis of this study?

The researchers gave attention both to complete as well as partial PTSD. It's a question of this latter category when the complaints are less intense or when not all the required symptoms are present. With regard to both these types, the study specified whether they had occurred to a veteran in the past (lifetime prevalence) or whether they were still affecting him (current prevalence). The statistics that were gathered can justly be called impressive. The study revealed that no less than 15.2 percent of all male veterans completely met the criteria of PTSD. This represented a total of 479,000 cases. When it came to women, the figure was 8 percent, which amounted to 160 cases. For partial PTSD the percentages were 11.1 for men and 7.8 for women. The total number of veterans with this disorder amounted to 350,000.

The figures become even more striking if we consider not only present-day cases but those in the past as well. The prevalence of PTSD turned out to be 30.9 percent among men and 26.9 percent among women. For those diagnosed with partial PTSD the figures were 22.5 and 21.2 percent respectively. This means that at a certain moment in their life 1.7 million veterans were confronted with serious stress disorders. It also became clear that PTSD represented a chronic illness. Approximately half of the veterans who had ever suffered from PTSD during their life, were still experiencing trouble from it at the time that the study was carried out.

Behind these overall figures were hidden differences in vulnerability to PTSD. Thus prevalence varied from one racial or ethnic group to another. Hispanics were the most susceptible, next came Afro-Americans, and finally whites. It appeared to be of crucial importance whether a person had actually taken part in combat. The soldiers who had done so had high scores of prevalence. Similarly, the study revealed that predisposing factors did play a considerable role, but that these by no means trivialized the significance of actual war experiences:

Taken together these results are consistent with a model of PTSD that posits a role for individual vulnerability (potentially including biological, psychological, and sociodemographic predisposing factors) *and* a role for exposure to environmental factors (specifically, war-zone stressors) in determining who among theater veterans gets PTSD. However, it is clear that exposure to war-zones stress makes a substantial contibution to the development of PTSD in war veterans that is independent of a broad range of potential predisposing factors.[16]

Furthermore, the same study revealed that those who took an active part in the fighting also had to pay a certain price in another sense. This group in particular came to face a disproportionate degree of personal and social problems. The veterans in question were plagued by moods of depression, struggled with drink problems and generally went through a difficult process of adaptation to the demands of civilian society. Thus the soldiers who belonged to the untis that were engaged in actual combat ran a much higher risk with regard to a whole range of other negative phenomena.

In order to present as realistic a picture of the significance of PTSD, the researchers attempted to investigate whether this illness had occurred in combination with other psychological and social disorders. As it turned out, this was indeed the case. It was clear that PTSD dominated the whole sphere of life of the individual involved. For example, veterans who had suffered from PTSD had a five times greater chance of becoming unemployed than veterans who had not had the illness. In addition, 70 percent of them were divorced (35 percent two or more times), 49 percent had marital problems and 55 percent experienced difficulties functioning as previously. Approximately half of them had been arrested or had spent time in prison. Displaying violent behavior was also not exceptional among this group. A final point, which should not be ignored here, is the fact that in the environment of those suffering from PTSD there are often other individuals who become victims. Spouses have become clinically depressed and children have suffered all kinds of behavioral difficulties. Therefore, PTSD not only has repercussions for the veterans themselves.

The influence that PTSD can have on the social environment of the patient has been aptly described by the wife of a Dutch career officer.[17] This serviceman was one of the Dutch UN observers who was sent to Lebanon at the beginning of the 1980s. After his return he was affected by an illness which lasted for ten years and had devastating consequences for his whole family. From Mrs. Mentink's account it is also clear that the military authorities themselves were not aware of the existence of PTSD. The army only took action when several hundred Lebanon veterans themselves sounded the alarm. By then it was already 1992. How assistance to the soldiers serving in Bosnia will be organized, for the time being remains an open question.

Conclusion

In 1980 psychiatry was enriched by the addition of a new concept: post-traumatic stress disorder. This bureaucratic expression sounds like it was the brain-child of a low-ranking civil servant. But nothing could be further from the truth. The phrase was formulated by the *crème de la crème* of American psychiatry and adopted in the official manual of the American Psychiatric Association.

Approval of the diagnosis PTSD meant not only that American psychiatry had officially accepted that traumtic events could lead to behavioral disorders but also that these disorders could become manifest after a delay of months or even years.

Not only war experiences were considered to be in this category of traumas. Natural disasters, traffic accidents and rape were included in the category as well. Thus the concept is more comprehensive than old terms like shell shock or combat exhaustion.

It is noteworthy that the veterans themselves took the initiative to win recognition for this illness. Former servicemen who took part in the Vietnam War at first met with no sympathy for the psychological problems they had to struggle with after they returned to civilian society.

At the end of the 1960s the idea was prevalent in psychiatry that the psychologically wounded soldier was a phenomenon of earlier times. The war in Vietnam appeared to show that a combination of preventive measures was capable of limiting cases of combat stress to a minimum. Reality turned out to be surprisingly different. In the end Vietnam produced a sizeable contingent of soldiers with behavioral disorders, even if these disorders only manifest themselves at a later date. The psychologically wounded soldier had given place to the psychologically wounded veteran.

XI - Final Conclusion

If you set about chopping wood, chips are bound to fly. When two armies confront one another in battle, there are bound to be dead and wounded. From time immemorial wounds were chiefly thought of in terms of physical injuries. However, in modern times it has become increasingly clear that in the fray of battle a human being can suffer damage to his psyche. Yet the psychologically wounded soldier is certainly not a new phenomenon. In previous centuries as well, when conflicts were more limited in character and war was fought with more primitive means, the lot of the fighting soldier was far from enviable. Testimony from diaries and other first-person documents reveal that direct encounter with physical violence on the battlefield was experienced as a very traumatic event. In earlier times too soldiers suffered breakdowns, individually or in groups, and were thus of no use for the rest of the battle or for the continuation of the campaign. In modern warfare, which among other things is characterized by the use of weapons of mass destruction, this category of wounded became so large that it could no longer be ignored by the military authorities.

Modern warfare emerged in the wake of the industrial revolution. New forms of industrial production provided the military with unknown possibilities in many areas. This development not only led to the introduction of new weapons and new weapon systems but included the provision of greatly improved medical and logistical facilities.

These changes have had consequences for the psychological pressure which soldiers undergo. Modern warfare has confronted them with death and destruction on a hitherto unknown scale. Similarly, they face weapon systems that have consciously been designed to exploit their fears and insecurities. Technological advances have seen to it that the natural rest periods which were available to the military throughout the centuries have come to be of less significance. Campaigns are no longer limited to particular seasons and even the difference between day and night is no longer as absolute as in previous times. Finally, the combat situation has changed from the social viewpoint as well. Combat in massive closed formations has given way to individual action and fighting in small open groups. The modern battlefield is inhabited by 'lonely' soldiers who frequently are unable to see their enemies but merely feel an anonymous threat. From this brief summing up one should not draw the conclusion that modern warfare is a homogeneous phenomenon. Nothing could be farther from the truth.

Recent history has displayed a broad spectrum of armed conflicts which differ greatly from one another in their nature, scale and intensity. For example, the great powers in the first half of this century were engaged in total, all-consuming world wars. Afterwards, they waged war on a much more limited scale in the colonies where independence movements contested European hegemony. Some conflicts such as the First World War, in which armies each totaling more than a million men bombarded one another from trenches, were endowed with a static character. The German *Wehrmacht*, whose example has been successfully followed by the Israeli army, demonstrated the offensive potential of modern military organization.

Modern warfare has many faces. The *Blitzkrieg* and trench warfare comprise two of the most extreme. In the first case it is a matter of tank units that can easily advance tens of kilometers a day. In the second case one may be dealing with fixed positions where neither side makes any gains in territory over a period of several years. Between these two extremes there are innumerable other combat situations, a few of which we have briefly described.

The sketched situations vary with regard to intensity of the psychological stress which they entail. Amphibious operations have always stirred up enormous feelings of anxiety. Likewise, storming fortified positions has given rise to disconcerting emotions. On the other hand, tensions associated with participating in a *Blitzkrieg* are not as extreme as those encountered in the other two examples.

The psychological pressures vary not only according to intensity but according to content as well. In this study three ideal type positions have been discussed in which soldiers can be involved in using violence, namely as victim, perpetrator or witness. The predominating feeling in the case of the victims is powerlessness. The perpetrators are primarily troubled by feelings of guilt. In the case of the witnesses a sense of frustration dominates. Thus the three positions entail quite divergent psychological consequences.

The psychologically wounded soldier appears in many variations. There are enormous differences between the symptoms exhibited, both in intensity and possible combinations. Pretty much every soldier who goes into battle experiences psychosomatic manifestations such as heart palpitations and increased transpiration. At the same time, many are gripped by more or less intense feelings of anxiety. Still others have problems with their ability to concentrate and with their memory. In extreme cases, deafness and blindness, and even symptoms of paralysis, can occur.

We have seen that the disorders are not the same in every war. During the First World War it was chiefly manifestation of hysteria which drew the attention of military psychiatrists. In the other larger or smaller conflicts of the twentieth century this form of manifestation was of less importance. In the Second World War functional organic disorders figured as an alternative to combat neurosis, at least to a certain degree. This symptom displacement has been related to changes that took place during the inter-war years both in psychiatry itself and in the social position of this discipline. In this connection reference has also been made to the developments that warfare underwent in the years after 1918.

Generally speaking, working psychiatrists have had few problems as far as recognizing symptoms is concerned. The diagnostic methods employed in war are a good reflection of what is available at any particular period in the way of intellectual models and concepts in civilian psychiatry. Military psychiatrists, just as their civilian colleagues, have made use of concepts such as neurasthenia, hysteria, anxiety syndrome and stress. But in addition to this they have also launched certain terms that were specific to an individual occasion. By means of these concepts a relation could be established between psychological disorders and the specific wartime situations in which these disorders manifested themselves. As a term, shell shock has undoubtedly made the strongest impression on the public imagination, whereas nowadays combat stress is the most frequently applied label one comes across.

The military organization received these labels and, more generally, the overall role of psychiatry with mixed feelings. Naturally, military psychiatry could work like a safety valve by means of which potentially more threatening forms of deviant behavior could be prevented. And, naturally, it was an attractive idea that soldiers who had suffered a breakdown could be made functional again. But there was a certain price to be paid. In fact, military psychiatry has come to question the deeply cherished traditional morality of the military. Heroism, a mentality of determination and self-sacrifice, the foundations on which this morality was built, have been relativized and reduced to human proportions. It is perfectly understandable that this has evoked considerable resistance. Consequently, military psychiatry has had to fight to win acceptance in the army. In the British armed forces resistance has always been especially strong.

What did this new group of medical practitioners have to offer the military in the way of therapies?

By now it will have become clear to the reader that the psychiatrists who worked in the various military medical services during the great wars of the twentieth century had a difficult task to perform. They were required to help large numbers of soldiers who had suffered a breakdown and where possible to make them fit to return to active duty again. In carrying out their work these doctors made use of what civilian psychiatry had to offer in the way of scientific theory and practical therapies.

However, the given situation, i.e. an army during wartime, imposed a procedure of selection and adaptation with regard to available therapies. Above all, simple, easy-to-apply therapies of short duration were chosen. Being in a state of war also made it possible to bend the ethical rules according to which treatment was to be provided. It appears that for various reasons many therapists were perfectly willing to take advantage of the new opportunities. Thanks to all these factors military psychiatry came to have its own specific countenance: one characterized by simplicity and harshness. On the other hand, the degree of harshness varied in accordance with the range of therapies in use at any given moment. In particular, electrotherapy in the hands of doctors such as Yealland, Kaufmann and Pansen could develop into a method which was dangerous as well as violent.

On the whole it can be said that the wars did not lead to important discoveries in the area of therapy. With regard to methods of treatment, military psychiatry was not very innovative. When military psychiatry first came into existence during the

First World War, it was even considered by some to be a step backwards in history –
indeed, to the period around 1800. That had been the period of moral treatment,
the period when the founders of modern psychiatry were active. Military psychiatry
did in a certain sense revive the ideas of Tuke, Pinel and Reil. These early pioneers
had viewed their patients as children, at times as rather naughty children, who had
to be directed to adulthood with a firm hand. Only the latter day military psychiatrists had less time at their disposal. Therefore the process of 'parental' upbringing
had to be accelerated and intensified. But this was not simply a question of making
the soldiers once again fit for active duty. Even patients who were only expected to
have a future in civilian life were dealt with in the same way. Military psychiatry was
not solely interested in maintaining the level of fighting power of the armed forces.
Keeping the number of potential pensioners to a minimum was also high on the
agenda. One of the most notorious therapies, the Kaufmann-method, was in fact
originally developed with this rather ignoble goal in mind.

Military psychiatrists seldom refer explicitly to the above-mentioned features in
studies concerning their discipline. They prefer, for the most part, to make reference to the existence of certain underlying assumptions which are meant to be characteristic for their branch of care. These basic principles form the core of combat
psychiatry. At the risk of exaggeration, one could say that immediacy, proximity
and positive expectancy are the gospel of military psychiatry. In some surveys maintaining the military setting which we have discussed as a subdivision of positive expectancy is introduced as a fourth principle. Similarly, simplicity with regard to the
therapies employed is sometimes presented as a separate basic assumption.

In practice the basic principles were discovered through the method of trial and
error. During the Russo-Japanese War, for the first time there was experimentation
to set up a system of care which corresponded to these principles. Within a system
of this kind the existing provisions for treatment are divided over different echelons. Although there are variations in practice, in theory three levels of differing
types of assistance can be distinguished. The first echelon is located among the
fighting units. These are usually the divisions, but sometimes the brigades as well.
Here one finds the out-patient and the semi-out-patient facilities. The period of
residence in these facilities is brief, usually not more than one week. Soldiers who
cannot be helped during this time span are moved on to the second echelon. Ideally, the facilities provided at the second level are still located in close proximity to
the front. In these facilities one reckons on a longer stay for the patient. One is
thinking here in terms of weeks rather than days. Military-base hospitals and specialized clinics situated far from the fighting zone constitute the final echelon.
These institutions form the concluding phase of combat psychiatry. The Germans
and the French, who were moreover unaware of the earlier Russian attempts, introduced forward psychiatry during the First World War. It was the American psychiatrist Thomas Salmon who formulated the basic principles in words. When the army
of the United States launched its own first offensive, from the very beginning it disposed over a system of psychiatric care based on these principles.

Psychiatrists have frequently presented combat psychiatry as a blueprint for absolute success. Recovery rates of between 80 and 90 percent were predicted. In reality, however, setting up an adequate system of psychiatric care entailed quite a number of problems. Moreover, there is not really all that much that can be claimed for the actual results of combat psychiatry. What is striking is the intermittent pattern of development of military psychiatry. This discontinuity is particularly evident in the Anglo-Saxon countries where in every war the psychiatric services almost had to be started up once again from scratch. The fact that in these countries military psychiatry met with great resistance, indeed even on the part of the regular army doctors, is a partial explanation for this state of affairs.

How then did these basic principles relate to the theory and practice of civilian psychiatry?

The idea of immediacy is as old as modern psychiatry itself. Around 1800 when this profession began to take shape, there was widespread unanimity concerning the view that treatment of the mentally ill should begin as quickly as possible. But in the course of the nineteenth century this idea, for practical as well as theoretical reasons, receded into the background. Many asylums had waiting lists and, therefore, speedy admission was by no means always possible. Moreover, speedy intervention according to the new up-and-coming bio-medical school of thought counted less than it had according to the traditional psychological model. Whereas bio-medical thought did offer a theoretical explanation for the occurrence of mental illness, to begin with it had little to say in the way of providing a starting point for setting up a concrete plan of treatment. The principle of positive expectancy is not clearly present in psychiatry as a constant factor. The introduction of other methods of treatment or new medicinal drugs has been, and to a great extent still is, accompanied by great therapeutic optimism. Most often this euphoria decreases with the lapse of time. Pessimism and optimism regularly alternate with one another in psychiatry. In the field of military psychiatry a positivist stance is always adopted, at least on paper. The principle of proximity is in direct opposition to classical psychiatry where until deep into the twentieth century primacy was accorded to asylum care. In the latter case patients were deliberately removed from their original social surroundings and banished to institutions where they were given treatment in total isolation. Only in the last decades, at least in some Western countries, have adequate out-patient and semi-out-patient facilities been provided, with the result that this process of banishment has more or less ended. The importance of proximity has been widely acknowledged in modern mental health care. Thus, in this respect, the military sector had been in advance of the rest of society. That does not mean that the military had fostered a completely new vision concerning the structure of mental health care. In any case, in the mental hygiene movement similar conceptions had been developed. What can be said is that the military setting made it possible actually to implement these ideas in practice. The military psychiatrists made use of these possibilities and saw to it that quite early on a whole new path was pursued in the army.

In some respects the characteristic ideas of military psychiatry show similarities with the world of ideas of antipsychiatry. They have in common their aversion to psychiatric asylums. They also have in common the distance they adopt *vis-à-vis* the medical model and their rejection of the role of patient. The most visible parallel has been their abandonment of the doctor's white coat. As early as the First World War, military practitioners exchanged their specialized medical clothing for an army uniform. At the end of the 1960s the antipsychiatrists traded in their professional dress for a sports jacket.

This does not cancel out the crucial differences which exist between the two groups. The movement of democratization has had virtually no effect on military psychiatry. The therapeutic relationship in the army has always been based on an authoritarian and hierarchical structure and remains so today. Non-directive therapies have never been able to thrive in the military environment. Of essential significance is the difference in their fundamental starting point. Antipsychiatry has been first and foremost concerned with 'the patient'. The latter must be given help and, if necessary, protected from an environment that may be malevolent or responsible for making an individual sick. In the military context, from the outset it was not a question of the requirements of 'the patient', but rather a question of the needs of the army or of society. The interests of the individual who is seeking help have been entirely subordinated to this higher priority.

After the psychiatrists in the First World War had shown that they could be of service to the army in treating soldiers who had suffered a breakdown, in the following war the further step was taken to implement prevention. Only in the American armed forces had the introduction of preventive and curative activity occurred more or less simultaneously and that had been during the final phase of the First World War.

An important part of prevention had to do with selection. In this case selection took place not only in order to keep potential psychiatric patients out of the army. It was also a method for distributing the soldiers in an optimal way throughout a military organization that had become extremely complex. The Anglo-Saxon countries had great trust in objective psychological tests. On the basis of these tests it was determined where someone should be assigned in the army. In the case of the Germans, however, the officers in the army units played a crucial role in deciding where personnel would be employed.

During the Second World War, the social scientists also got the chance to demonstrate their usefulness for running an army. In particular the American army made grateful use of the information that had been gathered by the sociologists and psychologists.

After 1945 military psychiatry could claim, with a certain degree of justification, that experience had been acquired in the army regarding the functioning of organized social-psychiatric care. This system the military psychiatrists held up as an example for civilian society. The actual influence emanating from the military model was, however, quite limited. Fundamental changes only began in mental health care in the 1960s, and military psychiatry had little or nothing to do with these developments.

In 1980 psychiatry was enriched by the addition of a new concept: post-traumatic stress disorder. This bureaucratic expression sounds like it was the brain-child of a high-ranking civil servant. But nothing could be farther from the truth. The phrase was formulated by the *crème de la crème* of American psychiatry and adopted in the official manual of the American Psychiatric Association.

Approval of the diagnosis PTSD meant not only that American psychiatry had officially accepted that traumtic events could lead to behavioral disorders but also that these disorders could become manifest after a delay of months or even years. Not only war experiences were considered to be in this category of traumas. Natural disasters, traffic accidents and rape were included in the category as well. Thus the concept is more comprehensive than old terms like shell shock or combat exhaustion.

It is noteworthy that the veterans themselves took the initiative to win recognition for this illness. Former servicemen who took part in the Vietnam War at first met with no sympathy for the psychological problems they had to struggle with after they returned to civilian society.

At the end of the 1960s the idea was prevalent in psychiatry that the psychologically wounded soldier was strictly a phenomenon of earlier times. The war in Vietnam appeared to show that a combination of preventive measures was capable of limiting cases of combat stress to a minimum. Reality turned out to be surprisingly different. In the end Vietnam produced a sizeable contingent of soldiers with behavioral disorders, even if these disorders only manifest themselves at a later date. The psychologically wounded soldier had given place to the psychologically wounded veteran.

NOTES

Chapter I

1. Clausewitz, *Oorlog*, 92-3.
2. Keegan, *Command*, 161.
3. Keegan, *op. cit.* 162.
4. See for example Holmes, *Firing Line*, 204 ff; Gabriel and Metz, *Military Medicine* II, 196-9.
5. Wondergem, *Anders terug*, 19.
6. In this connection see Deutsch, *Civil War*.
7. Gabriel and Metz, *op. cit.*, 235 ff.

Chapter II

1. Van Doorn, *Sociologie*, 86 ff.; Teitler, *Officierscorps*, 217 ff.
2. Teitler, *op. cit.*, 232 ff.
3. What follows is based on Van Creveld, *Supplying War*.
4. See also Spits, *Metamorfose*.
5. Bartov, *Hitler's Army*, 17.
6. Bartov, *op. cit.*, 76.
7. Van Creveld, *Transformation*, 106.
8. Keegan, *Warfare*, 301 ff.
9. What follows is based on Urlanis, *Menschenverluste*; see also Gabriel and Metz, *op. cit.*
10. Gabriel and Metz., *op. cit.*, 143 ff.
11. Gabriel and Metz., *op. cit.*, 179-96.
12. Gabriel and Metz., *op. cit.*, 226-33.
13. Gabriel and Metz., *op. cit.*, 222.
14. Teitler, *op. cit.*, 232-41.
15. Parker, *Het Spaanse leger*, 278 ff.
16. Holmes, *op. cit.*, 84.
17. Teitler, *op. cit.*, 232-41.
18. Horne, *Monty*, 127 ff.
19. Hastings, *Overlord*, 177-8.
20. Holmes, *op. cit.*, 251.

Chapter III

1. Strecker, 'Military Psychiatry', 385.
2. *Ibid.*

3.   Howard, *European History*, 94 ff.
4.   Simkins, *Kitchner's Army*, 57.
5.   Keegan, *Face of Battle*, 216 ff.
6.   Keegan, *op. cit.*, 250.
7.   On this subject see Dupuy, *Weapons and Warfare*.
8.   On the history of this weapon see Elles, *Machinegun*.
9.   Gabriel and Metz, *op. cit.*, 27.
10. Keegan, *Warfare*, 360; Terraine, *Smoke and Fire*, 47.
11. Keegan, *op. cit.*, 361.
12. Holmes, *op. cit.*, 186-7.
13. Holmes, *op. cit.*, 187.
14. The most accessible of these is Dupuy, *op. cit.*
15. Dupuy, *op. cit.*, 213.
16. Holmes, *op. cit.*, 151.
17. The standard work of du Picq is *Études sur le combat*.

Chapter IV
1.   A good summary is found in Stouffer, *The American Soldier*, 66-8.
2.   Horne, *Glory*, 56.
3.   Quoted in Winter, *Death's Men*, 119.
4.   Winter, *op. cit.*, 121.
5.   Winter, *op. cit.*, *passim*.
6.   Horne, *op. cit.*, 62.
7.   Ashworth, *Trench Warfare*.
8.   See Groen, *Militaire orde*.
9.   What follows is taken from Van Doorn, 'Een mammoet', 162 ff.
10. Van Creveld, *Transformation*, 208.
11. Regarding what follows see Wintle, *Viet Nam*, 152 ff.
12. McPherson, *Generation*, 9.
13. Wintle, *op. cit.*, 154.
14. Wintle, *op. cit.*, 145.
15. *Excessennota* bijlage 5, 57.
16. Van Doorn and Hendricks, *Geweld*.
17. Wintle, *op. cit.*, 155.
18. Wintle, *op. cit.*, 163.
19. Ashworth, *op. cit.*, 221.
20. Holmes, *op. cit.*, *passim*.
21. Wondergem, *Anders terug*, 89-90.
22. Wondergem, *op. cit.*, 37.
23. Quoted in Ulrich and Ziemann, *Frontalltag*, 102.
24. Gabriel and Metz, *op. cit.*, 25.
25. Bourne, *Stress*, XX ff.

Chapter V

1. Gabriel and Metz, *op. cit.*, 183.
2. What follows is based on Binneveld, *Filantropie*.
3. Quoted in Deutsch, 'Mental Hygiene', 343.
4. Deutsch, *op. cit.*, 356 ff.
5. On what follows see Goldstein, *Console*, 322 ff.
6. Brinkgreve, 'Zenuwlijders', 187.
7. Brinkgreve, *Psychoanalyse*, 34 ff.
8. On what follows see Binneveld and Wolf, *Een huis*, 75 ff.
9. Trimbos, *Antipsychiatrie*.
10. Roosens, *Unicum*.
11. Peeters, 'Historische fasen', 22 ff.
12. Van Doorn, *Verzorgingsstaat*.

Chapter VI

1. Myers (1915), 'Shell Shock I'. This was the first of a series of three articles.
2. Bogacz, 'War Neurosis', 234.
3. Myers (1916), 'Shell Shock II'.
4. Shoalter, *Female Malady*, 174.
5. Roth, 'Modernisierung', 16 ff.
6. Bogacz, *op. cit.*, 249.
7. In this regard see Myers (1919), 'Shell Shock III', 51; Elliot Smith, 'Shock', 815; Brown, 'Treatment', 197.
8. Gicklhorn, 'Freud', 943.
9. Turner, 'Neuroses', 614.
10. Carver, 'Shell Shock', 195.
11. Roussy, 'Troubles', 115.
12. Roussy, *op. cit.*, 115.
13. See for example Heldenhain, *Im Dienste der Wehrmacht*.
14. Lifton, *Nazi-dokters*, 170-1.
15. Roth, *op. cit.*, 36-9; Riedesser, *Militär*, 252.
16. Quoted in Riedesser and Verderber, *Aufrüstung*, 29.
17. Riedesser and Verderber, *op. cit.*, 30.
18. On this subject see Haase, *Deserteurs*, 36-7.
19. Ahrenfeldt, *Psychiatry*, 15.
20. Sargant and Slater, 'War Neuroses'.
21. Kleber, Brom and Defares, *Traumatische ervaringen*, 32-3.
22. Ahrenfeldt, *op. cit.*, 164.
23. Neill, 'Symptoms', 151.
24. Quoted in Bourne (1969), *Stress*, XVII.
25. Ahrenfeldt, *op. cit.*, 172-3.
26. Friedman, Kaplan and Sadock, *Synopsis*, 385.
27. Bourne, *op. cit.*, 98.

28. Bourne, *op. cit.*, 99-115.
29. Quoted in Bourne, *op. cit.*, 109.
30. Dasberg, *Trauma*, 6.
31. Leed, *No Man's Land*, 166 ff.
32. Dunn, *The War*, 100.
33. Dunn, *op. cit.*, 250-1.
34. Leed, *op. cit.*, 166.
35. Bogacz, *op. cit.*, 239.
36. Long, 'Patton'.
37. Ahrenfeldt, *op. cit.*, 26.
38. Ahrenfeldt, *op. cit.*, 164.
39. Ward, *Harrier*, 207 ff.
40. Dasber, *op. cit.*, 4.
41. Solomon, 'Denial'.
42. Quoted in Solomon, *op. cit.*, 277.
43. Cooter, 'Modern Medicine'.
44. Elliot Smith, 'Shock', 857.

Chapter VII
1. Kaufmann, 'Heilung', 802.
2. Kaufmann, *op. cit.*, 803.
3. Kaufmann, *op. cit.*, 804.
4. Hirschfeld, *Sittengeschichte*, 361.
5. 'Notes', 882.
6. Ulrich and Ziemann, *Frontalltag*, 106-7.
7. 'Notes', 882.
8. Yealland, *Hysterical Disorders*.
9. Yealland, *op. cit.*, 6-10.
10. Déjerine and Gauckler, 'Traitement', 521-3.
11. Rivers, 'Freud's Psychology', 913.
12. See Fussel, *The Great War*, *passim*.
13. What follows is based on Roth, *op. cit.*, 8-33.
14. Quoted in Ulrich and Ziemann, *op. cit.*, 105.
15. Roth, *op. cit.*, 21.
16. Gicklhorn, *op. cit.*, 945.
17. Roth, *op. cit.*, 26.
18. Sargant and Slater, *op. cit.*.
19. Kleber, Brom and Defares, *op. cit.*, 39.
20. Maxwell Jones, 'Group Psychotherapy', 276-8.
21. Maxwell Jones, *op. cit.*, 277.
22. Maxwell Jones, *op. cit.*, 277.
23. For what follows see Roth, *op. cit.*, 33-75.
24. Bartov, *op. cit.*, 29 ff.

25. Bartov, *op. cit.*, 139 ff.

26. Roth, *op. cit.*, 48 ff.

27. Roth, *op. cit.*, 64.

28. On this point see Riedesser and Verderber, *op. cit.*, 28 ff.

29. Peterson and Chambers, 'Combat Psychiatry', 252.

30. Colbach, 'Ethical Issues', 261.

31. Pettera, Johnson and Zimmer, 'Psychiatric Management', 675.

32. See for example Neumann and Levy, 'Treatment', 196-9.

33. Troelstra, *Gedenkschriften* III, 301.

34. Quoted in Riedesser and Verderber, *op. cit.*, 28.

35. Cooter, *op. cit.*, 15-55.

36. Gicklhorn, *op. cit.*, 947.

37. Messerschmidt and Wüllner, *Wehrmachtjustiz*, 235.

Chapter VIII

1. Friedman, Kaplan and Sadock, *op. cit.*, 1183.

2. See Gabriel and Metz, *op. cit.*, 233 ff.

3. Gabriel and Metz, *op. cit.*, 237.

4. Gabriel and Metz, *op. cit.*, 226 ff.

5. See Travers, 'The Offensive'.

6. Riedesser, *op. cit.*, 243.

7. Leed, *op. cit.*, 168.

8. Riedesser, *op. cit.*, 243.

9. See for example Déjerine and Gauckler, *op. cit.*

10. Bailey, 'Neuroses', 2149.

11. Strecker, *op. cit.*, 401 ff.

12. On what follows see Paschall, *Defeat*, 163 ff.

13. Strecker, *op. cit.,* 410.

14. Copp and McAndrew, *Exhaustion*, 101.

15. Neumann and Levy, 'Military Installation', 199.

16. *Ibid.*

17. Pettera, Johnson and Zimmer, *op. cit.*, 675.

18. Milligan, *War.*

19. Milligan, *op. cit.*, 259.

20. Ahrenfeldt, *op. cit.* 149.

21. Quoted in Copp and McAndrew, *op. cit.*, 122-3.

22. Copp and McAndrew, *op. cit.*, 110.

23. Quoted in Ahrenfeldt, *op. cit.*, 165.

24. Glass, 'Psychotherapy', 730.

25. Pettera, Johnson and Zimmer, *op. cit.*, 675.

26. Sargant and Slater, *op. cit.*.

27. Copp and McAndrew, *op. cit.*, 59.

28. De Swart, *Warfare*, 4-5.

29. McManners, *Scars*, 17 ff.
30. Rees, *op. cit.*, *passim*; Ahrenfeldt, *op. cit.*, *passim*.
31. Freidson, *Profession*.
32. Copp and McAndrew, *op. cit.*, 109.
33. L'Etang, 'A Criticism', 34.
34. Copp and McAndrew, *op. cit.*, 105.

Chapter IX

1. What follows is based on Van Heerde, *Sociologie*, 292 ff.
2. Rees, *op. cit.*, 43.
3. Rees, *op. cit.*, 45.
4. Riedesser, *op. cit.*, 251.
5. Feynman and Leighton, *Joking*, 138.
6. Feynman and Leighton, *op. cit.*, 143.
7. Bigler, *Soldaat*, 51.
8. Rees, *op. cit.*, 52 ff.
9. Bigler, *op. cit.*, 48.
10. Bigler, *op. cit.*, 48.
11. In this connection see *Personele aspecten*, 44 ff.
12. Rees, *op. cit.*, 150.
13. Talbott, 1237.

Chapter X

1. Scott, 'Veterans' Issues', 592.
2. Tiffany and Allerton, 'Army Psychiatry', 814 ff.
3. Bourne (1970), 'Military Psychiatry', 124 ff.
4. Tiffany and Allerton, *op. cit.*, 811.
5. Tiffany and Allerton, *op. cit.*, 813.
6. On what follows see Holmes, *op. cit.*, 86, 251.
7. Horowitz and Solomon, 'Prediction'.
8. In this connection see Scott, *op. cit.*.
9. These groups are described in detail in Lifton, 'The War'.
10. Quoted in Scott, *op. cit.*, 610.
11. Bourne, *op. cit.*, 129.
12. Quoted in Solomon, 'PTSD', 274.
13. Horowitz and Solomon, *op. cit.*.
14. McPherson, *Generation*, 218 ff.
15. Belenky, 'Combat Experience', 64.
16. Kulka *et alii*, *Trauma*, 268.
17. Mentink-Heshusius, *De plicht*.

BIBLIOGRAPHY

Ahrenfeldt, R.H., *Psychiatry in the British Army in the Second World War* (London 1957).

Ardant du Picq, C.J.J., *Études sur le combat. Part II: Le combat moderne (Nouvelle édition)* (Paris 1903).

Ashworth, T., *Trench Warfare 1914-1918. The Live and Let Live System* (London 1986).

Bailey, P., 'War Neuroses, Shell Shock and Nervousness in Soldiers' in: *JAMA* 71 (1918), nr. 26, 2148-2153.

Barker, P., *Regeneration* (London 1991).

Bartov, O., *Hitler's Army. Soldiers, Nazis, and War in the Third Reich* (New York/Oxford 1992), 139.

Belenky, G.L., 'Varieties of Reaction and Adaptation to Combat Experience' in: *Bulletin of the Menninger Clinic* 51 (1986), 64-79.

Bigler, R.R., *De naamloze soldaat* (Rotterdam 1966).

Binneveld, J.M.W., C. Brinkgreve, A.J. Lameijn, H.F.M. Peeters, P. Vandermeersch, C.P. de Vos, and J. Vijselaar, *Een psychiatrisch verleden. Uit de geschiedenis van de psychiatrie* (Baarn 1982).

Binneveld, H., *Filantropie, repressie en medische zorg. Geschiedenis van de inrichtingspsychiatrie* (Deventer 1985).

Binneveld, H. and R. Wolf, *Een huis met vele woningen; 100 jaar katholieke psychiatrie. Voorburg 1885-1985* ('s-Hertogenbosch 1985).

Binneveld, J.M.W., *Het leger als spiegel. Oorlog, psychiatrie en geestelijke gezondheidszorg* (Rotterdam 1989).

Bloch, J., *The Future of War in its Technical, Economic and Political Relation* (Boston 1902).

Bogacz, T., 'War Neurosis and Cultural Change in England, 1914-22: The Work of the War Office Committee of Enquiry into "Shell-Shock"' in: *Journal of Contemporary History* 24 (1989), 227-256.

Bourne, P.G., *The Psychology and Physiology of Stress. With Reference to Special Studies of the Viet Nam War* (New York/London 1970).

Bourne, P.G., 'Military Psychiatry and the Viet Nam Experience' in: *American Journal of Psychiatry* 127:4 (October 1970), 481-492.

Brinkgreve, C., 'De zorg voor zenuwlijders in Nederland rond de eeuwwisseling en de opkomst van de psychoanalyse' in: Binneveld, J.M.W. e.a. *Een psychiatrisch verleden uit de geschiedenis van de inrichtingspsychiatrie* (1982), 181-205.

Brinkgreve, C., *Psychoanalyse in Nederland. Synopsis* (Amsterdam 1984).

Brown, W., 'The Treatment of Cases of Shell Shock in an Advanced Neurological Centre' in: *The Lancet* (1918, 2), 197-200.

Carver, A., 'The Commotional Factor in the Aetiology of Shell Shock' in: *The Lancet* (1919, 2), 193-196.

Clausewitz, C. von, *On War*. Edited and Translated by M. Howard and P. Paret (Princeton University Press, New Jersey 1976). Original title: *Vom Kriege*.

Colbach, E.M., 'Ethical Issues in Combat Psychiatry' in: *Military Medicine* 150 C (1985), 256-265.

Cooter, R., 'War and Modern Medicine' in: W.F. Bynum and R. Porter, eds., *Companion Encyclopedia of the History of Medicine*, vol.2 (1993), 1536-1571.

Copp, T. and B. McAndrew, *Battle Exhaustion. Soldiers and Psychiatrists in the Canadian Army, 1939-1945* (Montreal 1990).

Creveld, M. van, *The Transformation of War* (New York 1991).

Creveld, M. van, *Supplying War. Logistics from Wallenstein to Patton* (Cambridge 1977).

Dasberg, H., S. Davidson, G.L. Durlacher, B.C. Filet, and E. de Wind, *Society and Trauma of War* (Assen 1987).

Deutsch, A., 'The History of Mental Hygiene' in: J.K. Hall, and G. Zilboorg, eds., *One Hundred Years of American Psychiatry* (New York 1945 [2nd edition]), 325-365.

Deutsch, A., 'Military Psychiatry I. The Civil War (1861-1865)' in: idem, 367-384.

Deutsch, A., 'Military Psychiatry III, World War II' in: idem, 417-441.

Déjerine, J. and E. Gauckler, 'Le traitement par l'isolement et la psychothérapie des militaires atteints de troubles fonctionnels du système nerveux' in: *La Presse Médicale* (décembre 1915).

Doorn, J.A.A. van, *Sociologie van de organisatie. Beschouwingen over organiseren in het bijzonder gebaseerd op een onderzoek van het militaire systeem* (Leiden 1956).

Doorn, J.A.A. van, and W.J. Hendrix, *Ontsporing van geweld. Over het Nederlands-Indisch-Indonesisch conflict* (Rotterdam 1970).

Doorn, J.A.A. van, and C.J.M. Schuyt, eds. *De stagnerende verzorgingsstaat* (Meppel/Amsterdam 1978).

Doorn, J.A.A. van, 'Een mammoet in een mijnenveld' in: J. Ramondt and H. Vrijhof, eds., *Besturing en beheersing van organisaties* (Rotterdam 1988), 155-173.

Dunn, Captain J.C., *The War the Infantry Knew 1914-1919* (London 1938) [published under the name P.S. King].

Dupuy, T.N., *The Evolution of Weapons and Warfare* (New York 1980).

Eder, M.D., 'The Psycho-pathology of the War Neuroses' in: *The Lancet* (1916, 2), 264-268.

Elliot Smith, G., 'Shock and the Soldier' in: *The Lancet* (1916, 1), 813, 853-857.

Excessennota. Nota betreffende het archiefonderzoek naar de gegevens omtrent excessen in Indonesië begaan door Nederlandse militairen in de periode 1945-1950. Ingeleid door J. Bank (Den Haag 1995).

Ellis, J., *The Social History of the Machinegun* (Baltimore 1986).

Feynman, R.P., and R. Leighton, *Surely You're Joking, Mr. Feynman!* (New York 1985).

Freedman, A.M., H.I. Kaplan, and B.J. Sadock, *Modern Synopsis of Psychiatry II* (Baltimore 1976 [2nd edition]).

Friedson, E., *The Profession of Medicine. A Study of the Sociology of Applied Knowledge* (New York 1970).

Fuller, J.F.C., *The Conduct of War 1789-1961* (Kent 1961).

Fussel, Paul, *The Great War and Modern Memory* (Oxford 1975) 363 pp.

Gabriel, R.A. and K.S. Metz, *A History of Military Medicine*, vol. II (New York/London 1992).

Gicklhorn, R., 'Sigmund Freud über Kriegsneurosen, Elektrotherapie und Psycho-analyse. Ein Auszug aus dem Protokoll des Untersuchungsverfahrens gegen Wagner-Jauregg im Oktober 1926' in: *Psyche* 26 (1972), II, 939-941.

Glass, A.J., 'Military Psychiatry and Changing Systems of Mental Health Care' in: *American Journal of Psychiatry* 104 (1947), 217-220.

Glass, A.J., 'Psychotherapy in the Combat Zone' in: *American Journal of Psychiatry* 110 (1954), 725-731.

Goldstein, J., *Console and Classify. The French Profession in the Nineteenth Century* (Cambridge 1987).

Grinten, T. van der, *De vorming van de ambulante geestelijke gezondheidszorg. Een historisch beleidsonderzoek* (Baarn 1987).

Groen, P.M.H., *Buiten de militaire orde* (Leiden 1995). An inaugural address.

Haase, N., *Duitse deserteurs tijdens de Tweede Wereldoorlog* (Berlin 1991).

Hastings, M., *Overlord. D-Day and the Battle for Normandy 1944* (London 1984; reprinted 1993).

Hausman, W. and D. McRioch, 'A Prototype of Social and Preventive Psychiatry in the United States' in: *Arch. Gen. Psychiat.* 16 (1967), 727-739.

Heerde, R.J.A.T. van, *Sociologie van de oorlogvoering* (Breda 1987). An unpublished manuscript.

Heldenhain, A., *Die Psychiatrie im Dienste der Wehrmacht* (Leipzig 1938).

Hirschfeld, M. and A. Gaspar, eds., *Sittengeschichte des Ersten Weltkrieges* (Hanau without date [reprint of 2nd revised edition]).

Holmes, R., *Firing Line* (Suffolk 1985).

Horne, A., *The Price of Glory. Verdun 1916* (London 1993).

Horne, A. and D. Montgomery, *Monty 1944-1945. The Lonely Leader* (London 1994).

Horowitz, M.J. and G.F. Solomon, 'A Prediction of Delayed Stress Response Syndromes in Vietnam Veterans' in: *Journal of Social Issues*, 31 (1975), no. 4, 67-80.

Howard, M., *War in European History* (Oxford 1976).

Jones, K., *A History of the Mental Health Services* (London 1972).

Kahn, S.M., *Between Tedium and Terror. A Soldier's World War II Diary, 1943-45* (Urbana/Chicago 1993).

Kaufmann, Dr F., 'Die planmässige Heilung komplizierter psychogener Bewegungsstörungen bei Soldaten in einer Sitzung' in: *Münchener Medizinische Wochenschrift* 30, Mai 1916. Feldärztliche Beilage Nr. 22, 354-357.

Keegan, J., *The Face of Battle* (Suffolk 1976).

Keegan, J., *The Mask of Command* (New York 1987).

Keegan, J., *A History of Warfare* (London 1993).

Kentsmith, D.K., 'Principles of Battlefield Psychiatry' in: *Military Medicine* 151 (February 1986), 89-96.

Kleber, R.J., D. Brom and P.B. Defares, *Traumatische ervaringen, gevolgen en verwerking* (Lisse 1986).

Kulka, R.A. *et alii*, *Trauma and the Vietnam War Generation* (New York 1990).

Leed, E.J., *No Man's land. Combat and Identity in World War I* (Cambridge 1979).

Lifton, R.J., *Nazi-dokters. De psychologie van de rassenmoord in het Derde Rijk* (Utrecht 1987).

Long, P.H., 'Patton... and the Slap heard "round the World"' in: *Medical Times* 98 (1970), 244-254.

MacDonald, L., *They Called It Passchendaele. The Story of the Third Battle of Ypres and the Men Who Fought in It* (London 1978).

MacDonald, L., *The Roses of No Man's Land* (London 1980).

MacDonald, L., *Somme* (London 1983).

MacPherson, M., *Long Time Passing. Vietnam and the Haunted Generation* (New York 1984).

Maxwell Jones, M.B., 'Group Psychotherapy' in: *British Medical Journal* (Sept. 1942), 276-278.

McManners, H., *The Scars of War* (London 1993).

Mentink-Heshusius, M., *De plicht tot hulp: De post-traumatische stress-stoornis van een Nederlandse VN-militair* (Amsterdam 1993).

Messerschmidt, M. and F. Wullner, *Die Wehrmachtjustiz im Dienste des Nationalsozialismus. Zerstörung einer Legende* (Baden-Baden 1987).

Milligan, S., *Milligan's War* (London 1989).

Mott, F.W., 'War Psycho-neurosis' in: *The Lancet* (1918, 1), 127-129.

Myers, C.S., 'A Contribution to the Study of Shell Shock' in: *The Lancet* (1915, 1), 316-320.

Myers, C.S., 'Contributions to the Study of Shell Shock' in: *The Lancet* (1916, 1), 65-69.

Myers, C.S., 'The Study of Shell Shock' in: *The Lancet* (1919, 1), 51-54.

Neill, J.R., 'How Psychiatric Symptoms Varied in World War I and II' in: *Military Medicine* 158 (3:149, 1993).

Neumann, M. and A. Levy, 'A Specific Military Installation for Treatment of Combat Reactions During the War in Lebanon' in: *Military Medicine* 149 (April 1984), 196-199.

'Notes from German and Austrian Medical Journals, Disciplinary Treatment of Shell Shock' in: *British Medical Journal* (ii-1916), 882.

Noy, S., R. Levy and Z. Solomon, 'Mental Health Care in the Lebanon War, 1982' in: *Israel Journal of Medical Sciences* 20 (1984), 360-363.

Parker, G., *Het Spaanse leger in de Lage Landen* (Haarlem 1978).

Paschall, R., *The Defeat of Imperial Germany 1917-1918* (New York 1989).

Peeters, H.F.M., 'Historische fasen in aard en behandeling van geesteszieken' in: J.M.W. Binneveld *et alii*, *Een psychiatrisch verleden. Uit de geschiedenis van de psychiatrie* (Baarn 1982), 11-26.

Personele aspecten van het moderne gevecht, (gevechts)stress en (gevechts)stressmanagement Directie personeel Koninklijke Landmacht, afdeling gedragswetenschappen, rapporteur L. Fintel ('s-Gravenhage 1988).

Peterson, D.B. and R.E. Chambers, 'Restatement of Combat Psychiatry' in: *American Journal of Psychiatry* 109 (1952), 249-254.

Pettera, R.L., B.M. Johnson and R. Zimmer, 'Psychiatric Management of Combat Reactions with Emphasis on a Reaction Unique to Vietnam' in: *Military Medicine* (1969), 673-678.

Rees, J.R., *The Shaping of Psychiatry by War* (New York 1945).

Rennie, Th. and L.E. Woodward, *Mental Health in Modern Society* (New York 1948).

Riedesser, P., 'Militär und Medizin. Materialien zur Kritik des Sanitätsmedizin am Beispiel der Militärpsychiatrie' in: *Das Argument*, Sonderband 4 (1974), 231-279.

Riedesser, P. and A. Verderber, *Aufrüstung der Seelen. Militärpsychologie und Militärpsychiatrie in Deutschland und Amerika* (Freiburg 1985).

Rivers, W.H.R., 'Freud's Psychology of the Unconscious' in: *The Lancet* (12 June 1917), 912-914.

Roosens, E., *Een unicum in de psychiatrie* (Leuven 1977).

Roth, K.H., 'Die Modernisierung der Folter in den beiden Weltkriegen: Der Konflikt der Psychotherapeuten und Schulpsychiater um die deutschen "Kriegsneurotiker" 1915-1945' in: *Forschung 1999*, Heft 3 (1987), 8-75.

Roussy, M.G., 'Troubles nerveux psychiques' in: *La Presse Médicale* 15 (1915), 115-117.

Sargant, W. and N. Craske, 'Modified Insulin Therapy in War Neuroses' in: *The Lancet* (23 August 1941), 212-214.

Sargant, W. and E. Slater, 'Acute War Neuroses' in: *The Lancet* (6 July 1940).

Scott, W.J., 'PTSD and Agent Orange: Implications for a Sociology of Veterans' Issues' in: *Armed Forces & Society* 18 (Summer 1992), no. 4, 592-612.

Showalter, E., *The Female Malady. Women, Madness and English Culture 1830-1980* (London 1985).

Simkins, P., *Kitchener's Army. The Raising of the New Armies, 1914-16* (Manchester/New York 1988).

Solomon Z., 'Oscillating between Denial and Recognition of PTSD: Why are Lessons Learned and Forgotten?' in: *Journal of Traumatic Stress* 8 (1995), no. 2, 271-282.

Spits, F.C., *De metamorfose van de oorlog in de achttiende en de negentiende eeuw* (Assen 1971).

Stouffer, S.A. ed., *The American Soldier: Combat and its Aftermath* (New Jersey 1949).

Strecker, E.A., 'Military Psychiatry: World War I 1917-1918' in: J.K. Hall, G. Zilboorg, eds., *One Hundred Years of American Psychiatry* (New York 1945), 385-416.

Swaan, A. de, *Zorg en de staat. Welzijn, onderwijs en gezondheidszorg in Europa en de Verenigde Staten in de nieuwe tijd* (Amsterdam 1989).

Swart, H.W. de, *Human Implications of Modern Warfare. Recovery Units for Combat Stress Victims*, Executive summary, Directorate of Personnel (RNLA), Behavioural Sciences Department (Den Haag 1989), 1-11.

Talbott, J.A., 'Community Psychiatry in the Army' in: *JAMA* 2 10 (1969), nr. 7, 1233-1237.

Teitler, G., *De wording van het professionele officierscorps* (Rotterdam 1974).

Terraine, J., *The Smoke and the Fire. Myths and Anti-myths of War, 1861-1945* (London 1992).

Tiffany Jr., W.J. and W.S. Allerton, 'Army Psychiatry in the Mid-'60s' in: *American Journal of Psychiatry* 123:7 (January 1967), 810-820.

Travers, T.H.E., 'The Offensive and the Problem of Innovation in British Military Thought 1870-1915' in: *Journal of Contemporary History* 13 (London and Beverly Hills 1978), 531-53.

Trimbos, K., *Antipsychiatrie, een overzicht* (Deventer 1975).

Troelstra, P.J., *Gedenkschriften III. Branding* (Amsterdam 1929), 301.

Turner, W.A., 'Neuroses and Psychoses of War' in: *The Lancet* (1918, 2), 613-617.

Ulrich, B. and B. Ziemann, eds., *Frontalltag im Ersten Weltkrieg. Wahn und Wirklichkeit. Quellen und Dokumente* (Frankfurt am Main 1994).

Urlanis, B.Z., *Bilanz der Kriege: Die Menschenverluste Europas vom 17. Jahrhundert bis zur Gegenwart* (Berlin 1965).

Ward, N.D., *Sea Harrier over the Falklands* (London 1993).

Wiersma, E., *Pathologisch! Nederlandse psychiaters en hun beeldvorming van militaire dienstweigeraars rond de Tweede Wereldoorlog*. Thesis for the Faculty of History at the University of Amsterdam (1987).

Winter, D., *Death's Men. Soldiers of the Great War* (London 1979).

Wintle, J., *The Viet Nam Wars* (London 1991).

Wondergem, G., *Je komt anders terug. Aantekeningen uit het dagboek van een VN-waarnemer in Sarajevo en Kostajnica (sector Noord)* (Amsterdam 1993).

Yealland, L., *Hysterical Disorders of Warfare* (London 1918).

Source of Illustrations

p29.   Friedrich, E., *Krieg dem Kriege* (Frankfurt am Main 1986)

p47.   Gilbert, M., *The Routledge Atlas of the First World War* (London 1994)

p110.   Hirschfeld, Magnus und Andreas Gaspar ed., *Sittengeschichte des Ersten Weltkrieges* (Hanau z.j. [Nachdruck der 2. neubearbeiteten Auflage]).

p85, 115.   *Historial de la grande guerre*, (Peronne 1991)

p36.   Keegan, J., *The Face of Battle* (London 1976)

p142.   MacDonald, L., *The Roses of No Man's Land* (London 1988)

p96.   Roeder, G.H., *The Censored War* (Yale University, 1993)

INDEX